INTERNATIONAL SERIES OF MONOGRAPHS ON
PURE AND APPLIED MATHEMATICS
GENERAL EDITORS: I. N. SNEDDON, S. ULAM and M. STARK

VOLUME 22

FUNDAMENTAL CONCEPTS
OF
MATHEMATICS

FUNDAMENTAL CONCEPTS
OF
MATHEMATICS

by
R..L. GOODSTEIN
University of Leicester

PERGAMON PRESS
OXFORD · LONDON · EDINBURGH · NEW YORK
PARIS · FRANKFURT

PERGAMON PRESS LTD.
Headington Hill Hall, Oxford
4 and 5 Fitzroy Square, London, W.1

PERGAMON PRESS INC.
122 East 55th Street, New York 22, N.Y.

GAUTHIER-VILLARS ED.
55 Quai des Grands-Augustins, Paris, 6^e

PERGAMON PRESS G.m.b.H.
Kaiserstrasse 75, Frankfurt am Main

Distributed in the Western Hemisphere by
THE MACMILLAN COMPANY · NEW YORK
pursuant to a special arrangement with
Pergamon Press Limited

First Published 1962
Reprinted 1964

*Printed by Photo-lithography in Great Britain
by Compton Printing Works Ltd., London*

PREFACE

THE title of this book *Fundamental Concepts of Mathematics* correctly describes one aim of the book, to give an account of some of the notions which play a fundamental part in modern mathematics. The book makes no claim to be exhaustive and what has been omitted is not thereby judged to be of less importance; I have written about the ideas which interest me most at the moment. The class of readers for whom the book is intended is rather more difficult to specify. Certainly I am not writing for the professional mathematician, who does not need the help I try to give the reader. Nor am I writing for the student who is seeking training in a technique. The cultivated amateur is one whose needs I had in mind, but above all this account is intended for teachers of mathematics who feel that their background knowledge is out of date, and for teachers in training. There is a great hunger in the world for mathematicians and a great hunger for mathematics, and both these needs can be met only by means of an immense increase in the number of teachers of mathematics with a thorough comprehension of fundamental concepts.

R. L. GOODSTEIN

CONTENTS

CHAPTER 1

NUMBERS FOR COUNTING

CHAPTER 2

NUMBERS FOR PROFIT AND LOSS
AND NUMBERS FOR SHARING

CHAPTER 3
NUMBERS UNENDING

CHAPTER 4
CLASSES AND TRUTH FUNCTIONS

CHAPTER 5
NETWORKS AND MAPS

NUMBERS FOR COUNTING

THE whole structure of mathematics, rich in its three thousand years of development and with an almost bewildering variety of growing points, has both its foundation and its origin in the numbers with which we count.

What do we do when we count the objects in a collection? Our first answer might be that we use the numbers as labels, and give each object in turn a label, one, two, three, and so on, just as we name our children. To make the situation more definite let us suppose we have a stock of number labels, from which we draw the numbers to be attached to the objects counted. When each of the objects has been assigned its label, what has been accomplished, apart, that is, from just affixing the labels? Can we say that we have now found out the number of objects in the collection, that this number is that on the last label we used? For instance, let me count a row of squares:

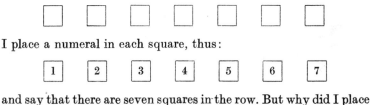

I place a numeral in each square, thus:

| 1 | 2 | 3 | 4 | 5 | 6 | 7 |

and say that there are seven squares in the row. But why did I place just *these* numerals in the squares? Why did I not perhaps fill the squares in this way:

Counting therefore cannot be simply a process of naming. Our next suggestion may be that the labels must be kept, and used, in a definite order. That the label 1 must be used first, then the label 2, and so on. This would safeguard us against the error we committed above, but how is the *order* of the labels to be determined? We might of course rely upon an order established by custom, as with the letters of the alphabet; in fact both the Greeks and the Hebrews used the letters of their alphabets as number labels in this way. Thus we might label the row of squares with letters:

and say that we have g squares, the established order of the letters of the alphabet guarding us against error. For counting sufficiently small collections such a procedure would be adequate, but it does not take us to the heart of the matter. Our stock of labels is necessarily limited, yet we know that we can number any collection, however great. And the need to commit to memory, or record in some other form, an established order of number names becomes increasingly burdensome as the collection of number labels increases. Concealed beneath our counting process there is in fact a remarkable mechanism for generating numbers as large as we like and for ordering them automatically. The familiar process of counting is really a combination of two operations. One of these is a number generating process and the other a process of translation or abbreviation. To separate these two aspects of counting, let us start by recognising the number names: "two", "three", "four", and so on, as abbreviations for "one and one", "two and one", i.e. "one and one and one", "three and one", and so on. Thus one part of counting consists in reciting the definitions "one and one is two", "two and one is three", "three and one is four", and so on, only, in counting, we do not repeat the whole of the definition, we just say "one, two, three, ..." omitting the "and one" or rather replacing it by looking at the object counted, or by touching it. The other part of the process of counting is a process of *copying* the objects counted, or matching them, by dots, or strokes, or match sticks, or words. Thus counting may be said to have originated in the practice of making a copy of a collection, perhaps in pebbles on the ground, or in strokes on sand, or cuts in a length of wood; but this making a copy is by no means the whole of counting. The essential step lies in organising the copy into a readily identifiable whole, as we do when we translate "one and one" into "two", "one and one and one" into "three", and so on. It is instructive to look at this organising process in other settings. Instead of using number words, let us work with dot patterns, named according to the following scheme:

one   two   three   four   five   six   seven

eight   nine   ten

Faced with a row of dots

we seek to organize the dots into one of the named patterns to determine its number. This bears a certain relationship to counting, but lacks one essential feature; counting is systematic, and is entirely free from trial and error, but with the above dot patterns we must try each pattern afresh, to see which we can make. This is because the dot patterns have no internal connections, we do not pass from one to the next by adding a fresh dot, as we pass from "one and one" to "two" and from "two and one" to "three" and so on by adding one. We can remedy this by redesigning the patterns:

one   two   three   four   five   six

seven   eight   nine   ten

Each pattern is now contained in its successor, and to count a row of dots we *form the patterns in turn,* adding one dot at a time until the collection of dots is exhausted. If we work with stick patterns instead of dots we can produce patterns which bear some resemblance to the arabic numerals themselves. Probably the set which bears the closest resemblance is this:

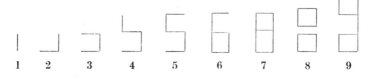

Surprising though the resemblance is, there is no historical evidence of a connection between the arabic numerals and stick patterns, but the patterns themselves may nevertheless prove of value in teaching children to count and in introducing them to the arabic numerals. The child would make the pattern in match sticks, and name it, before learning to write the arabic numeral. Stick pattern making would provide an activity to accompany the learning of the definitions "one and one is two", "two and one is three", and so on, and would provide both a visual and a tactile aid.

The use of stick patterns shows how curious an operation counting would be if it really consisted in assigning a pattern (number name) not to the whole collection but to each separate object. Thus to count the row of sticks

$$| \quad | \quad | \quad | \quad | \quad |$$

instead of organising the sticks into the single pattern

we should need a stock of sticks from which to draw twenty-one sticks just to count six, as the following diagram shows.

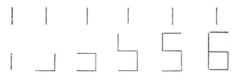

Addition

After counting, the next operation of arithmetic is *addition*. Addition of numbers may be thought of as uniting two collections. Thus to add two and three, we unite the collections .., ... to form

. . . . .

and count the new collection. It soon becomes apparent that if we start with one collection in pattern form, we can perform addition without having to count the united collection; we simply exhaust the second collection, a stick at a time, to make fresh patterns from the pattern of the first collection. Thus to add five and three we start with the pattern five and three spare sticks:

and form in turn

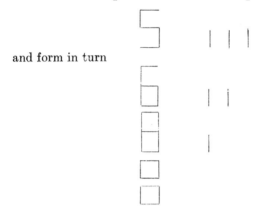

showing that the sum is eight. Translated into words the addition of five and three consists in the steps:

five and (one and one and one)

is

(five and one) and (one and one)

which is six and (one and one)
and this is

(six and one) and one

that is seven and one
which is eight.

I have used brackets to help the eye follow the transfer of a 'one' from one collection to the other.

The fact that the order of addition is irrelevant may most readily be seen by setting out the objects of the collections to be united in a row. For instance to show that the result of adding three to five is the same as the result of adding five to three, we set out collections of five and three side by side:

$$\times \ \times \ \times \ \times \ \times \ \bullet \ \bullet \ \bullet$$

reading from left to right we have five to which three is added, but reading from right to left we have three to which five is added. The fact that the order in which addition is performed is irrelevant is usually expressed by saying that addition is *commutative*.

In stating general properties of numbers, like the commutative property of addition, it is very convenient to have a symbol to express the idea of "any number". In suitable contexts we can use single letters for this purpose, generally letters from the end of the alphabet. Instead of talking about "a sum of two numbers" we write "$x + y$", the plus sign "$+$" standing as usual for addition and the "x" and "y" each standing for any numeral. We use two letters "x" and "y" rather than just "x", to avoid suggesting that we are considering a sum of the same two numbers. The expression

$$x + y$$

stands for the sum of any two numbers whatever.

The x and the y are like blank squares on an income tax form, which are to be filled by numerals. The commutative property of addition may now be expressed by the equation

$$x + y = y + x$$

the equals sign "$=$" between "$x + y$" and "$y + x$" affirming that the two numbers between which it stands (or rather the numbers obtained by filling in the blanks) are the same. Of course "x" and "y" are not themselves numerals; their role is the same as that of words like "he" and "she" in language, which stand in place of names, but are not themselves names. Since "he" is a pronoun, "x" and "y" in the equation

$$x + y = y + x$$

may be called *pronumerals*. But in fact the parallel is not an exact one, for in the equation

$$x + y = y + x$$

we may replace "x" and "y" by any numerals we please, whereas in common usage, "he" refers to a particular person in a particular context. The equation
$$x + y = y + x$$
summarizes all such instances of the commutative property of addition as
$$2 + 3 = 3 + 2, \ 4 + 5 = 5 + 4, \ 2 + 5 = 5 + 2, \text{ etc.}$$

The equation $2 + 3 = 3 + 2$ does not of course say that $2 + 3$ and $3 + 2$ are the same sign — they obviously are not — but that each denotes the same number, or in a sense we shall later explain, that each may be transformed into the other.

Let us repeat the process whereby we added three to five, taking this time any number x in place of five and writing numerals in place of words:
$$x + 3$$
$$= x + (2 + 1), \text{ using the definition } 3 = 2 + 1,$$
$$= (x + 1) + 2, \text{ transferring a "}+1\text{" from 2 to } x,$$
$$= (x + 1) + (1 + 1)$$
$$= ((x + 1) + 1) + 1, \text{ transferring "}+1\text{" again.}$$

If we now fill in any numeral for the x, we have before us the sum of that numeral and 3. For instance, with "6" for "x":
$$6 + 3 = ((6 + 1) + 1) + 1.$$

If we now use the definitions $6 + 1 = 7, \ 7 + 1 = 8, \ 8 + 1 = 9$ we arrive at the result
$$6 + 3 = 9.$$

Of course the chain of definitions $1 + 1 = 2, \ ..., \ 8 + 1 = 9$, may be continued as far as we please, but, as is well known, the numerals after 9 are not individual signs but are compounded of the numerals 1 to 9, by means of a most ingenious device, *positional notation*, according to which the number a numeral denotes depends upon the position the numeral occupies. Positional notation is most easily described in terms of the bead frames from which it originated.

Let us suppose that we are going to match some collection in beads, storing the beads on a wire. We choose a wire which can

hold exactly ten beads. At first we might use a great many wires
in exactly the same way; we fill the wires and store each full wire
until the whole collection has been matched. This is very uneconom-
ical both in beads and wires, and one day it occurred to some one
that it was not really necessary to store the full wires, provided
that we matched the full wires by beads on another wire. Now
we should need only two wires, one to hold the beads which we
match with the given collection, and another to hold the beads
which match the full wires. Instead of recording a collection of
thirty-four by means of three full wires, and four over

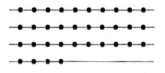

we introduce an upright wire on which we match the full wires
by additional beads, and the record now takes the form

which records 3 full wires and 4. This two-wire device would be
adequate for quite small collections, but faced with a large collection (of several hundred, say) we should find the single upright
wire insufficient, and be obliged to introduce a third wire on
which we placed beads to match the full upright wires. Thus for
instance, using only wires which hold ten beads, a collection of
two hundred and seventy-four would be recorded in the form

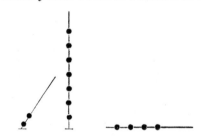

Each bead on the sloping wire represents a full upright wire, and since each bead on an upright wire represents a full horizontal wire, it follows that a bead on the sloping wire represents the following array of beads

. . . .
. . . .
. . . .
. . . .
. . . .
. . . .
. . . .
. . . .
. . . .
. . . .

in which we have attached a full horizontal row of beads to each bead on the full vertical wire. Thus a single bead on the sloping wire represents a full ten by ten array of beads, a hundred beads in all. Matching collections of more than ten hundred would necessitate the introduction of a fourth wire, and by this time no doubt it would have been realised that the special devices of horizontal, upright and sloping wires are quite unnecessary and that the relative positions of the wires alone serve to distinguish them, and we arrive at the abacus with vertical wires.

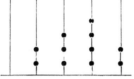

We have represented the result of matching a collection of two and four-tens and three-ten-tens and two-ten-ten-tens (i.e. two thousand, three hundred and forty-two). In talking about the abacus, the right-hand end wire is called the *unit* wire, then from right to left the successive wires are known as the *tens* wire, *hundreds* wire, *thousands* wire, *ten-thousands* wire. Of course the number words one, two, three, four themselves provide a more logical nomenclature (a fact which we shall exploit when we come to the study of indices) the tens wire being one from the end, the hundreds two from the end, the thousands three from the end, and so on.

Since each wire necessarily contains fewer than ten beads, the number of beads on a wire is denoted by one of the numerals 1, 2, 3, 4, 5, 6, 7, 8, 9, and to indicate the wire on which the beads stand, the position of the numeral is made to correspond to the position of the wire. Let us return to our previous example and write beneath each wire the numeral of the number of beads on the wire:

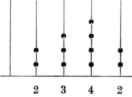

2   3   4   2

As a record of the collection the row of numerals 2342 serves as well as the beads, and we take "2342" as the numeral of the number of beads (i.e. two thousand three hundred and forty-two). However, unless we have a way of indicating an empty wire, we shall fail to distinguish between, for instance, the following three situations

1   1   1

each of which is represented by the single numeral 1. Clearly what is needed is an indicator for an empty wire, and this part is played by the numeral "0" (zero). Since we are counting position from the right-hand end wire we do not need to mark empty wires on the left and the above three positions are adequately denoted as follows

1   1   0   1   0   0

where instead of a single numeral, we now have three distinct numerals "1", "10", "100", and these are the numerals for the number represented by a bead on the end wire, a bead on the one-from-end wire, and a bead on the two-from-end wire respectively.

Addition in positional notation is of course precisely addition on the abacus. To add 243 to 672 we start with an abacus set up to represent a collection of 672 objects

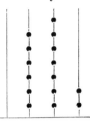

and then add three beads to the units wire; then one-by-one we start to add four beads to the tens wire, which is filled after three have been added, so that we empty the wire and add a bead to the hundreds wire, at which stage the abacus looks like this

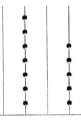

Next we add the remaining tens-wire bead to its wire, and place two more beads on the hundred wire. The steps we have taken are paralleled exactly in the familiar process of addition in positional notation:

$$
\begin{array}{r}
1 \\
672 \\
243 \\
\hline
915 \\
\hline
\end{array}
$$

The units present no difficulty. In adding the tens we add to 7 to make ten, three of the four (tens) in the second row, and place the one (ten) remaining in the answer row, and the new hundred that has been formed in the hundreds column, and finally add the entries in the hundreds column.

If we dispense with positional notation, and write t for ten, t^2 for a hundred (the 2 merely indicating the wire position two from the end, t^3 for a thousand, and so on, the number 672 takes the form

$$6t^2 + 7t + 2$$

(six hundreds and seven tens and 2).

The general notion of a three place numeral may be represented by

$$at^2 + bt + c,$$

a two place numeral by

$$at + b,$$

and a four place numeral by

$$at^3 + bt^2 + ct + d.$$

If we add two numbers represented by two place numerals, say $at + b$, $ct + d$, we add the units to form $b + d$, and the tens to form $(a + c) t$, giving the sum

$$(a + c) t + (b + d)$$

(whether or not $b + d$ exceeds nine is of course unknown here). Thus

$$(at + b) + (ct + d) = (a + c) t + (b + d).$$

In this addition two fundamental general properties of addition are contained. One is the *associative property* of addition, which may be expressed by the equation

$$(a + b) + c = a + (b + c)$$

which says that in adding three numbers, we may first add the first two and then add the third to the result, or we may add the second and third first, afterwards adding the result to the first. We prove this property by observing that a row of beads separated into three groups of a, b and c beads (from left to right) contains c and b and a beads (from right to left). For instance the row

. .   . .

expresses both the sum $(2 + 3) + 5$ (read from left to right) and the sum $(5 + 3) + 2$ (read from right to left), but since addition is commutative

$$5 + 3 = 3 + 5$$

and $(5 + 3) + 2 = 2 + (5 + 3)$

so that finally

$$(5 + 3) + 2 = 2 + (3 + 5)$$

and therefore

$$(2 + 3) + 5 = 2 + (3 + 5).$$

The second general property implicit in addition in positional notation is one to which we shall return after we have discussed multiplication.

To give an account of the addition of numbers, which is independent of operations with collections, we may take certain properties of addition as *defining* addition of numbers and derive the remaining properties from the definitions alone, without further reference to collections. Ignoring the abbreviations "two", "three", "four" and so on, we shall write our numerals in the form 1, $1 + 1$, $(1 + 1) + 1$, $((1 + 1) + 1) + 1$, and so on. Thus if n is a numeral, $n + 1$ is the next. We take as the definition of addition a particular instance of the associative property of addition, namely

$$m + (n + 1) = (m + n) + 1,$$

which says that to add the number after n, to m, we add n itself to m, and then take the next number. To see how this definition achieves its object we consider the addition of $(1 + 1) + 1$ to 1. We start by writing 1 for m and $(1 + 1)$ for n, and the definition yields

$$1 + ((1 + 1) + 1) = (1 + (1 + 1)) + 1;$$

starting again we take 1 for m and 1 for n and we find

$$1 + (1 + 1) = (1 + 1) + 1$$

and using this value of $1 + (1 + 1)$ on the right-hand side of the previous equation we find

$$1 + ((1 + 1) + 1) = ((1 + 1) + 1) + 1.$$

The definition we have given of addition is not a definition in the more usual sense of the term for we have not explained addition in terms of some other concept. All that we have given is a rule for transforming one sum into another. This rule is known as a *recursive definition* (or an inductive definition) because it defines the sum of two numbers in terms of the sum of smaller numbers.

Re-introducing abbreviations for the moment, we can illustrate the use of the definition by observing that the recursive definition gives the sum $7 + 5$, say, in terms of $7 + 4$, and this in terms of $7 + 3$, and this in terms of $7 + 2$, and finally $7 + 2$ in terms of $7 + 1$. This process of leading us back to some initial term is what gives definition by recursion its name. Putting it another way, a recursive definition does not immediately eliminate the operation defined (in this case the operation of addition) but serves to eliminate the operation in stages. The object of the definition is, for example, to turn "$+ n$" into a string "$+ 1 + 1 + \cdots + 1$", i.e. to define addition of numbers in terms of the repeated addition of ones.

Mathematical Induction

To prove that all numbers have a certain property, mathematics makes frequent appeal to a fundamental principle known as "induction" (more strictly mathematical induction). Induction is a principle of inheritance. If every man necessarily transmits some trait to his offspring, then *all* the descendants of a man with this trait will have this trait. *If every number necessarily transmits a certain property to the next number, then all numbers have this property which follow some number with the property.* This is the principle of mathematical induction, the keystone in the whole structure of arithmetic. To illustrate the use of the principle we give a proof of the commutative property of addition

C $$a + b = b + a$$

by means of induction.
As a first step we prove that

C_1 $$(b + a) + 1 = (b + 1) + a;$$

this equation closely resembles the defining equation for addition, but differs in that we add one to the first of the two numbers in the sum, not the second.
We look upon equation C_1 as a property of the number a which we have to show holds for all a.

Since both sides of equation C_1 are the same when we replace "a" by "1", we see that the number 1 has the property C_1. Suppose now that some number n has the property. Then

$$(b + (n + 1)) + 1 = ((b + n) + 1) + 1.$$

by the definition of addition,

$$= ((b + 1) + n) + 1,$$

since n has the property C_1,

$$= (b + 1) + (n + 1),$$

again by definition,

which shows that the number $n + 1$ has the property C_1. We have shown that 1 has the property in question, and that *if* any number n has the property, so has the next number $n + 1$. By induction therefore all numbers a have the property, that is to say the equation C_1 has been proved for any number a whatever. Throughout the proof the number b had no *particular* role to play, which shows that we could carry through the proof with any number b whatever. It is very important in using induction not to make any substitution for the number which is the subject of the induction. When we seek to show that if some number n has a certain property P, say, then the next number $n + 1$ has the property, we must not change n during the proof. The number n, though unspecified, is to be thought of as some one definite number. We could for instance take n to be 7 in the proof, *provided* that we did not use any special property of the number 7, which some other number might not have. Since we are seeking to show that *every* number transmits the property P to its successor, the passage from "n has the property P" to "$n + 1$ has the property P" must hold for any number n whatever, and must not appeal to any particular property of the number n. Thus we cannot prove, by induction, that *all* numbers have a certain property, without appealing to some other property which all numbers have. Our only source of such a property at this stage is the definition of addition, but step by step further properties are found which may be used in later proofs by induction. It is easy to see that nonsense would result if we were allowed to change the number n which is assumed to have the property P, during the proof that $n + 1$ has the property too. For instance, let us seek to prove the false equation

$$a + a = a + 1.$$

The number 1 has this property, since $1 + 1 = 1 + 1$. Suppose that n has the property; then if we were allowed to change n into $n + 1$, it would immediately follow that $n + 1$ has the property, and so by induction, that all numbers have the property. Taking $1 + 1$ for a however, the left-hand side of the equation has the value $(1 + 1) + (1 + 1) = ((1 + 1) + 1) + 1$, but the right-hand side has the different value $(1 + 1) + 1$. Such a misuse of induction would amount to nothing more than the assumption that whatever property some one number has, the next number necessarily has the same property which is no more true than the assumption that every son is identically the same as his father.

Let us now return to the proof of equation C, which we regard as a property of the number b. It is not immediately apparent that the number 1 has this property, i.e. that

$$a + 1 = 1 + a$$

and so our first task is to establish that all numbers a have this property. Certainly the number 1 has the property, and if some number n has the property then

$(n + 1) + 1 = (1 + n) + 1$, since n has the property,
$\qquad\qquad\quad = 1 + (n + 1)$, by the definition of addition,

and this shows that $n + 1$ has the property, whence by induction, all numbers a have the property.

Thus we have proved that the number 1 has the property C. Suppose now that some number n has the property C; then

$a + (n + 1) = (a + n) + 1$, by the definition of addition,
$\qquad\qquad\quad = (n + a) + 1 = (n + 1) + a$,

which shows that $n + 1$ has also the property C, and so by induction all numbers b have this property. As a further illustration of the use of the principle of induction, we prove the associative property of addition

A $\qquad\qquad\qquad (a + b) + c = a + (b + c)$.

We look upon this equation as a property A of the number c, and we have to show that all numbers c have the property A. The definition of addition

$$a + (b + 1) = (a + b) + 1$$

shows that 1 has the property in question. Suppose now that some number n has the property A.
Then

$$(a + b) + (n + 1) = ((a + b) + n) + 1,$$

by the definition of addition,

$$= (a + (b + n)) + 1,$$

since n has property A,

$$= a + ((b + n) + 1),$$

by the definition of addition,

$$= a + (b + (n + 1)),$$

for the same reason,

showing that n + 1 has property A.

Thus we have shown that the property A is transmitted from any number n to its successor n + 1, and that 1 has the property. It follows by the principle of induction that all numbers c have the property, so that addition is associative.

Inequality

If a is a sum of two numbers b and c, i.e. if

$$a = b + c$$

we say that a is *greater than* b and write $a > b$. The relation $a > b$ is called an *inequality*. If a is either greater than, or equal to, b we write $a \geqslant b$. If $a > b$ we say also that b is *less than a*, and write $b < a$. The two relations $a > b$, $b < a$ are fully equivalent; each leads to the other. There are many simple but important properties of inequalities. For instance

if $\qquad a > b \quad$ and $\quad b \geqslant c \quad$ then $\quad a > c$.

For if $a > b$ there is a number d, say, such that

$$a = b + d;$$

if $b = c$ then $a = c + d$ and so $a > c$; if $b > c$ there is a number e such that $b = c + e$ and therefore

$$a = (c + e) + d = c + (e + d)$$

so that again $a > c$.

Another important property is that if $a > b$ then $a + c > b + c$, i.e. an inequality (like an equality) is preserved by adding the same amount to both sides. For from $a > b$ we know that there is a number d such that $a = b + d$, and therefore $a + c = (b + d) + c = b + (d + c) = b + (c + d) = (b + c) + d$ proving that $a + c > b + c$.

An even simpler inequality is $a \geqslant 1$, which holds for all a. For $1 \geqslant 1$, and if $n \geqslant 1$, then $n + 1 \geqslant 1 + 1 > 1$, so that $a \geqslant 1$ for all a, by induction. Again by induction we may prove the fundamental property of *order* that for any a, b

$$a = b \quad \text{or} \quad a > b \quad \text{or} \quad b > a.$$

Subtraction

When $a > b$, so that there is a number d such that $a = b + d$, d is called the *difference* between a and b and we write

$$d = a - b.$$

Thus $b + (a - b) = a$: the difference between a and b is what must be added to b to make a.

For instance $17 = 11 + 6$ so that $17 - 11 = 6$.

The operation of taking the difference between two numbers is called *subtraction*. We observe that $a - b$ is defined only for $a > b$; the definition we have given is, however, an indirect one. To find the difference between 7 and 3 for instance we must try in turn $3 + 1, 3 + 2, 3 + 3, 3 + 4$ until we reach the sum 7. We can, however, carry out subtraction directly by formulating the definition rather differently.

Let us define:
$$(a + 1) - 1 = a$$
$$(a + 1) - (b + 1) = a - b.$$

Then to find for instance $7 - 3$ we pass through the differences $7 - 3 = 6 - 2 = 5 - 1 = 4$ (using the definitions $7 = 6 + 1$, $6 = 5 + 1$, etc.).

To justify this new definition we have to prove that, if $a > b$, then
$$b + (a - b) = a.$$

We start by proving, by induction over c, that

$$(b + c) - c = b;$$

this equation holds when $c = 1$; if it holds for some value n of c then

$$(b + n + 1) - (n + 1) = (b + n) - n, \text{ by definition}$$
$$= b, \text{ by assumption,}$$

and so if the equation holds for $c = n$, it holds for $c = n + 1$ and so for all c.

In fact the rather more general equation

$$(a + c) - (b + c) = a - b$$

may be proved in exactly the same way.

Now if $a > b$, there is a number d such that $a = b + d$ and therefore

$$b + (a - b) = b + ((d + b) - b) = b + d = a$$

as we wished to show.

The two definitions of subtraction are therefore seen to be equivalent.

There are several further interesting relations between addition and subtraction which we mention without proof:

If $a > b$, then $a - (a - b) = b$;

if $a > b > c$, then $(a - c) - (a - b) = b - c$;

if $a > b + c$, then $a - (b + c) = (a - b) - c$.

Unlike addition, subtraction is neither commutative, nor associative. For if $a > b$, only the first of $a - b$, $b - a$ is defined (e.g. there can be no number x such that $2 + x = 1$, since $2 + x > 1$ for all x, and so there is no such number as $1 - 2$). And $(a - b) - c$ is never equal to $a - (b - c)$ for

$$((d + b + c) - b) - c = (d + c) - c = d,$$

whereas

$$(d + b + c) - (b - c) = ((d + b + c + c) - c) - (b - c)$$
$$= (d + b + c + c - b) = d + c + c.$$

For example

$$(7 - 3) - 2 = 4 - 2 = 2, \text{ and } 7 - (3 - 2) = 7 - 1 = 6.$$

In terms of collections of objects, subtraction is the operation of taking away or removing objects from a collection. For instance a row of seven dots consists of four dots and three dots,

. . . . . .

and if we remove three, then four are left, and it is this residue which must be combined with the three we removed to complete the original set; thus the number of the collection which is left when part of a collection is removed, is what must be added to the number of the objects taken away to make the original number, showing that the number which remains when a part is removed, is the *difference* between the number in the original collection, and the number removed.

In terms of collections such properties of differences as for instance

$$(a - b) - c = a - (b + c)$$
$$a - (b - c) = (a - b) + c$$

may readily be proved.

The first of these is shown in the following diagram

• • • •   ○ ○ ○   □ □

in which we have nine dots (four black, three round and two square). We take away the two square dots, and then the three round ones, and only the black remain; and of course we may take away the two square and three round ones together, still leaving only the black dots.

The same diagram serves also to prove the second relation. We have nine dots, four black and five others. From the five other dots we remove the two square ones leaving the three round dots, and we then remove these from the row of nine dots leaving the black dots and the square dots

• • • •   □ □

If, however, we start by removing *all* the other dots, leaving only the black dots, then we must add on the two square dots to be left with the same collection. The relation we have proved is $9 - (5 - 2) = (9 - 5) + 2$, but of course the proof is perfectly general.

Multiplication

Repeated addition of the same number is called *multiplication*. For $3 + 3$ we write 2×3, read *two times three* (two threes), for $3 + 3 + 3$ we write 3×3, three times three, for $3 + 3 + 3 + 3$ we write 4×3, four times three, and so on. 4×3 is also called the *product* of 4 and 3 (and 3 and 4 are called the factors of the product), or the result of multiplying 3 by 4. Considering four rows of three dots

```
. . .
. . .
. . .
. . .
```

as three columns of four dots we see that

$$4 \times 3 = 3 \times 4$$

so that multiplication, like addition, is commutative. When we consider products with unspecified factors, we generally omit the multiplication sign $\times$, and write for instance $3a$ for $a + a + a$, and ab for $b + b + \cdots + b$ with a b's in the sum.

Multiplication is also associative, that is

$$(ab)\, c = a\,(bc).$$

For instance in the following diagram

```
. . . . .
. . . . .
. . . . .
```

```
. . . . .
. . . . .
. . . . .
```

```
. . . . .
. . . . .
. . . . .
```

```
. . . . .
. . . . .
. . . . .
```

we have three rows taken four times, that is 4×3 rows, each row containing 5 dots making $(4 \times 3) \times 5$ dots in all; but we also have three rows of five dots in each frame making 3×5 dots in a frame, and so

$$4 \times (3 \times 5)$$

dots. Thus

$$4 \times (3 \times 5) = (4 \times 3) \times 5.$$

The same argument may be carried out with any number of frames, with any number of rows in each frame and any number of dots in each row, which establishes the associative property of multiplication.

There is a very interesting joint property of addition and multiplication which can be seen in the following array of dots

In each row we have $3 + 4$ dots, and so in the five rows there are

$$5(3 + 4)$$

dots (we have omitted the multiplication sign in front of the bracket); but in the first frame we have five rows of three dots, making 5×3 dots, and in the second five rows of four dots, making 5×4 dots, so that in the two frames together there are $(5 \times 3) + (5 \times 4)$ dots. Thus we have shown that

$$5(3 + 4) = (5 \times 3) + (5 \times 4).$$

This joint property of addition and multiplication is called the *distributive* property; with unspecified numbers, a, b, c it takes the form

$$a(b + c) = ab + ac.$$

Short cuts in multiplication

There are some simple short cuts in multiplication. For instance, to multiply 83 by 87 we simply take $8 \times 9 = 72$, $3 \times 7 = 21$ and the product $83 \times 87 = 7221$; as another example of the same method $114 \times 116 = 13224$, where $132 = 11 \times 12$ and $24 = 4 \times 6$. The short cut works only when the numbers to be multiplied differ

only in the last digit, and the sum of the final digits is 10 (when 10 is the scale base.) To see why the device works consider the product
$$(10a + b)(10a + c);$$
by the distributive property this product is equal to
$$10a(10a + b) + (10a + b)c$$
$$= 100a \times a + 10ab + 10ac + bc$$
$$= 100a \times a + 10a(b + c) + bc.$$

If, therefore $b + c = 10$, the product is equal to
$$100a \times a + 100a + bc = 100a(a + 1) + bc.$$

To take again the first example, the steps in the proof for this example are
$$83 \times 87 = (8 \times 10 + 3)(8 \times 10 + 7)$$
$$= 8 \times 8 \times 100 + 8 \times 10(3 + 7) + 3 \times 7$$
$$= 8 \times 9 \times 100 + 21 = 7221.$$

We can also illustrate the proof by means of a diagram. Consider a rectangle ABCD of sides 24 units and 26 units in length respectively, containing a square APQR of sides 20 units long.

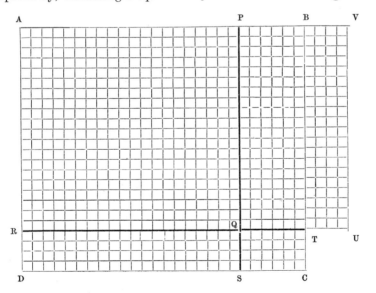

Cut out the rectangle QSDR and place it along the side BC of the rectangle ABCD, in position BTUV.

The rectangles ABTR and BTUV together form a rectangle ARUV of sides of lengths 30 units and 20 units respectively. Now the rectangle ABCD has been rearranged into the rectangle ARUV and the rectangle QSCT. The rectangle ABCD contains 24×26 unit squares; the rectangle ARUV contains $20 \times 30 = 600$ unit squares, and the rectangle QSCT contains $4 \times 6 = 24$ unit squares, showing that

$$24 \times 26 = 600 + 24 = 624.$$

Another short cut is based on the property

$$(a + b)(a - b) = (a \times a) - (b \times b)$$

i.e. the product of the sum and difference of two numbers is the difference of the products of each number by itself.

To exhibit this property consider seven rows of 3 crosses and $7 - 3$ dots; remove three rows of crosses

```
×  ×  ×  ┊  ·  ·  ·  ·
×  ×  ×  ┊  ·  ·  ·  ·
×  ×  ×  ┊  ·  ·  ·  ·
×  ×  ×  ┊  ·  ·  ·  ·
×  ×  ×  ┊  ·  ·  ·  ·
×  ×  ×  ┊  ·  ·  ·  ·
×  ×  ×  ┊  ·  ·  ·  ·
```

and there remain 7 rows of $7 - 3$ dots, and (turning the page round) 3 rows of $7 - 3$ crosses making $7 + 3$ rows of $7 - 3$ marks; in all we have 7×7 marks and we removed 3×3 marks, and so

$$7 \times 7 - 3 \times 3 = (7 + 3)(7 - 3).$$

With unspecified numbers a and b, $a > b$, consider now a row of b crosses and $(a - b)$ dots. Remove b rows of crosses, and there remain a rows of $(a - b)$ dots and b rows of $(a - b)$ crosses, making $a + b$ rows of $a - b$ marks, that is a total of

$$(a + b)(a - b)$$

marks. But from a rows of a marks we removed b rows of b marks, leaving

$$(a \times a) - (b \times b)$$

marks, showing that
$$(a + b)(a - b) = (a \times a) - (b \times b).$$

This property enables us to work out for instance 47×53 in our heads. We have $47 = 50 - 3$ and $53 = 50 + 3$ so that
$$47 \times 53 = (50 - 3)(50 + 3) = 2500 - 9 = 2491.$$

As another example consider,
$$94 \times 106 = (100 - 6)(100 + 6) = 10000 - 36 = 9964.$$

Another simple short cut may be used to multiply any number by itself. For instance
$$57 \times 57 = 50 \times 50 + 2 \times 50 \times 7 + 7 \times 7$$
$$= 2500 + 700 + 49 = 3249;$$
and
$$83 \times 83 = 80 \times 80 + 2 \times 80 \times 3 + 3 \times 3$$
$$= 6400 + 480 + 9 = 6889.$$

In terms of unspecified numbers a and b the property in question is
$$(a + b)(a + b) = (a \times a) + 2ab + (b \times b),$$

which is exhibited in the following diagram:

Consider a rows of a crosses and b dots, and a further b rows of a dots and b rings, making $(a + b)(a + b)$ marks in all; since there are $a \times a$ crosses, $(a \times b) + (b \times a) = 2ab$ dots and $b \times b$ rings, therefore
$$(a + b)(a + b) = (a \times a) + 2ab + (b \times b).$$

Since multiplication is repeated addition, we can obtain the product $(a + 1)b$, i.e. b added $(a + 1)$ times, by taking b first a times, giving the product ab and then adding another b so that
$$(a + 1)b = ab + b;$$

from this property, together with the initial equation $1 \times b = b$ which we formulate purely for notational completeness, we can deduce all the properties of multiplication without further reference to collections.

For instance, the distributive property

D $$a(b + c) = ab + ac.$$

We regard this equation as a property of the number a; in virtue of the definition $1 \times b = b$, the equation D holds when a has the value 1; if the number n has the property D, then

$$(n + 1)(b + c) = n(b + c) + (b + c), \text{ by definition,}$$
$$= (nb + nc) + (b + c), \text{ since n has property D,}$$
$$= ((nb + nc) + b) + c, \text{ by the associative property of addition,}$$
$$= (nb + (nc + b)) + c, \text{ by the associative property again,}$$
$$= (nb + (b + nc)) + c, \text{ by the commutative property for addition,}$$
$$= ((nb + b) + nc) + c, \text{ by the associative property,}$$
$$= ((n + 1)b + nc) + c, \text{ by the definition of multiplication,}$$
$$= (n + 1)b + (nc + c), \text{ by the associative property,}$$
$$= (n + 1)b + (n + 1)c, \text{ by means of the definition.}$$

Thus we have shown that if n has the property D then so has $(n + 1)$, and therefore all numbers a have this property. An immediate consequence is that

$$a(b + 1) = ab + a$$

(the companion equation to $(a + 1)b = ab + b$), because it is quite easy to show that $a \times 1 = a$ and hence we may prove $ab = ba$; we shall omit the details. Another simple consequence is the associative property $\quad a(bc) = (ab)c$

(proved by induction over c).

An inequality, like an equality, is preserved when both sides are multiplied by the same number. For if $a > b$, then there is a number d such that

$$a = b + d$$

and therefore

$$ca = c(b + d) = cb + cd$$

using the distributive property, which proves that $ca > cb$. The distributive property for subtraction may be obtained from that for addition, for if $b > c$ so that $b = c + d$, for some d, then

$$a(b - c) = ad$$

and

$$ab - ac = a(c + d) - ac = (ad + ac) - ac = ad$$

which proves that, if $b > c$,

$$a(b - c) = ab - ac.$$

Prime Numbers

Multiplication opens the door to many fascinating properties of numbers. We have already remarked that the numbers a, b are called the factors of the product. In virtue of the associative property we can write products of three factors abc without brackets since abc may stand for either $(ab)c$ or $a(bc)$ without it making any difference. Step by step the property extends to any number of factors, $abcd$, standing for $((ab)c)d$ or for $(ab)(cd)$, or for any other arrangement into pairs, and $abcde$ for any grouping into pairs whatever, for instance $(ab)((cd)e)$, and so on. Some numbers can be expressed as a product of factors in many ways, for instance

$$288 = 2 \times 144 = 3 \times 96 = 4 \times 72 = 8 \times 36 = 8 \times 9 \times 4,$$

and so on, whereas other numbers, like 7, are not expressible as a product except trivially with a unit factor. Thus $13 = 1 \times 13 = 13 \times 1$ but no other factorisation of 13 is possible; to see that this is so, observe first that if $a > 13$ then $ab > 13b \geqslant 13$, i.e. $ab > 13$, and therefore any factor of 13 must be less than or equal to 13. It is easy to see that each of the numbers $1, 2, ..., 12$ are less than 13; for instance $13 = 6 + 7$ so that $13 > 6$. Moreover these are the only numbers less than 13, for the successors of 13 are

13 + 1, (13 + 1) + 1 = 13 + 2; (13 + 2) + 1 = 13 + 3, and so on, which are therefore all greater than 13. Finally we form the product of any two of the numbers 2, 3, ..., 11, 12 and observe that none of these products has the value 13. A number which, like 13, has only the trivial factors 1 and the number itself, is called a *prime* number. The number 1 itself is prime in this definition, but it proves to be convenient to start the primes with 2. The first 20 prime numbers are:

2, 3, 5, 7, 11, 13, 17, 19, 23, 29, 31, 37, 41, 43, 47, 53, 59, 61, 67, 71.

Prime numbers may be obtained readily by a method known as the *Sieve of Eratosthenes*. Numbers which have the factor 2 are $2 \times 1 = 2$, $2 \times 2 = 4$, $2 \times 3 = 6$, $2 \times 4 = 8$ and so on, those with the factor 3 (the first number after 2, which is not a product) are $3 \times 1 = 3$, $3 \times 2 = 6$, $3 \times 3 = 9$, and so on, those with the factor 5 (the first number after 3 which has not yet appeared as a product) are $5 \times 1 = 5$, $5 \times 2 = 10$, $5 \times 3 = 15$, and so on, those with the factor 7 (the first number after 5 which has not appeared as a product) are $7 \times 1 = 7$, $7 \times 2 = 14$, $7 \times 3 = 21$, ...; the first number after 7 which has not yet appeared as a product is 11, which is the next prime number, and so we proceed as far as we please. It has been known* for over 2000 years that there is no greatest prime. To prove this we start with the observation that if $a \geqslant 2$ and $b > 2$ then $ab + 1$ has not the factor b (nor the factor a). For consider all numbers with the factor b: $1b$, $2b$, $3b$, $4b$, ... (called the *multiples* of b); if $r \leqslant a$, then $rb \leqslant ab < ab + 1$, and if $r > a$, so that $r = a + d$, then $rb = (a + d)b = ab + db \geqslant ab + 2d \geqslant ab + 2 > ab + 1$, which shows that none of the multiples of b is equal to $ab + 1$.

Next we observe that the smallest factor (greater than 1) of any number is necessarily prime, for if $f > 1$ is the smallest factor of F and if f itself has a factor g (other than the trivial factors 1 and f), then g would be a factor of F smaller** than f, which contradicts the choice of f as the smallest factor of F; thus f is prime.

---

* Proved by Euclid.
** By hypothesis $F = fe$, for some number e, and $f = gh$, so that $F = g(he)$, showing that g is a factor of F; furthermore $h > 1$, so that $f = gh > g$.

Consider now the number

$$N = (2 \times 3 \times 4 \times 5 \times \cdots \times n) + 1$$

where the product is taken up to any number n we please. The number N has none of the factors $2, 3, 4, 5, \ldots, n$ and so the *least* factor of N is greater than n, which proves that there is a prime number greater than n; but n may be chosen as big as we please. N may itself be prime, or have a prime factor greater than n. Although, as we have just shown, there can be no greatest prime, the largest number actually known to be prime (at the time of writing) is one less than a product of 3217 twos (i.e. $2 \times 2 \times \cdots \times 2$ with 2 appearing 3217 times) a number which, written out in full (with digits $0, 1, \ldots 9$) contains 969 digits.

If we look at the set of prime numbers we wrote above it will be noticed that there are several prime pairs $p, p + 2$ where both p and $p + 2$ are prime. For instance 3, 5; 5, 7; 11, 13; 17, 19; 29, 31; 41, 43; 59, 61. Very large prime pairs are known, and it has long been conjectured that prime pairs exist as large as we like, but this has not yet been proved. Another unproved conjecture* is that every even number (multiple of 2) after 2 itself is a sum of two primes, as for instance $8 = 3 + 5$, $10 = 3 + 7$, $12 = 5 + 7$, $14 = 3 + 11$. As far as the conjecture has been tested no case of failure has been found, but proof that *every* even number is so expressible is still lacking.

Division

If $a = bq + r$, $1 \leqslant r < q$, we say that q is the *quotient*, and r the *remainder*, when a *is divided by* b. For instance $7 = (3 \times 2) + 1$ so that when 7 is divided by 3, the quotient is 2 and the remainder 1, and since $68 = (7 \times 9) + 5$, the quotient is 9 and the remainder 5 when 68 is divided by 7. When a is a multiple of b so that $a = bq$ for some q, we say that a is divisible by b without remainder, and q is called the quotient of a divided by b.

---

* Known as Goldbach's conjecture (proposed by C. Goldbach (1690–1764) in a letter to L. Euler in 1742).

For any two numbers a, b with $1 < b < a$, where a is not just a multiple of b, there exist q and r, with $1 \leqslant r < q$, such that

$$a = bq + r.$$

We consider in turn the multiples of b; $2b$, $3b$, $4b$, ... Since $b > 1$, therefore $ab > a$, and so amongst the multiples $2b$, $3b$, ..., ab there will be a *first* which exceeds a, so that the previous multiple is less than a; let this multiple of b which is less than a be qb, then we have

$$qb < a, \quad (q+1)b > a, \quad \text{i.e.} \quad qb + b > a.$$

Consider now the numbers

$$qb, \ qb + 1, \quad qb + 2, \ ..., \ qb + b.$$

The first of these is less than a, the last greater than a, so that a is one of the numbers between qb and $qb + b$; that is to say there is an r between 1 and b (including 1 but excluding b) such that

$$a = qb + r$$

as was to be proved. The proof shows that quotient and remainder are unique.

For example the multiples of 17 are 34, 51, 68, 85, ...; the number 75 lies between the multiples 68 and 85, i.e. between 68 and 68 + 17 (excluding these end values). We consider in turn 68 + 1, 68 + 2, ... until we reach 68 + 7 = 75, showing that 7 is the remainder when 75 is divided by 17, and since 68 = 4 × 17, therefore 4 is the quotient.

Division bears the same relation to subtraction that multiplication bears to addition; that is to say division is equivalent to repeated subtraction. The question "what is the quotient when 75 is divided by 17" is the same as the question "how many times can 17 be subtracted from 75".

For

$$(75 - 17) - 17 = 75 - (17 + 17) = 75 - 2 \times 17$$
$$(75 - 2 \times 17) - 17 = 75 - (2 \times 17 + 17) = 75 - 3 \times 17$$
$$(75 - 3 \times 17) - 17 = 75 - (3 \times 17 + 17) = 75 - 4 \times 17 = 7.$$

Further subtraction is not possible since $7 < 17$. Consider now two general numbers a, b with $a > b$. Let us prove that the number of times that b may be subtracted from a is equal to the quotient of a divided by b. First we observe that if we subtract $b\,m$ times from a, the remainder is $a - b\,m$; for this is certainly true for $m = 1$. Let it be true for $m = \mathrm{n}$; when we subtract $b\,\mathrm{n} + 1$ times, we necessarily start by subtracting $b\,\mathrm{n}$ times which by assumption gives the remainder $a - \mathrm{n}b$; and then subtract b once more giving

$$(a - \mathrm{n}b) - b = a - (\mathrm{n}b + b) = a - (\mathrm{n} + 1)\,b$$

proving the property for the value $\mathrm{n} + 1$ of m, whence by induction, all numbers m have the property. If now q is the quotient and r the remainder when a is divided by b, so that

$$a = bq + r$$

then $a - bq = (r + bq) - bq = r$; thus when we subtract $b\,q$ times from a the remainder is r, and since $r < b$, no further subtraction is possible, and so q is precisely the number of times which we can subtract b from a. The familiar so-called "long division" of school arithmetic is based on this connection between division and subtraction. For instance to divide 75219 by 17 by long division we proceed as follows

$$
\begin{array}{r}
17)\,75219\,(4424 \\
68 \\
\hline
72 \\
68 \\
\hline
41 \\
34 \\
\hline
79 \\
68 \\
\hline
11
\end{array}
$$

The first step is to subtract 17 four thousand times, which, without abbreviation, would appear in the form

$$75219 - 17 \times 4000 = 75219 - 68000 = 7219;$$

however we omit the zeros after the 4 and after 68, and leave the final figures 19 waiting in the first line to be "brought down" when needed. Thus we start by subtracting 17 as many *thousands* of times as possible. From the remainder 7219 we then subtract 17 as many hundreds of times as possible (in this case 4 hundred) leaving a remainder 419 (the 9 is still left in the first line). Next we subtract 17 as many ten times as possible (two tens in fact) leaving 79 and from this 17 is subtracted a further 4 times leaving a remainder 11 too small to admit of further subtraction of 17.

If a is divisible by b, we write the quotient in the form $\dfrac{a}{b}$; by means of this notation we may express the sum, difference and product of the quotient of a divided by b, and the quotient of c divided by d, entirely in terms of a, b, c, d. For if $a = bp$ and $c = dq$ then

$$ad = bdp, \quad bc = bdq$$

and so

$$ad + bc = bd(p + q), \quad ad - bc = bd(p - q)$$

so that

$$p + q = \frac{ad + bc}{bd}$$

$$p - q = \frac{ad - bc}{bd}$$

and therefore

$$\frac{a}{b} + \frac{c}{d} = \frac{ad + bc}{bd}, \quad \frac{a}{b} - \frac{c}{d} = \frac{ad - bc}{bd}.$$

Moreover $ac = bd\,pq$, so that

$$pq = \frac{ac}{bd}$$

and therefore

$$\frac{a}{b} \times \frac{c}{d} = \frac{ac}{bd}.$$

If p is also divisible by q, then

$$\frac{a}{b} \div \frac{c}{d} = \frac{ad}{bc} = \frac{a}{b} \times \frac{d}{c},$$

for from $a = bp$, $c = dq$ and $p = qr$, $q \geqslant 1$, it follows $bcp = adq$ and so $qbcr = qad$, whence

$$bcr = ad,$$

(for the quotient of $qbcr$ by q is *unique*, and this quotient is both bcr and ad) i.e.

$$r = \frac{ad}{bc}$$

that is

$$\frac{a}{b} \div \frac{c}{d} = \frac{ad}{bc}.$$

We observe also that

$$\frac{a}{b} = \frac{ac}{bc}$$

for from $a = bp$ follows $ac = bcp$ and therefore

$$p = \frac{ac}{bc}.$$

Exponentiation

Repeated addition is called multiplication, and repeated multiplication is called *exponentiation*. The number of factors in a repeated multiplication is indicated by means of an *index*. Thus $a \times a$ is written a^2, $a \times a \times a$ is written a^3 and so on. From a^n we pass to a^{n+1} by multiplication by a, that is

$$a^{n+1} = a^n \times a.$$

The number n in a^n is the index, or power of a. For notational completeness we shall write a^1 for a itself in certain contexts. If we multiply a^m by a^n we obtain a product consisting in all of $m + n$ a's so that

$$a^m \times a^n = a^{m+n};$$

this may also be shown very simply by induction. And if we multiply a^m by itself n times we obtain a product of $m \times n$ a's so that

$$(a^m)^n = a^{mn}$$

which is also readily proved by induction since

$$(a^m)^{n+1} = (a^m)^n \times a^m$$

and

$$a^{m(n+1)} = a^{mn+m} = a^{mn} \times a^m.$$

Another important property of indices is that

$$(ab)^m = a^m \times b^m$$

for the product $(ab)^m$ contains m a's and m b's, (for an inductive proof observe that $(ab)^{m+1} = (ab)^m \times ab$ and

$$a^{m+1}b^{m+1} = a^m \times a \times b^m \times b = a^m b^m \times ab).$$

Representation in a scale

Since a hundred is ten tens we have $100 = 10^2$, and then, in turn, $1000 = 10 \times 100 = 10^3$, $10,000 = 10 \times 1000 = 10^4$, and so on. A number like four thousand seven hundred and sixty-three may now be written

$$4 \times 10^3 + 7 \times 10^2 + 6 \times 10 + 3,$$

which is called the expression of the number in the scale of ten, or the expression with the base ten. As another example we observe that

$$2^{12} = 4 \times 10^3 + 9 \times 10 + 6.$$

Of course expression in a scale is only an explicit form of positional notation. When we write a number as 4763 the positions of the digits, as we have already observed, correspond with the abacus wires, so that the 6 denotes 6 tens, the 7 denotes 7 hundreds, and so on. The indices of the powers of ten in the representation

$$4 \times 10^3 + 7 \times 10^2 + 6 \times 10 + 3$$

serve exactly the same purpose, the 3 in 10^3 pointing to the wire three from the right-hand end, the 2 in 10^2 pointing to the wire two from the end, and finally the 1 in $10^1 = 10$ pointing to the wire one from the end. Of course we may take any number we please (except 1, why?) as base. For instance with base 3, and digits 0, 1, 2 (the base, remember, is the number on a full wire, and so one more than the largest digit) the numbers from one to twenty in positional notation are

$$1, 2, 10, 11, 12, 20, 21, 22,$$

$$100, 101, 102, 110, 111, 112, 120, 121, 122, 200, 201, 202,$$

and the same numbers to the base 3 in explicit notation are

$$1, 2, 1 \times 3, 1 \times 3 + 1, 1 \times 3 + 2, 2 \times 3, 2 \times 3 + 1, 2 \times 3 + 2,$$

$$1 \times 3^2, 1 \times 3^2 + 1, 1 \times 3^2 + 2,$$

$$1 \times 3^2 + 1 \times 3, 1 \times 3^2 + 1 \times 3 + 1,$$

$$1 \times 3^2 + 1 \times 3 + 2, 1 \times 3^2 + 2 \times 3, 1 \times 3^2 + 2 \times 3 + 1,$$

$$1 \times 3^2 + 2 \times 3 + 2, 2 \times 3^2, 2 \times 3^2 + 1, 2 \times 3^2 + 2.$$

Of course we cannot read "110" as 'one hundred and ten' because the base is now 3; '110' must be read now as 'one three-threes and three' or simply as 'one-one-zero'.

Of all bases, the base 2 is particularly interesting because of the simplicity of the addition and multiplication tables. The addition table is simply $1 + 1 = 10$, and the multiplication table $1 \times 1 = 1$, for in the scale of 2 the only digits are 0, 1. For instance to add the numbers 1011 and 1101 we proceed in the familiar way to add a column at a time

```
    1 1 1 1
...................
      1 0 1 1
      1 1 0 1
    _____
    1 1 0 0 0
```

writing the carry figure on the top of the appropriate column; to translate into the scale of ten, we observe that

$$1011 = 1 \times 2^3 + 1 \times 2 + 1 = 8 + 2 + 1 = 10 + 1$$

$$1101 = 1 \times 2^3 + 1 \times 2^2 + 1 = 8 + 4 + 1 = 10 + 3$$

and the sum is $2 \times 10 + 4$; of course

$$11000 = 1 \times 2^4 + 1 \times 2^3 = 1 \times 10 + 6 + 8 = 2 \times 10 + 4.$$

This illustrates the conversion from the scale of 2 to the scale of 10. The conversion down from base ten to base two, is illustrated in the following example. To convert the number 75 from the base ten to the base two we simply divide 75 repeatedly by 2:

$$
\begin{array}{r|l}
2 & 75 \\ \hline
2 & 37 + 1 \\ \hline
2 & 18 + 1 \\ \hline
2 & 9 \\ \hline
2 & 4 + 1 \\ \hline
2 & 2 \\ \hline
 & 1 \\ \hline
\end{array}
$$

for each division without remainder we record a 0, and when the remainder is 1 we record this remainder, starting on the right and working to the left, and finally we record the last quotient, thus

$$1001011$$

which represents the number

$$2^6 + 2^3 + 2 + 1.$$

The first division by 2 shows that 75 contains 37 twos with one left over. The second division shows that 37 contains 18 twos with one left over; since the 37 records the number of twos, what is left over is a *two* (not a unit), and the 18 tells us that there are 18 twos in 37 and therefore 18 *fours* in 75 (since $2 \times 2 = 4$). Then we see that 18 contains 9 twos, but this 18 counts the *fours* in 75 and so the quotient 9 counts the *eights* in 75 ($2 \times 4 = 8$); the next quotient 4 counts the *sixteens* ($2 \times 8 = 16$) in 75 and there is one eight left over, then we find 2 *thirty-twos* ($2 \times 16 = 32$), and the final quotient counts the *sixty-fours* ($2 \times 32 = 64 = 2^6$) in 75. The series of divisions therefore shows that there is one sixty-four (2^6) in 75, one eight, one two and a one.

The scale of two is used in electronic digital computers because it requires only two digits, which may be represented by the off-on position of a switch, i.e. the opening and closing of a circuit, or the presence or absence of a current in a wire.

The scale of 2 provides a very simple solution of the following problem, which once seemed quite difficult. Can we place a 0 or 1 at each of 2^n points round a circle so that as we pass round the circle we meet all possible arrangements of n 0's and 1's? For instance, with $2^3 = 8$ points the following arrangement provides a solution:

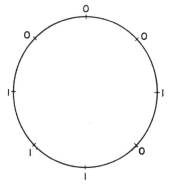

Starting at the top and moving anticlockwise we pass in turn through the following eight groups of three 0's and 1's:

$$001, 011, 111, 110,$$

$$101, 010, 100, 000.$$

These comprise all possible groups of three 0's and 1's for we have three places to fill, and each place may be filled in two ways, giving $2 \times 2 \times 2 = 8$ arrangements. Of course this is precisely what the representation of the numbers 1 to 8 in the scale of 2 shows; the first three wires of the abacus (the wires holding no more than a single bead each) suffice to represent the numbers 1 to 7, each wire being either empty or holding one bead. The number 8 is represented by leaving the first three wires empty, and placing a bead on the fourth wire. Thus all possible groups of three 0's and 1's correspond exactly to the numbers 1 to 8 in the scale of 2. To enumerate, we have

$$001 = 1, 010 = 2, 011 = 3,$$

$$100 = 4, 101 = 5, 110 = 6,$$

$$111 = 7 \quad \text{and} \quad 1000 = 8.$$

A method of finding such an arrangement in every case is the following. We consider again the case of 8 points round a circle. Starting with the number 1, we double and add one repeatedly, subtracting 8 if the result exceeds 8, and stop if we reach a number that has already been obtained; we then decrease by one and start again. The process ends when all the numbers from 1 to 8 have been obtained, thus: from 1 we pass to $2 \times 1 + 1 = 3$, from 3 to $2 \times 3 + 1 = 7$, from 7 to $2 \times 7 + 1 = 15$ and $15 - 8 = 7$, which we have already obtained, so we take $7 - 1 = 6$ instead. Starting again with 6 we form $2 \times 6 + 1 = 13$ and $13 - 8 = 5$; from 5 we pass to $(2 \times 5 + 1) - 8 = 3$, and since 3 has occurred before we take instead $3 - 1 = 2$; from 2 we pass to $(2 \times 2 + 1) = 5$, and as we have met this before we take 4; from 4 we pass to 8 (since $(2 \times 4 + 1) - 8 = 1$, so that we take $2 \times 4 = 8$ instead of $2 \times 4 + 1$), and the list now reads

$$1, 3, 7, 6, 5, 2, 4, 8.$$

Writing these in the scale of 2 we obtain

$$1, 11, 111, 110, 101, 10, 100, 000$$

(ignoring the fourth wire); we write these figures round the circle, taking each time just the right hand (unit digit) and we obtain the solution depicted above. If we apply the same process to the case of 16 points the solution runs as follows:

$$1, 3(= 2 \times 1 + 1), 7(= 2 \times 3 + 1), 15(= 2 \times 7 + 1),$$

$$\underline{14}(= 2 \times 15 - 16), 13(= 2 \times 14 + 1 - 16),$$

$$11(= 2 \times 13 + 1 - 16), 6(= 2 \times 11 - 16), \underline{12}(= 2 \times 6),$$

$$9(= 2 \times 12 + 1 - 16), 2(= 2 \times 9 - 16), 5(= 2 \times 2 + 1),$$

$$\underline{10}(= 2 \times 5), 4(= 2 \times 10 - 16), \underline{8}(= 2 \times 4), \underline{16}(= 2 \times 8),$$

(the numbers underlined are those where doubling and adding one fails to produce a new number, so that we simply double, without adding one); writing these numbers in the scale of 2 we obtain the sequence

$$1, 11, 111, 1111, 1110, 1101, 1011, 110, 1100, 1001, 10,$$
$$101, 1010, 100, 1000, 0000$$

and the final digits in order give the arrangement:

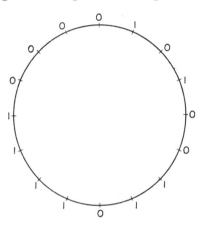

as we pass round the circle from point to point we pass all possible groups of four 0's and 1's beginning, say, at 0000, and passing in turn through 0001, 0011, 0111, 1111, 1110, and so on.

Another problem which admits a very simple solution by using the expression of numbers in a scale is the counterfeit penny problem. The problem is to find which one of twelve pennies is counterfeit, by means of three weighings on a balance, and whether the bad penny is light or heavy. We separate the 27 numbers of 3 digits in the scale of 3 into 3 groups. In one group we place the three numbers 000, 111, 222 in which the digits are all the same; we divide the remaining 24 into two groups, one of which is:

010	011	012	001
120	121	122	112
200	201	202	220

and the other contains the *duals* of these numbers, where the dual of *abc* is obtained by interchanging the digits 0.2 and leaving the digit 1 unchanged. The twelve numbers in the above array contain four numbers with initial digit 0, four with initial 1, four with initial 2, and four with second digit 0, and so on. We label the twelve pennies with the numbers in this array and start by weighing the four with an initial 0 on the label against the four with initial 2 on the label. If the two loads balance we record a 1, otherwise we record the initial digit of the labels of the pennies which descend. We repeat the process weighing the pennies with second digit 0 on their labels against the pennies with second digit 2, and finally we weigh the pennies with third digit 0 on their labels, against those with third digit 2. The number recorded, or its dual, is the number on the label of the bad penny; if the number recorded is on one of the labels, that penny is heavy; if the dual of the label on a penny is recorded, that penny is light. Suppose, for example, the label on the bad penny is 201 and that this penny is heavy; at the first weighing the pennies with first digit 2 on their labels descend and we record 2. Next we record 0. At the third weighing the bad penny is not weighed and the remainder balance. If penny 201 is light we find that the recorded number is 021.

By means of exponentiations we can more readily discuss some further properties of prime numbers. We remarked before that the largest prime known at present is

$$2^{3217} - 1.$$

Writing in 1640, the great French mathematician Pierre Fermat conjectured that *all* numbers of the form $2^n + 1$ are prime if n is a power of two.

In fact when we give n in turn the values 2, $4 = 2^2$, $8 = 2^3$, $16 = 2^4$ we find that the values of $2^n + 1$ are respectively

$$5, 17, 257, 65\,537$$

and all of these are prime.

The next value of n is $32 = 2^5$, and $2^{32} + 1 = 4{,}294{,}967{,}297$; after exhaustive tests Fermat was unable to find a factor of this number, but Leonhard Euler showed that $2^{32} + 1$ has the factor 641, disproving Fermat's conjecture. If we name the numbers $2^n + 1$ according to the power of 2 in the index n, denoting $2^2 + 1$ by $\mathfrak{F}_1$, $2^4 + 1$ by $\mathfrak{F}_2$, $2^8 + 1$ by $\mathfrak{F}_3$, and so on (the $\mathfrak{F}$ reminding us of Fermat) then we can sum up the position by saying $\mathfrak{F}_5$ is the first non-prime Fermat number. In the two centuries which have passed since Euler proved $\mathfrak{F}_5$ is non-prime, no further prime $\mathfrak{F}_n$ has been discovered. The first $\mathfrak{F}_n$ of which it is still not known whether it is prime or non-prime is $\mathfrak{F}_{13}$. Recently a number as gigantic as $\mathfrak{F}_{1945}$ was shown to have the factor $5 \times 2^{1947} + 1$.

In 1795, C. F. Gauss, then a boy of 18, and destined to become the greatest mathematician of all time, discovered a connection between the Fermat numbers and the problem of dividing the circumference of the circle into equal parts using only ruler and compasses. Gauss discovered that the circumference can be divided into n parts if and only if n is a power of 2, or a Fermat prime or a product of a power of 2 and distinct Fermat primes (calling 3 the Fermat prime $\mathfrak{F}_0$ for a reason to be discussed later). Apart from the well-known divisions of the circle into 3, 4, 5 and 6 parts Gauss' discovery showed that division into 17, 257 and 65,537 parts, by ruler and compass, is possible. The question whether division into a greater prime number of parts is possible waits on the discovery of another Fermat prime.

Tetration

Repeated addition $a + a + \cdots + a$ is called multiplication, repeated multiplication $a \times a \times \cdots \times a$ is called exponentiation, but repeated exponentiation $a^{a^{\cdots^a}}$ has no established name; we shall call it *tetration*, the fourth process, and shall denote the repeated exponentiation of a with b factors by $T(a, b)$. Of course the earlier operations like multiplication and exponentiation may be represented in the same way, with $M(a, b)$ standing for $b \times a$, and $E(a, b)$ for a^b, for example. The relationship between $M(a, b)$ and addition is

$$M(a, b + 1) = M(a, b) + a,$$

that between $E(a, b)$ and $M(a, b)$ is

$$E(a, b + 1) = M(a, E(a, b)),$$

and that between $E(a, b)$ and $T(a, b)$ is

$$T(a, b + 1) = E(a, T(a, b)).$$

From tetration we may pass in turn through new operations, pentation, hexation, septation, and so on, the relations between the new operation and the one before being

$$P(a, b + 1) = T(a, P(a, b))$$
$$H(a, b + 1) = P(a, H(a, b))$$
$$S(a, b + 1) = H(a, S(a, b))$$

and so on, where P, H, S denote, of course, pentation, hexation and septation respectively. If we tried to proceed much further with this notation we should soon run out of letters, and it becomes desirable to have a notation which will serve to name an endless succession of operations. A simple way of effecting this is to use a suffix to indicate which operation we are using, writing $O_1(a, b)$ for $a + b$, $O_2(a, b)$ for the second operation $a \times b$, $O_3(a, b)$ for the third operation a^b, $O_4(a, b)$ for the fourth operation, tetration, and so on. We can now write down *a single definition which covers all the operations at once*. For the relationship between $O_{n+1}(a, b)$ and $O_n(a, b)$ is simply

$$O_{n+1}(a, b + 1) = O_n(a, O_{n+1}(a, b))$$

which together with the initial conditions

$$O_n(a, 1) = a \text{ for } n \geqslant 2, \quad O_1(a, 1) = a + 1 \text{ and } O_0(a, b) = b + 1,$$

completely determines the value of $O_n(a, b)$ for any n, a, b. To see this we note that $O_0(a, b)$ is given for any a, b, and that if for some p, $O_p(a, b)$ is known for any a, b then $O_{p+1}(a, b)$ may be determined, since $O_{p+1}(a, 1)$ is given, and if we know $O_{p+1}(a, q)$ for some q, then $O_{p+1}(a, q + 1) = O_p(a, O_{p+1}(a, q))$ so that $O_{p+1}(a, q+1)$ is determined, and so by induction $O_{p+1}(a, b)$ is determined for any b, whence by a second induction it follows that $O_n(a, b)$ is determined for any n.

It is known to be impossible to define $O_{n+1}(a, b)$ directly in terms of $O_n(a, b)$ instead of, as above, in terms of $O_n(a, c)$ where c itself depends upon $O_{n+1}(a, b)$, and equally impossible to define $O_{n+1}(a, b + 1)$ in terms of $O_{n+1}(a, b)$ alone, without introducing also the function $O_n(a, b)$.

The arithmetic of remainders

When we divide a number a by a number $b > 1$, we may obtain any of the remainders $1, 2, 3, \ldots, b - 1$, or there may be no remainder. We shall denote the absence of a remainder by the same symbol 0 which we used to denote an empty wire. Since any number a, divided by itself, leaves no remainder we have $a = 1 \times a + 0 = a + 0$; hence we write also $a - a = 0$ (since we defined this to mean $a + 0 = a$) and we further *define* $0 + 0 = 0$, $a \times 0 = 0 \times a = 0 \times 0 = 0$. The commutative, associative and distributive properties of addition and multiplication are preserved as may readily be verified; thus $a(b + c) = ab + ac$ also when one or more of a, b, c is zero; for instance, if $c = 0$, we have

$$a(b + 0) = ab, \ ab + (a \times 0) = ab + 0 = ab$$

so that $a(b + 0) = ab + a \times 0$, and if for instance $a = b = 0$,

$$0(0 + c) = 0 \times c = 0, \ 0 \times a + 0 \times c = 0 + 0 = 0$$

so that again
$$0(0 + c) = 0 \times 0 + 0 \times c.$$

Let us now consider a fragment of arithmetic in which only the remainders on division by some number are retained. As a first example let us consider only the remainders on division by 5. These remainders are 0, 1, 2, 3, 4. The arithmetic we are going to construct is just like ordinary arithmetic with 0, 1, 2, 3, 4, except that after addition or multiplication we retain only the remainder on division by 5. For instance, if we add 3 and 4 we write 2 for the answer, not 7, because on division by five, 7 leaves the remainder 2; and if we multiply 3 by 4 the answer is again 2, since $3 \times 4 = 12$ and 12 leaves the remainder 2 on division by 5. To avoid confusion with ordinary arithmetic we denote addition now by $\oplus$, and multiplication by $\otimes$. Thus we have, for instance,

$$2 \oplus 4 = 1, \ 3 \oplus 2 = 0, \ 2 \otimes 4 = 3.$$

The complete addition and multiplication tables for remainders on division by 5 are:

$\oplus$	1	2	3	4
1	2	3	4	0
2	3	4	0	1
3	4	0	1	2
4	0	1	2	3

and

$\otimes$	1	2	3	4
1	1	2	3	4
2	2	4	1	3
3	3	1	4	2
4	4	3	2	1

To find a sum or product from the tables we look for the first factor in the left-hand column and the second factor in the top row; the square which lies in the chosen row and column gives the answer. In the multiplication table for instance, if we seek $2 \otimes 3$ we look for 2 in the left-hand column, and 3 in the top row, and then in the *row* through 2 and the *column* through 3 we find the entry 1, so that $2 \otimes 3 = 1$.

These tables reveal some remarkable features of this "little arithmetic". First we notice that, unlike ordinary arithmetic, there is no restriction on *subtraction*, (when as usual we define $a - b$ so that $b + (a - b) = a$); for in each row we find the number which must be added to the leading number in that row to give any chosen sum. For instance, to work out $2 \ominus 3$ we look for the number to add to 3 to produce 2; in the row through 3 we find the entry 2 in the column headed 4, so that 4 must be added to 3 to produce 2, i.e. $2 \ominus 3 = 4$. Similarly in the row through 4 we find the entry 2 in the column through 3, so that $2 \ominus 4 = 3$. The multiplication table reveals a corresponding completeness with respect to division; any number may be divided by any other, unlike the situation in ordinary arithmetic where divisibility is the exception rather than the rule (e.g. only one of 15, 16, 17, 18, 19, 20 is divisible by 6). The simplest way to check this is to observe that there is a 1 in every row and in every column, so that given any a, we can always find c, so that $a \otimes c = 1$; it follows that $a \otimes c \otimes b = b$, i.e. $a \otimes (b \otimes c) = b$, showing that $b \otimes c$ is what a must be multiplied by to give b, in other words, b is divisible by a with quotient $b \otimes c$. For example, $3 \otimes 2 = 1$, and so $3 \otimes 2 \otimes 4 = 4$, that is $2 \otimes 4 = 3$ is the quotient when 4 is divided by 3. Addition and multiplication in this arithmetic of remainders have all the familiar properties, and in fact, we have already taken the associative and commutative properties of multiplication for granted in finding the quotient. Since the number of numbers involved is only five (including 0) the verification of these properties may be made by a simple enumeration of all the cases, but these properties necessarily hold in the arithmetic of remainders just because they hold in ordinary arithmetic. For instance, since $a(b + c) = ab + ac$, for any a, b, c, therefore $a(b + c)$ and $ab + ac$ leave the same remainder on division by 5; now $b \oplus c$ is the remainder when $b + c$ is divided by 5, so that, if q is the quotient, $b + c = 5q + (b \oplus c)$, and therefore $a(b + c) = 5qa + a(b \oplus c)$; next let Q be the quotient when $a(b \oplus c)$ is divided by 5, so that $a(b \oplus c) = 5Q + a \otimes (b \oplus c)$, and therefore

$$a(b + c) = 5(Q + qa) + a \otimes (b \oplus c)$$

which shows that $a \otimes (b \oplus c)$ is the remainder when $a(b + c)$ is divided by 5. Next we write B and C for the quotients when ab and ac are divided by 5, so that

$$ab = 5B + a \otimes b$$
$$ac = 5C + a \otimes c$$

and therefore

$$ab + ac = 5(B + C) + a \otimes b + a \otimes c;$$

finally let A be the quotient when $a \otimes b + a \otimes c$ is divided by 5, so that

$$a \otimes b + a \otimes c = 5A + (a \otimes b) \oplus (a \otimes c)$$

and therefore

$$ab + ac = 5(A + B + C) + (a \otimes b) \oplus (a \otimes c)$$

showing that $(a \otimes b) \oplus (a \otimes c)$ is the remainder when $ab + ac$ is divided by 5. Since, as we have already observed, $a(b + c)$ and $ab + ac$ leave the same remainder, therefore

$$a \otimes (b \oplus c) = a \otimes b \oplus a \otimes c$$

proving the distributive law in the arithmetic of remainders.

The arithmetic of remainders on division by a number q is called the *arithmetic modulo q*. For any q, addition and multiplication in the arithmetic modulo q, is commutative, associative and distributive, and subtraction is unrestricted, but division is unrestricted *only* if q is a prime number. For instance, in the arithmetic modulo 4 the multiplication table is

$\otimes$	1	2	3
1	1	2	3
2	2	0	2
3	3	2	1

and in this table we see that 1 is missing from the second row, so that we cannot find an a such that $2 \otimes a = 1$, and therefore division of 1 by 2 is not now possible.

What is more remarkable, a product of two non-zero factors may be zero, since $2 \otimes 2 = 0$, whereas in ordinary arithmetic — and in the arithmetic modulo a prime number — a product is not zero unless a factor is zero. The effect of this is that *cancellation* is not possible in the arithmetic modulo 4, that is to say, we cannot proceed from

$$ax = bx$$

to

$$a = b,$$

even when x is different from zero (e.g. $2 \times 3 = 2 \times 1$ but it does not follow that $3 = 1$).

In common arithmetic the passage from

$$ax = bx,$$

with a non-zero x, to $a = b$, relies on the distributive law $(a - b)\,x = ax - bx$, which takes us from $ax = bx$ to $(a - b)x = 0$, and since x is not zero, and no product cd is zero with non-zero c, d, this entails that $a - b = 0$, whence $a = b$. This proof is equally valid in the arithmetic modulo a prime number, but fails in the arithmetic modulo a non-prime number.

An arithmetic in which addition and multiplication, subtraction and division (excluding division by zero) are possible for any pair of numbers without restriction is called a *field*. Thus the arithmetic modulo 5 is a field, but the arithmetic modulo 6 is *not*, nor is common arithmetic. An arithmetic in which addition, multiplication and subtraction are unrestricted (but division may not be) is called a *ring*. Thus the arithmetic modulo 6 is a ring, but common arithmetic is not. We shall later meet further examples of rings and fields. To make the notion of field and ring more precise, let us enumerate their properties in detail.

A field has two operations (which we call addition and multiplication and denote by $+$ and $\times$).

These operations are commutative, associative and distributive, and both are freely reversible, that is to say, for any a and b there are numbers d and q such that $b + d = a$ and $bq = a$ (provided that, in the latter case, b does not satisfy $a + b = a$).

A ring also has two operations which are commutative, associative and distributive, but only one of these, addition, is freely reversible.

(Rings and fields may be divided into commutative and noncommutative rings and fields according as their multiplication is commutative or not; if the multiplication is not commutative it is necessary that two forms of the distributive law, namely

$$a\,(b + c) = ab + ac$$
$$(b + c)\,a = ba + ca$$

both be satisfied.)

The fundamental theorem of arithmetic

It is one of the most fundamental properties of prime numbers that a prime can only divide a product of two numbers (without remainder) if it divides one of its factors. For instance, if both a and

b are odd numbers, so that neither is divisible by 2, then ab is also odd; for if a', b' are the quotients when a, b are divided by 2, so that

$$a = 2a' + 1, \; b = 2b' + 1$$

then $ab = 2(2a'b' + a' + b') + 1$, showing that ab is not divisible by 2, but leaves the remainder 1.

To show that every prime has this property, we start by noting some simple properties of divisibility. If a and b are both divisible by c, then so are $a + b$, and $a - b$; for denoting the respective quotients by a', b' we have

$$a = ca', \; b = cb', \text{ and so } a + b = c(a' + b'),$$

$$a - b = c(a' - b').$$

It follows that if a is not divisible by c then neither $a + c$ nor $a - c$ is divisible by c (for if $a - c$ were divisible by c, then $(a - c) + c$ would be divisible by c, i.e. a would be divisible by c). If a and b leave the same remainder on division by c, and $a > b$, then $a - b$ is divisible by c, for denoting the remainder by r and the quotients by a', b', we have $a - b = (ca' + r) - (cb' + r) = c(a' - b')$; conversely if $a - b$ is divisible by c, then both a and b leave the same remainder on division by c; for if $b = cb' + r$ and $a - b = cd$, then $a = b + cd = c(d + b') + r$, showing that a, too, leaves the remainder r on division by c.

Suppose now that there is a prime number which divides some product without dividing one of its factors; let p be the smallest such prime, and let ab be the smallest product which p divides without dividing either of the factors a, b. Necessarily both a and b are smaller than p, since if one of them, a suppose, is greater than p, then $(a - p)b = ab - pb$ is a smaller product than ab which is divisible by p without either of its factors $a - p$, b being divisible by p. Let q be the quotient when ab is divided by p, so that

$$ab = pq;$$

let f be a prime factor of a, then f divides pq and so (since $f < p$) f divides q (for p is prime). If a', q' are the respective quotients when f divides a, q, then

$$fa'b = fpq'$$

and so
$$a'b = pq'$$

which shows that $a'b$ is divisible by p; but $a'b < ab$ and neither a' nor b is divisible by p, which contradicts our supposition that ab is the smallest such product. Since the assumption that there is a prime which divides some product without dividing one of its factors has proved to be false, it follows that a prime can only divide a product if it divides one of the factors. Another way of expressing this is to say that the *only* products divisible by p are the multiples of multiples of p, $a \times bp$.

A simple, but very important consequence of this result, is that if a number a is divisible by a prime p and by a prime q, then it is divisible by the product pq; for if a' is the quotient when a is divided by p, then
$$a = pa';$$

since a is divisible by q, therefore either p or a' is divisible by q, and since p is prime, it follows that a' is divisible by q, with quotient a'' say, so that
$$a = pqa''$$

showing that a is divisible by pq.

Every number is expressible as a product of primes. For if we divide a number a by one of its prime factors, p, say, with quotient a' we have
$$a = pa', \text{ and } a' < a;$$

next divide a' by one of its prime factors p', with quotient a'' so that
$$a' = p'a'', a'' < a',$$
and therefore,
$$a = pp'a'', a'' < a' < a;$$

divide a'' by one of its prime factors p' with quotient p'' then
$$a = pp'p''a''', \text{ with } a''' < a'' < a' < a,$$

and so on. Since there are at most $a - 1$ numbers less than a (the numbers $1, 2, 3, \ldots, a - 1$) the process comes to an end in at most $a - 1$ steps, giving a as a product of at most $a - 1$ prime factors
$$pp'p'' \ ..$$

The primes $p, p', p'', \ldots$ are not necessarily all different. For example

$$12250 = 7 \times 1750$$
$$= 7 \times 7 \times 250$$
$$= 7 \times 7 \times 5 \times 50$$
$$= 7 \times 7 \times 5 \times 5 \times 10$$
$$= 7 \times 7 \times 5 \times 5 \times 5 \times 2.$$

Apart from changes in the *order* of the factors, *a number can be represented in only one way as a product of primes.* For if a is expressed both as a product of primes $pqr \ldots$ and as a product of primes $p'q'r' \ldots$ then

$$pqrs \ldots = p'q'r's' \ldots;$$

thus $p'q'r's' \ldots$ is divisible by p; either $p' = p$, or p', being prime, is *not* divisible by p. If p' is different from p it follows that $q'r's' \ldots$ is divisible by p; hence again, either $q' = p$ or $r's' \ldots$ is divisible by p. Continuing in this way we see that one of the primes $p', q', r', \ldots$ must be equal to p, and (perhaps by changing the arrangement) we may take this prime to be p'. Since $p = p'$, therefore

$$qrs \ldots = q'r's' \ldots$$

and exactly as before we may show that one of $q', r', s', \ldots$ is equal to q, and so on. Thus every one of the primes $p, q, r, \ldots$ appears on the right as often as it appears on the left. Exactly the same argument shows that every prime $p', q', r', \ldots$ appears on the left as often as it appears on the right, and therefore $p', q', r', s', \ldots$ consists precisely of the primes $p, q, r, s, \ldots$.

If b and c have no common prime factor and if ab is divisible by c, then a itself must be divisible by c. For if c is a product of primes $pqr \ldots$ and if the quotient of ab divided by c is k, then

$$ab = kpqr \ldots;$$

thus p divides ab, but not b, and so p divides a, with quotient a', say, whence $a = a'p$,

$$pa'b = kpqr \ldots$$

and therefore,

$$a'b = kqr \ldots;$$

hence q divides a', with quotient a'', and therefore $a = a''pq$, and

$$a''b = kr \ldots;$$

proceeding in this way until all the factors of c are exhausted we find

$$a = Apqr \ldots$$

for some A and all the prime factors $p, q, r, \ldots$ of c repeated as often as they occur in c.

We come now to a general result of which we noticed particular cases when we considered the arithmetic of remainders. It is this: if a and $b > 1$ have no common factor, then there is a number x such that

$$ax = 1, \text{ modulo } b,$$

i.e. ax leaves the remainder 1 on division by b. Consider the multiples of a

$$1 \times a, \ 2a, \ 3a, \ \ldots, \ (b-1)a;$$

none of these is divisible by b, for a and b have no common factor and r is not divisible by b, if $1 \leqslant r < b$; nor is the difference $(r - s)a$ of any two of these multiples ra, sa for the same reason. Hence these $b - 1$ multiples of a all leave different remainders on division by b; but there are only $b - 1$ possible remainders, namely $1, 2, \ldots, b - 1$, and so the multiples

$$a, \ 2a, \ 3a, \ \ldots, \ (b-1)a$$

leave the remainders $1, 2, 3, \ldots, b - 1$ in *some order*. In other words one of these multiples, xa, say, leaves the remainder 1. Incidentally we have shown that if r is any number from 1 to $b - 1$, then there is some multiple of a, say ka, which leaves the remainder r on division by b, and therefore if l is the quotient,

$$ka - r = lb,$$

that is,

$$ka - lb = r.$$

In particular, if y is the quotient when xa is divided by b, we have

$$\mathbf{xa - yb = 1.}$$

Thus we have shown that if a, b have no common factor, then there exist numbers x and y such that xa and yb differ by unity.

Suppose now that a, b have a common factor; let h be their *greatest* common factor, so that a, b are both divisible by h, with quotients a', b' say. Then a', b' have no common factor, for otherwise we can find $k > 1$ and a'', b'' so that $a' = ka''$, $b' = kb''$, and so $a = hka''$, $b = hkb''$ and a, b have the common factor hk which is greater than h. Since a', b' have no common factor there exist x, y such that

$$xa' - yb' = 1$$

and therefore

$$xha' - yhb' = h,$$

i.e.

$$xa - yb = h,$$

showing that the greatest common factor is expressible as the difference of a multiple of a and a multiple of b. It follows that every number which divides both a and b also divides h, so that h is the greatest common factor in this sense also.

We shall illustrate a method of *finding* values of x and y such that

$$xa - yb = 1$$

by means of examples.

The equation $ax - by = 1$

Our first example is to find x and y such that

$$5x - 11y = 1;$$

consider the cyclic rearrangement of the numbers 1 to 11 in which 1 is carried into $1 + 5 = 6$; this rearrangement is shown in the following figure

1	2	3	4	5	6	7	8	9	10	11
6	7	8	9	10	11	1	2	3	4	5

(note that 5 stands below 11, and this fixes the rearrangement quite mechanically.)

Starting with 5 in the upper row, we pass to 10 in the line below, then look for 10 in the upper row and pass to 4 below it, continuing in this way through the sequence 9, 3, 8, 2, 7, 1, and stopping when we reach 1. The complete sequence is

$$5, 10, 4, 9, 3, 8, 2, 7, 1$$

which contains 9 numbers; then 9 is the value of x and we find y simply by dividing $5 \times 9 - 1 = 44$ by 11, giving $y = 4$. Thus values of x and y are 9 and 4 respectively; of course these values are not unique for we can add any multiple of 11, to the value of x, provided we add the same multiple of 5 to the value of y. For

$$5(x + 11k) - 11(y + 5k) = 5x - 11y.$$

The same method enables us to find values of x and y to satisfy

$$5x - 11y = r$$

for any r between 1 and 11. For instance to find values of x, y such that

$$5x - 11y = 3,$$

we run through the same sequence as before

$$5, 10, 4, 9, 3$$

stopping this time when we reach 3; the sequence now has 5 terms, so that a value of x is 5 and the corresponding value of y is found on dividing $5 \times 5 - 3 = 22$ by 11, giving y the value 2. (If r is greater than 11 we subtract a multiple of 11 from both sides; for instance if $5x - 11y = 25$, then $5x - 11(y + 2) = 3$, subtracting 2×11 from both sides.) As a last example we consider

$$13x - 9y = 1;$$

this time (because $13 > 9$) we start by writing $13x$ in the form $4x + 9x$ and the equation becomes

$$4x - 9(y - x) = 1$$

and proceeding exactly as before we obtain the sequence

$$4, 8, 3, 7, 2, 6, 1$$

which contains 7 numbers, so that the value of x is 7; the value of y is $13 \times 7 - 1 = 90$ divided by 9, i.e. $y = 10$.

To see why the method works let us consider again the first example, $5x - 11y = 1$.

In the rearrangement

1	2	3	4	5	6	7	8	9	10	11
6	7	8	9	10	11	1	2	3	4	5

to find the number *below* a number n in the top line we take the remainder when $n + 5$ is divided by 11. The sequence of numbers

$$5, 10, 4, 9, 3, 8, 2, 7, 1$$

are therefore the remainders when we divide the multiples of 5,

$$1 \times 5, \ 2 \times 5, \ 3 \times 5, \ 4 \times 5, \ 6 \times 5, \ 7 \times 5, \ 8 \times 5, \ 9 \times 5$$

in turn by 11. The number of numbers in this sequence (viz. 9) is precisely the multiple of 5 (9×5) which leaves the remainder 1, as required. That there always is such a multiple we proved before.

The measuring problem

This same method also solves a rather harder problem, of great antiquity, that of measuring a chosen amount of water with two measuring jars of known capacity. Suppose for instance that we wish to measure 1 pint of water with two jars of capacities 5 pints and 11 pints. We consider the same cyclic rearrangement as before;

1	2	3	4	5	6	7	8	9	10	11
6	7	8	9	10	11	1	2	3	4	5

and the same sequence of numbers

$$5, 10, 4, 9, 3, 8, 2, 7, 1.$$

These numbers tell us the quantities of water we must measure in turn to obtain 1 pint. We start by filling the 5 pint jar, transfer its contents to the larger jar and then pour in another 5 pints. Fill the 5 pint jar again, fill the 11 pint jar from it (only 1 pint goes in) leaving 4 pints. Empty the large jar and pour the 4 pints into it, followed by a further 5 pints, making 9 in all. Fill the large jar from the small again, leaving now 3 pints in the small jar, which we again transfer to the large jar (after emptying it). Continuing in this way to fill the larger jar from the small one, and then transferring the contents to the large jar, we produce in turn 2, 7 and finally 1 pint. The explanation is simply that in passing from a number in the first row to one in the second we add 5 (the contents of the smaller jar) or, if the sum is greater than 11, we add 5 and take away 11 (i.e. empty the contents of the large jar).

The explorer problem

A problem which may be solved using both scales of notation and equations of the form

$$ax - by = 1$$

is the explorer problem. Five explorers keep a monkey to pick nuts for them. After some nuts have been collected they go to sleep. One explorer awakens, gives a nut to the monkey and takes a fifth of the rest for himself. Then the second awakens, gives the monkey two nuts and takes for himself two-fifths of the remainder. The third explorer then gives the monkey three nuts and takes three-fifths of the remainder for himself. The fourth gives the monkey four nuts and takes four-fifths, and the last gives the monkey five nuts and keeps the remainder. What is the smallest number of nuts which make such a share-out possible? Let the number be

$$a + b \times 5 + c \times 5^2 + d \times 5^3 + \cdots;$$

since the first explorer gives the monkey only 1 nut and then has left a multiple of 5, we take $a = 1$, so that the remainder after the first man takes his share is

$$4b + 4 \times 5c + 4 \times 5^2 d + \cdots.$$

If a multiple of 5 remains after subtracting 2, $4b - 2$ is divisible by 5, and solving the equation

$$4b - 5b' = 2$$

we find $b = 3$, $b' = 2$, and the remainder after the second man takes his share is

$$3 \times 2 + 3 \times 4c + 3 \times 4 \times 5d + \cdots.$$

Since a multiple of 5 remains after subtracting 3, $12c + 3$ is divisible by 5, and solving the equation

$$12c + 3 = 5c'$$

we find $c = 1$, $c' = 3$, and the remainder after the third share has been taken is

$$2 \times 3 + 2 \times 3 \times 4d + \cdots.$$

Subtracting 4 leaves a multiple of 5 if

$$24d + 2 = 5d',$$

a solution of which is $d = 2$, $d' = 10$, and the remainder after the fourth has his share is

$$10 + \cdots.$$

Thus the smallest number which fulfills the given conditions is

$$1 + 3 \times 5 + 1 \times 5^2 + 2 \times 5^3$$

which equals 291.

Groups

Rearrangements, like the rearrangement of the numbers one to eleven we have been considering, exemplify one of the most fundamental structures in mathematics, the structure known as a *group*. Consider first all the arrangements of the three numbers 1, 2, 3. Since any one of the three may come first, there are three ways of starting an arrangement; when the first number has been chosen there remain two from which to choose the second number, and when the first two are in place, the third is then fixed, so that there are in all $3 \times 2 \times 1 = 6$ arrangements, which we exhibit below, giving each arrangement a name

$$I = \begin{pmatrix} 1 & 2 & 3 \\ 1 & 2 & 3 \end{pmatrix}, \qquad A = \begin{pmatrix} 1 & 2 & 3 \\ 1 & 3 & 2 \end{pmatrix}, \qquad B = \begin{pmatrix} 1 & 2 & 3 \\ 2 & 1 & 3 \end{pmatrix},$$

$$C = \begin{pmatrix} 1 & 2 & 3 \\ 2 & 3 & 1 \end{pmatrix}, \qquad D = \begin{pmatrix} 1 & 2 & 3 \\ 3 & 1 & 2 \end{pmatrix}, \qquad E = \begin{pmatrix} 1 & 2 & 3 \\ 3 & 2 & 1 \end{pmatrix},$$

the notation showing which number occupies the first, second and third place respectively.

In the arrangement called I there has been no change of position at all; in A we have changed 2 into 3 and 3 into 2; in C all three numbers have been changed, 1 into 2, 2 into 3 and 3 into 1. The rearrangements may therefore be looked upon as replacements, D for instance being regarded as an order to replace 1 by 3, 2 by 1 and 3 by 2.

We are going to see the effect of first carrying out one change of order and then following it by another. For instance if we first perform order change A, and then order change E, we find that 1 first remains unchanged and is then changed to 3; 2 is carried into 3 (in A) and then 3 is carried into 1 (in E); 3 is carried into 2 (in A) and then 2 is carried into 2 (in E). Thus the effect of carrying out first the rearrangement A and then E is to take 1 into 3, 2 into 1 and 3 into 2, which is rearrangement D. Thus the effect of A followed by E is D, which we denote by

$$A * E = D$$

the * simply being the operation 'followed by'.

If we perform E first and then A, we obtain not D, but C, thus

$$E * A = C.$$

The complete list of 'multiplications' is

$$A * I = I * A = A, \ B * I = I * B = B, \ C * I = I * C = C,$$
$$D * I = I * D = D, \ E * I = I * E = E,$$

$$A * B = C, \quad A * C = B, \quad A * D = E, \quad A * E = D,$$
$$B * A = D, \quad C * A = E, \quad D * A = B, \quad E * A = C,$$

$$B * C = E, \quad B * D = A, \quad B * E = C,$$
$$C * B = A, \quad D * B = E, \quad E * B = D,$$

$$C * D = I, \quad C * E = B, \quad D * E = A,$$
$$D * C = I, \quad E * C = A, \quad E * D = B,$$

and finally

$$I * I = I, \quad A * A = I, \quad B * B = I, \quad C * C = D,$$
$$D * D = C, \quad E * E = I.$$

These results are far more readily surveyed in the form of a multiplication table

*	I	A	B	C	D	E
I	I	A	B	C	D	E
A	A	I	C	B	E	D
B	B	D	I	E	A	C
C	C	E	A	D	I	B
D	D	B	E	I	C	A
E	E	C	D	A	B	I

The table exhibits a number of interesting features.

Clearly I behaves exactly like unity in ordinary multiplication, leaving every number unchanged. Next we notice that each row and each column contains all the names I to E exactly once, and in particular that there is an I in each row and in each column.

In one striking respect the table differs from a multiplication table for the operation is *not commutative*; note for instance that $A * B = C$, but $B * A = D$. The operation $*$ is, however, associative. It would be very tiresome to test every group of three names to verify this fact, but fortunately it is not necessary.

Let us denote three arbitrary arrangements by

$$\begin{pmatrix} 1 & 2 & 3 \\ a & b & c \end{pmatrix}, \qquad \begin{pmatrix} 1 & 2 & 3 \\ 1' & 2' & 3' \end{pmatrix}, \qquad \begin{pmatrix} 1 & 2 & 3 \\ 1° & 2° & 3° \end{pmatrix},$$

where a, b, c; $1', 2', 3'$; $1°, 2°, 3°$ are each some arrangement of the numbers 1, 2, 3, ($1'$ denoting the number 1 is changed to in the second arrangement, $1°$ denoting the number 1 is changed to in the third, and so on). Then

$$\begin{pmatrix} 1 & 2 & 3 \\ a & b & c \end{pmatrix} * \begin{pmatrix} 1 & 2 & 3 \\ 1' & 2' & 3' \end{pmatrix} = \begin{pmatrix} 1 & 2 & 3 \\ a' & b' & c' \end{pmatrix},$$

$$\begin{pmatrix} 1 & 2 & 3 \\ a' & b' & c' \end{pmatrix} * \begin{pmatrix} 1 & 2 & 3 \\ 1° & 2° & 3° \end{pmatrix} = \begin{pmatrix} 1 & 2 & 3 \\ a'° & b'° & c'° \end{pmatrix},$$

(where a' denotes the number a is transformed to in the second arrangement, and a'° what a' is changed to under the third arrangement, etc.)

$$\begin{pmatrix} 1 & 2 & 3 \\ 1' & 2' & 3' \end{pmatrix} * \begin{pmatrix} 1 & 2 & 3 \\ 1^\circ & 2^\circ & 3^\circ \end{pmatrix} = \begin{pmatrix} 1 & 2 & 3 \\ 1'^\circ & 2'^\circ & 3'^\circ \end{pmatrix},$$

and finally

$$\begin{pmatrix} 1 & 2 & 3 \\ a & b & c \end{pmatrix} * \begin{pmatrix} 1 & 2 & 3 \\ 1'^\circ & 2'^\circ & 3'^\circ \end{pmatrix} = \begin{pmatrix} 1 & 2 & 3 \\ a'^\circ & b'^\circ & c'^\circ \end{pmatrix}$$

which shows that

$$\left[\begin{pmatrix} 1 & 2 & 3 \\ a & b & c \end{pmatrix} * \begin{pmatrix} 1 & 2 & 3 \\ 1' & 2' & 3' \end{pmatrix} \right] * \begin{pmatrix} 1 & 2 & 3 \\ 1^\circ & 2^\circ & 3^\circ \end{pmatrix}$$

$$= \begin{pmatrix} 1 & 2 & 3 \\ a & b & c \end{pmatrix} * \left[\begin{pmatrix} 1 & 2 & 3 \\ 1' & 2' & 3' \end{pmatrix} * \begin{pmatrix} 1 & 2 & 3 \\ 1^\circ & 2^\circ & 3^\circ \end{pmatrix} \right]$$

that is, the operation $*$ is associative.

Thus in relation to the elements I, A, B, C, D, E the operation $*$ has the following properties:

1. For any elements $X, Y, X * Y$ is another element.
2. The operation $*$ is associative.
3. There is an element I such that $I * X = X * I$ for all elements X; I is called the neutral element or unity.
4. To each element X there is an element Y such that $X * Y = Y * X = I$

(this is revealed by the presence of an I in each row and column of the table); X and Y are called *inverse* elements.

A set of elements with an operation which has all these four properties is called a *group*. (More precisely the elements form a group with respect to the operation.)

We have already had examples of groups in the arithmetic of remainders. For instance the remainders *modulo* 3 form a group with respect to addition and the non-zero remainders form a group with respect to multiplication. The addition and multiplication tables are

+	0	1	2
0	0	1	2
1	1	2	0
2	2	0	1

×	1	2
1	1	2
2	2	1

For addition the neutral element is 0, the inverses of 0, 1, 2, are 0, 2, 1 respectively; (this group is commutative). For multiplication the neutral element is 1 and each of 1, 2 is its own inverse (and the group is again commutative).

A geometrical example is the group of rotations which restore an equilateral triangle to its original position. We may, for instance, rotate the triangle round its centre through a third of a revolution, or two thirds of a revolution, (clockwise or anticlockwise); or we may give it half a revolution round an altitude.

If we name the three vertices 1, 2, 3 and the original positions they occupy A, B, C, then the result of making a third of a revolution about the centre is shown in Fig. 2, and that of two-thirds of a revolution in Fig. 3. A half-turn round the altitude through A is shown in Fig. 4, and half-turns round the other two altitudes are shown in Figs. 5, 6. To see that these revolutions form a group, we remark, first, that the result of two consecutive rotations is a rotation; for instance, if we make a third of a turn round the centre, and then half a turn round the altitude through A we pass from Fig. 1 to Fig. 2 and then to Fig. 5, which may be obtained directly by a rotation round the altitude through B. The inverse of any rotation is of course a rotation in the opposite sense, or what comes to the same thing, a forward rotation to complete a full turn.

Let us denote a rotation around the centre by a third of a revolution by r, and rotation by two-thirds of a revolution by s. Next denote a rotation round the altitude through A by a, and similarly rotations round the altitudes through B, C by b, c respectively; using a cross $x \times y$ to denote a rotation x followed by a rotation y, we readily construct the following multiplication table, by studying the Figs. 1 to 6. We denote by i any rotation which leaves the

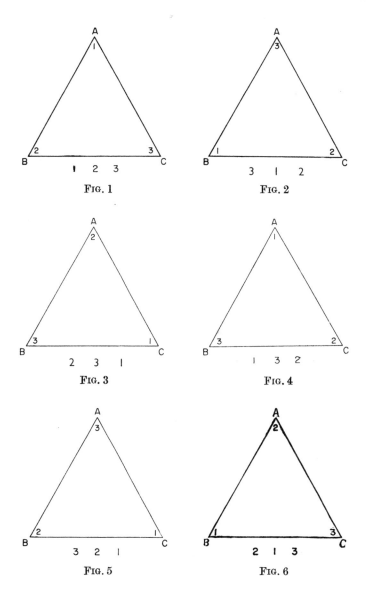

FIG. 1

FIG. 2

FIG. 3

FIG. 4

FIG. 5

FIG. 6

vertices in their original position (for instance a full turn around an altitude or about the centre).

×	i	r	s	a	b	c
i	i	r	s	a	b	c
r	r	s	i	b	c	a
s	s	i	r	c	a	b
a	a	c	b	i	s	r
b	b	a	c	r	i	s
c	c	b	a	s	r	i

Let us now match the rotations with the rearrangements of the vertices, using the names for these rearrangements on page 56. For instance, Fig. 2 shows the rearrangement

$$\begin{pmatrix} 1 & 2 & 3 \\ 3 & 1 & 2 \end{pmatrix}$$

i.e. D. Matching all the figures with rearrangements in this way, we obtain

$$i \leftrightarrow I, \quad r \leftrightarrow C, \quad s \leftrightarrow D, \quad a \leftrightarrow A, \quad b \leftrightarrow E, \quad c \leftrightarrow B$$

If we now compare the multiplication table above with that for rearrangements on page 58, the interesting fact emerges that this matching is *preserved under multiplication*. For instance,

$$s \leftrightarrow D,$$
$$b \leftrightarrow E,$$
$$s \times b = a \leftrightarrow A = D \times E$$

and

$$r \leftrightarrow C,$$
$$a \leftrightarrow A,$$
$$r \times a = b \leftrightarrow E = C \times A.$$

Groups which may be matched in such a way that the group operations are preserved, are said to be *isomorphic*. Thus the group of rotations which leave an equilateral triangle *in situ*, and the groups of arrangements of three things, are isomorphic. Not all groups of the same number of terms are isomorphic. For instance, the group with elements

$$1, k, k^2, k^3, k^4, k^5$$

(where $k^6 = 1$, so that $k^3 \times k^4 = k$, $k^3 \times k^5 = k^2$, etc.) is not isomorphic to the foregoing groups; groups in which all the elements are powers of a single element are said to be cyclic. Two cyclic groups with the same number of elements are isomorphic (and in fact *any* two groups with the same prime numbers of elements are isomorphic, being necessarily cyclic groups). A group isomorphic to a cyclic group is itself cyclic, but the rotations group is not cyclic, for the powers of r are

$$r^2 = s, \quad r^3 = i,$$

the powers of s are

$$s^2 = r, \quad s^3 = i,$$

and the powers of a, b, c are simply

$$a^2 = b^2 = c^2 = i,$$

showing that no single element can generate the whole group.

A geometrical example of a cyclic group of six elements is the group of rotations of a regular hexagon round its centre, through one-sixth of a revolution, one third, one half, two-thirds, and five-sixths of a revolution.

If we look again at the multiplication table of the group of rotations of a triangle, we see that the pair i, a by itselfs forms a group, as indeed do the pairs, i, b; i, c. So too the three elements i, r, s form a group. These groups are called *subgroups* of the triangle group. The number of elements in a subgroup is always a factor of the number of elements in the group. The triangle group itself is not commutative (for instance $a \times b = s$, $b \times a = r$), but all the subgroups i, a; i, b; i, c; i, r, s are commutative (the element i by itself forms a group and this group, together with the whole group, is also counted as a subgroup, a trivial or improper subgroup).

If x and y are any elements of a group and if $\bar{y}$ is the inverse of y, then the element

$$\bar{y} \times x \times y$$

is called the *transform* of x by y. For instance, in the triangle group the transform of a by r is

$$s \times a \times r = b$$

since s is the inverse of r $(r \times s = i)$; the transform of r by a is

$$a \times r \times a = s;$$

but the transform of r by s is

$$r \times r \times s = r$$

so that r is unchanged, *invariant*, under transformation by s.

If every element of a subgroup is unchanged or changed into another element of the subgroup, by transformation by *any* element of the group, the subgroup is said to be *normal*, or *invariant*. For instance, in the group of rotations of a triangle the subgroup i, r, s is normal, for i itself is unchanged by transformation by any element, and r, s are either unchanged or are changed into each other.

In a non-commutative group there may be some elements whose product is commutative; for instance, the elements r, s in the group of the triangle. If we fix our attention on any particular element x, say, in a group, the elements which commute (multiply commutatively) with x all lie in a subgroup called the *normalisor* of x. In the triangle group the normalisor of a is the subgroup i, a and the normalisor of r is the subgroup i, r, s. Those elements of a group which commute with every element of the group, also form a subgroup called the *centre* of the group; the centre of the triangle group contains only the single element i.

If N is a normal subgroup of a group G, then the set of elements obtained by multiplying each element of N by some element g of G is called the *coset* of g and denoted by gN (the order of multiplication is indifferent, N is normal and so for any element n of N, $\bar{g} \times n \times g$ is also an element n' say of N, where $\bar{g}$ is the inverse of g, and from

$$\bar{g} \times n \times g = n'$$

multiplying on the left by g we obtain

$$n \times g = g \times n',$$

showing that multiplying n on the right by g gives the same element as multiplying n' on the left by g). Each element of a group belongs to exactly one coset, for if a belongs to the coset of b then the coset of b coincides with the coset of a; for if there is some element n of N, (with inverse $\bar{n}$) such that $a = b \times n$, then $a \times \bar{n} = b$, so that b belongs to the coset of a, and if c is any element of the coset of b there is an element n_1 of N such that

$$b \times n_1 = c$$

and so

$$a \times n \times n_1 = c,$$

and since $n \times n_1$ is an element of N, this shows that c belongs to the coset of a. Similarly, every element of the coset of a belongs to the coset of b.

If we *define* the product of two cosets gN, hN as the coset $(g \times h)N$, then the class of cosets of a normal subgroup N of a group G forms a group called the *factor group* G/N. The cosets of the normal subgroups i, r, s of the triangle group are

$$F_1 = (i, r, s); \quad F_2 = (a, b, c)$$

and these form a group ($F_1^2 = F_1$, $F_1 \times F_2 = F_2 = F_2 \times F_1$, and $F_2^2 = F_1$, so that F_1 is the group unit, and F_2 is its own inverse). The number of elements in N, G are 6, 3 respectively and the number of elements in the factor group is $6/3 = 2$.

Semigroups

If we drop the requirement that each element shall have an inverse, and that there should be a unit element, then the system that results is called a semigroup. Thus the elements of a semigroup satisfy only two conditions:

(1) if a, b are elements, then ab is an element;

(2) $a(bc)$ is the same element as $(ab)c$.

A semigroup is *generated* by its *alphabet*, that is a collection of elements from which all other elements may be obtained by the semigroup operation (which we are denoting simply by juxtaposition). The elements generated by the alphabet are called *words*. Thus in a semigroup with alphabet a, b, c some of the words are

$$abcca, \quad ababba, \quad cccbca.$$

Just as in a group, there may be coincidences between words, for instance aba and bac may be the same element. We denote such coincidences by means of equations, writing for instance

$$aba = ccba.$$

When two words are equal one may be substituted for the other in a longer word which contains it. For instance, if

$$aba = ccba,$$

then

$$ccabacb = ccccbacb.$$

The problem we consider is the problem of finding out whether two words in a semigroup are equal or not. If there is a quite mechanical procedure for determining in a finite number of steps whether *any* two words in a given semigroup are equal or not, we say that the *word problem* for this semigroup is solvable.

As a first example we consider the semigroup (due to G. S. Zeitin) with alphabet a, b, c, d, e and word equalities

1. $ac = ca$ 5. $abac = abacc$
2. $ad = da$ 6. $eca = ae$
3. $bc = cb$ 7. $edb = be$.
4. $bd = db$

Let us consider whether or not the words $abaacd$ and $acbdad$ are equal. To see that they are not we observe that in every equation the letter a appears equally often on the left and right hand sides of the equation, and so no substitution can change the number of a's in the word. Since the word $abaacd$ contains 3 a's, and the word $acbdad$ only two, they cannot be equal.

Consider next the *commutative* semigroup with alphabet a, b, c, d, e. This semigroup has 10 equations of the form $xy = yx$ (where x and y are to be replaced by letters of the alphabet) and no other equations. It is easy to see that this semigroup has a solvable word problem, for in each equation a letter appears *once only* on each side, and so no substitution can alter the number of times a letter appears in a word. Thus two words can be equal if, and only if, each letter appears the same number of times in the two words. And if two words contain the same letters repeated the same number of times (but in different orders), then the words are equal, for in a commutative semigroup, the order of letters is irrelevant.

An interesting variation of the word problem arises when we allow, not just substitution of one word for another, but also deletions of words. To show that a word may be deleted we add a symbol $\square$ to our alphabet and equate the word which may be deleted to $\square$. For instance, in the semigroup with alphabet a, b, c, and equation $ab = \square$, the word $aaabbbc$ may be successively transformed into $aabbc$, abc, c, by striking out ab.

As a final example of the word problem we consider the semigroup with alphabet a, b, c and equations

$$b = acc, \quad ca = accc, \quad aa = cccc = \square.$$

We solve the word problem for this semigroup by showing that each word has a unique standard form.

To construct the standard form of a word we carry out the following substitutions,

$$b \to acc, \quad ca \to accc, \quad aa \to \square, \quad cccc \to \square.$$

These substitutions are all allowed by the equations of the semigroup (and are only a few of the allowable substitutions, since, for instance, the equation $b = acc$ allows both the substitutions $b \to acc$, and $acc \to b$).

The substitutions we have listed have the following effects. The substitution $b \to acc$ allows us to eliminate the letter b from a word, and so too the substitutions $aa \to \square$ and $cccc \to \square$ eliminate a recurrence of the letter a, and reduce any recurrence of c's to three. Furthermore whenever c comes before an a we can exchange them by writing $accc$ for ca. It follows that the result of these substitutions is to bring any word to one of the standard forms

$$\square, c, cc, ccc, a, ac, acc, accc,$$

for if we seek to write either an a or ac in front of, or behind, any one of these words, we obtain one of the other standard words, or the word itself, after substitution. For instance $aaccc$ goes into $accc$ and cca into $ccaccc$ and then, in turn, into $caccccc$, $cacc$, $acccc$, ac. As examples of reduction to standard form we consider the word $cacb$. Eliminating b first, and then making the appropriate substitutions we obtain in turn the chain of words

$$ca\mathbf{c}b, \quad \mathbf{c}acacc, \quad acccca cc, \quad accca ccccc,$$

$$ac\mathbf{c}accccccc, \quad aca ccccccccccc,$$

$$\mathbf{a}accccccccccccc, \quad cccccccccccccc,$$

$$ccccccccc, \quad ccccc, \quad cc,$$

the letters in bold print being the letters on which a substitution is made.

If a word W is reduced to the standard form S, then $W = S$, for the substitutions which take us from W to S *keep words equal*. Thus if two words are equal they will have equal standard forms. If we can show that no two of the standard forms are in fact equal, then it will follow that two words are equal if, and only if, they have the *same standard form*, and this provides us with a solution of the word problem for this semigroup. The procedure for determining whether two words are equal or not is simply to reduce the words to standard form. It remains to show that no two of the standard words are equal, and this is the hardest part of our task.

We observe first that if we pass from a word V to a word W by allowable substitutions, passing through words $V_1, V_2, ..., V_k$, and if V and W do not contain the letter b, then we can obtain a passage from V to W by allowable substitutions passing through words $W_1, W_2, ..., W_k$ *which also do not contain the letter b*. For if one of the V's, say V_r, contains the letter b, then we replace b (wherever it occurs) by acc forming the word W_r and since V_{r-1}, V_r, V_{r+1} are equal, so too W_{r-1}, W_r, W_{r+1} are equal (or the same word). Leaving aside the substitution $b \to acc$, the remaining allowable substitutions do not change the parity of the number of times a letter a occurs (that is the even or oddness of this number is unchanged).

The same is true of the letter c. This shows that none of the pairs of words

$\square, c;$	$\square, ccc;$	$\square, a;$	$\square, ac;$	$\square, acc;$	$\square, accc;$
$c, cc;$	$c, a;$	$c, ac;$	$c, acc;$	$c, accc;$	
$cc, ccc;$	$cc, a;$	$cc, ac;$	$cc, acc;$	$cc, accc;$	
$ccc, a;$	$ccc, ac;$	$ccc, acc;$	$ccc, accc;$		
$a, ac;$	$a, accc;$	$ac, acc;$	$acc, accc;$		

is equal. It remains only to consider the four pairs

$$\square, cc; \quad c, ccc; \quad a, acc; \quad ac, accc.$$

Now if any of the first three pairs were equal it would follow that $ac = accc$ and so it suffices to show that ac is not equal to $accc$. To show this we introduce the notions of the *degree* of the *position* of a letter a in a word, and the *grade* of a word. The degree of the position of a letter a in a word is the number of c's that precede it. The grade of a word is the sum of the degrees of the positions of the a's in it. For instance, in the word

$$accaca$$

the first a has degree 0, the second degree 2 and the third degree 3, so that the grade of this word is 5. Each of the substitutions $aa = \square$, $cccc = \square$, does not change the *parity* of the grade of a word (for consider the word $VaaW$; if V contains k c's, then the contribution to the grade from the pair of a's between V and W is $2k$, and this contribution drops to zero when we delete this pair).

However, the substitution $ca \to accc$ does change the parity of a word, for if we pass from the word $VcaW$ to the word $VacccW$, then the degree of every a in V remains unchanged but the degree of *each* a in W increases by 2; and the degree of the a between V and W drops by 1, so that the grade of the whole word is changed by an odd amount.

Since the words ac, $accc$ have the same grade (namely zero), it follows that if there is an allowable series of substitutions which takes us from ac to $accc$, then the substitution

$$ca \to accc$$

must be used an *even* number of times; but each application of the substitution increases the number of c's in the word by 0 or 2, and so after an even number of applications of the substitution the change in the number of c's in the word is divisible by 4. The substitution $aa = \square$ does not change the number of c's, and the substitution $cccc = \square$ changes the number of c's by 4. Thus the effect of all the allowable substitutions is to change the number of c's by a multiple of 4. Since the number of c's in $accc$ differs from the number of c's in ac by 2, these words are unequal, which completes the proof.

The word problem for groups

We have just seen that there are semigroups for which one can construct a *completely mechanical test* by which one may decide whether any two words are equivalent in the semigroup or not. For many years it was an open question whether such a mechanical decision procedure existed for *all* semigroups or not, but in 1946 and 1947 A. A. Markov in Russia and E. Post in the United States found examples of semigroups for which *no purely mechanical decision procedure is possible*. Markov's and Post's examples were very complicated but quite recently another Russian mathematician G. S. Zeitin constructed the very simple example we gave above (p. 66) of a semigroup which admits no mechanical decision procedure for word equivalence.

A group may be thought of as a semigroup with units such that to every letter a of its alphabet corresponds a letter a^* and an allowable substitution

$$a a^* = \square .$$

Thus groups are particular kinds of semigroups with substitutions, and the word problem arises also for groups. The examples which Markov, Post and Zeitin gave of undecidable semigroups are all examples of semigroups which are *not* groups, and the extraordinarily difficult *word problem for groups*, the problem of finding whether or not there is a mechanical decision procedure for word equivalence in groups, was solved only in 1955 and 1956 when the Russian mathematician P. S. Novikov and the young American, W. W. Boone, gave examples of groups for which no purely mechanical decision procedure is possible.

Congruences

A very convenient notation in which to express properties of remainders was introduced by C. F. Gauss. If a, b leave the same remainder on division by c, then a and b are said to be *equal modulo c* and we write

$$a = b \pmod c .$$

The notation is helpful because, as we saw when we considered the arithmetic of remainders, equality modulo c has many of the properties of ordinary equality. For instance,

if
$$a = b \pmod c$$
and
$$a' = b' \pmod c,$$
then
$$a + a' = b + b' \pmod c$$
and
$$aa' = bb' \pmod c$$
$$ka = kb \pmod c,$$

for if q is the quotient when $a - b$ is divided by c, and q' the quotient when $a' - b'$ is divided by c, then

$$a = b + qc, \quad a' = b' + q'c$$
and so
$$a + a' = b + b' + (q + q')c, \quad ka - kb = kqc,$$
and
$$aa' = bb' + c(qq'c + bq' + b'q)$$

showing that each pair

$$a + a', \quad b + b'; \quad ka, \quad kb$$

leaves the same remainder, on division by c. The relation

$$a = b \pmod c$$

is called a *congruence*.

Fermat's Theorem

We have already had occasion to remark that if a and $b > 1$ are without a common factor, then the $b - 1$ multiples of a

$$a, 2a, 3a, \ldots, (b - 1)a$$

all leave different remainders on division by b, so that these remainders are necessarily $1, 2, \ldots, b - 1$ in some order; that is to say, modulo b, the numbers $a, 2a, \ldots, (b - 1)a$ are equal to the numbers $1, 2, \ldots, b - 1$ in some order and therefore, forming their product, we have

$$1 \times 2 \times 3 \times \cdots \times (b - 1) \times a^{b-1} = 1 \times 2 \times \cdots \times (b - 1) \pmod{b},$$

i.e.

$$1 \times 2 \times 3 \times \cdots \times (b - 1) \, [a^{b-1} - 1]$$

is divisible by b. If b is a prime number, then since b does not divide any of the numbers $2, 3, \ldots, b - 1$, it follows that b does not divide their product, and therefore b divides $a^{b-1} - 1$. In congruence notation, we have proved a theorem, first discovered by Fermat, that:

if p is prime and not a factor of a, then $a^{p-1} = 1 \pmod{p}$.

For example $10^{40} = 1 \pmod{41}$, i.e. the number $99 \ldots 9$ with the digit 9 repeated 40 times is divisible by 41.

The necessary modification in the theorem in the case when b is not prime was discovered by Euler. If b^* denotes the number of numbers less than b which have no common factor with b, and if a, b have no common factor, then

$$a^{b*} = 1 \pmod{b}.$$

For instance, of the numbers $1, 2, 3, 4, 5, 6, 7, 8, 9$ which are less than 10, only $2, 4, 5, 6, 8$ have a factor in common with 10, so that there are 4 numbers $(1, 3, 7, 9)$ less than 10 and without a factor in common with 10. Hence

$$a^4 = 1 \pmod{10}$$

for any number a which is not divisible by 2 or 5 (the factors of 10); this is another way of saying that the fourth power of an odd number which does not end in 5, ends in 1 (in the scale of 10).

To prove Euler's extension of Fermat's theorem we use the same method as before, but instead of considering *all* the multiples of a we consider only the products of a by the numbers $1, b', b'', \ldots,$ $b - 1$ which are less than b and have no factor in common with b. When we divide the products

$$a, ab', ab'', \ldots, a(b - 1)$$

by b the possible remainders are just $1, b', b'', \ldots, b-1$, for if one of the products, let us say ac, leaves a remainder r which has a prime factor f in common with b, and if q is the quotient when ac is divided by b, so that

$$ac = bq + r,$$

then bq and r are divisible by f, so that ac is divisible by f, which is impossible since neither a nor c is divisible by f (which is a factor of b). Multiplying the b^* multiples of a together we find

$$a^{b^*} \times b'b'' \ldots (b-1) = b'b'' \ldots (b-1) \pmod{b}$$

that is

$$(a^{b^*} - 1) \, b'b'' \ldots (b-1)$$

is divisible by b; none of $b', b'', \ldots (b-1)$ has a prime factor in common with b, so that the product $b'b'' \ldots (b-1)$ has no prime factor in common with b, and therefore

$$a^{b^*} - 1$$

is divisible by b, as we had to show.

Fermat's Theorem and its extension explain many interesting structural patterns which may be observed in elementary arithmetic. Consider for instance the successive powers of 2

$$2, 4, 8, 16, \ldots;$$

on division by 5 the sequence of remainders is

$$2, 4, 3, 1, 2, 4, 3, 1, \ldots;$$

the remainders recur because

$$2^4 = 1 \pmod{5}$$

and therefore

$$2^{n+4} = 2^n \cdot 2^4 = 2^n \pmod{5}.$$

Of course successive powers of any number have the same property. The successive powers of 3 are

$$3, 9, 27, 81, 243, \ldots$$

and on division by 10 the remainders are

$$3, 9, 7, 1, 3, 9, 7, 1, \ldots.$$

The recurrence here depends upon the congruence

$$3^4 = 1 \quad (\text{mod } 10)$$

(there are 4 numbers less than 10 and prime to 10) from which we deduce

$$3^{n+4} = 3^n \cdot 3^4 = 3^n \quad (\text{mod } 10).$$

The exponent $p - 1$ in Fermat's Theorem

$$a^{p-1} = 1 \quad (\text{mod } p)$$

is not necessarily the smallest exponent which satisfies the congruence. For instance

$$2^3 = 1 \quad (\text{mod } 7),$$

so that the remainders on division by 7, recur every three numbers.

A rather more elaborate example of recurrence depending upon Fermat's Theorem is the following: Let us call the remainder of any number greater than 9 divided by 9 the reduce of that number.

Take any five digit number, say 34217. Replace each digit by the sum of the remaining digits, or by the reduce of this sum if it exceeds nine; then 3 is replaced by the remainder on dividing $4 + 2 + 1 + 7$ by 9, that is by 5; 4 is replaced by 4 itself since $3 + 2 + 1 + 7$ leaves the remainder 4, 2 is replaced by 6, 1 by 7 and the final 7 by 1. Thus 34217 is turned into 54671; repeating the process we obtain in turn the numbers 91874, 21347, 67541, 87914, 34217, the original number returning after six transformations. It will be found that any five-figure number has the same property, but a three-figure number needs 18 transformations to bring it back to its starting value, and yet a twenty-digit number needs only six transformations. To see why the original number recurs, consider a five-digit number

$$abcde$$

and let

$$s = a + b + c + d + e;$$

after the first transformation this number becomes

$$a'b'c'd'e'$$

say, where, modulo 9,

$$a' = s - a, \quad b' = s - b, \quad c' = s - c, \quad d' = s - d, \quad e' = s - e.$$

Since $a' + b' + c' + d' + e' = 4s$, repeating the process gives the number

$$a''b''c''d''e''$$

where, modulo 9,

$$a'' = 4s - a' = 3s + a \quad \text{etc.}$$

a'' in turn is replaced by $16s - a'' = 13s - a$, and then by $51s + a$, and so on.

The numbers $1, 3, 13, 51, \ldots$ are formed by multiplying by 4 and adding and subtracting 1 alternately; thus $3 = 4 \times 1 - 1$, $13 = 4 \times 3 + 1, 51 = 4 \times 13 - 1$, and so on, which may be written in the form

$$3 = 4 \times 1 - 1, \quad 13 = 4(4 \times 1 - 1) + 1 = 4^2 - 4 + 1,$$
$$51 = 4(4^2 - 4 + 1) - 1 = 4^3 - 4^2 + 4 - 1,$$
$$205 = 4 \times 51 + 1 = 4^4 - 4^3 + 4^2 - 4 + 1,$$
$$819 = 4 \times 205 - 1 = 4^5 - 4^4 + 4^3 - 4^2 + 4 - 1,$$

and so on.

Now one of the numbers $3s + a$, $51s + a$, $819s + a$, $\ldots$ will be equal to a modulo 9, if we can find one of $3, 51, 819, \ldots$ which divides by 9.

If we multiply $4^3 - 4^2 + 4 - 1$ by 4 we obtain

$$4^4 - 4^3 + 4^2 - 4$$

and if we add the original $4^3 - 4^2 + 4 - 1$ to this we obtain

$$4^4 - 1,$$

thus

$$(4 + 1)(4^3 - 4^2 + 4 - 1) = 4^4 - 1;$$

in exactly the same way we can show that

$$(4 + 1)(4^5 - 4^4 + 4^3 - 4^2 + 4 - 1) = 4^6 - 1,$$

and

$$(4 + 1)(4^7 - 4^6 + 4^5 - 4^4 + 4^3 - 4^2 + 4 - 1) = 4^8 - 1,$$

and so on. But for any number x, $5x$ is divisible by 9 only if x itself is divisible by 9, and so we need one of the numbers

$$4^2 - 1, \quad 4^4 - 1, \quad 4^6 - 1, \quad 4^8 - 1, \ldots$$

to be divisible by 9.

The numbers less than 9 and having no factor in common with 9 are 1, 2, 4, 5, 7, 8 of which there are six. By the extension of Fermat's Theorem therefore,

$$4^6 - 1$$

is divisible by 9, showing that the digits repeat after six transformations. Of course if the sum of the digits is divisible by 3, then two transformations suffice, for $3s$ is then divisible by 9.

Tests for divisibility

Tests for divisibility expressed in terms of the representation of a number in a scale are of both practical and theoretical interest. In the scale of ten, for instance, a number is divisible by nine if, and only if, the sum of its digits is divisible by nine. This depends on the fact that $a^n - b^n$ is divisible by $a - b$, $a \neq b$, for any value of n; to prove this we observe that it is certainly true for $n = 1$ ($a - b$ is divisible by $a - b$) and since

$$a^{k+1} - b^{k+1} = a(a^k - b^k) + b^k(a - b),$$

therefore $a^{k+1} - b^{k+1}$ is divisible by $a - b$ if $a^k - b^k$ is so divisible, and therefore by induction $a^n - b^n$ is divisible by $a - b$, for any value of n. Consider now any number $N = d_0 + 10d_1 + 10^2 d_2 + \cdots$ (the digits $d_0, d_1, d_2, \ldots$ lying, of course, between 0 and 9 inclusive, but this plays no part in the proof). The difference between N and the sum of its digits $d_0 + d_1 + d_2 + \cdots$ is

$$(10 - 1)d_1 + (10^2 - 1)d_2 + (10^3 - 1)d_3 + \cdots$$

and each of $10 - 1, 10^2 - 1, 10^3 - 1, \ldots$ is divisible by $10 - 1$, i.e. by 9, so that N and $d_0 + d_1 + d_2 + \cdots$ are either both divisible by 9 or both not divisible by 9 (in which case they still leave the same remainder on division by 9). Incidentally N and $d_0 + d_1 + d_2 + \cdots$ are both or neither divisible by 3, since their difference is divisible by 3 (being divisible by 9).

Exactly the same proof shows that a number is divisible by $r - 1$ if, and only if, the sum of its digits, in the scale of r, is divisible by $r - 1$.

There is a similar test for divisibility by 11, (in the scale of 10). We observe first that $a^{2n} - b^{2n}$ is divisible by $a + b$; for $a^2 - b^2 = (a - b)(a + b)$ and

$$a^{2k+2} - b^{2k+2} = a^2(a^{2k} - b^{2k}) + b^{2k}(a^2 - b^2)$$

from which a proof by induction readily follows. Also $a^{2n+1} + b^{2n+1}$ is divisible by $a + b$ for

$$a^3 + b^3 = (a + b)(a^2 - ab + b^2)$$

and

$$a^{2k+3} + b^{2k+3} = a^2(a^{2k+1} + b^{2k+1}) - b^{2k+1}(a^2 - b^2).$$

Hence

$$d_0 + d_1 10 + d_2 10^2 + d_3 10^3 + d_4 10^4 + \cdots$$
$$- (d_0 - d_1 + d_2 - d_3 + \cdots)$$
$$= d_1(10 + 1) + d_2(10^2 - 1) + d_3(10^3 + 1) + d_4(10^4 - 1) + \cdots$$

which is divisible by $10 + 1 = 11$, since each of $10 + 1$, $10^2 - 1$, $10^3 + 1$, $10^4 - 1, \ldots$ is divisible by $10 + 1$. Thus $d_0 + d_1 10 + d_2 10^2 + \cdots$ is divisible by 11, if, and only if, $d_0 - d_1 + d_2 - d_3 + \cdots$ is so divisible by 11. The same proof of course shows that $d_0 + d_1 s + d_2 s^2 + d_3 s^3 + \cdots$ is divisible by $s + 1$ if and only if $d_0 - d_1 + d_2 \ldots$ is divisible by $s + 1$. For example, 1234575 (in the scale of 10) is divisible by 9 since

$$1 + 2 + 3 + 4 + 5 + 7 + 5 = 27 = 9 \times 3;$$

and

$$1\ 2\ 3\ 4\ 5\ 4\ 5$$

is divisible by 3, but not by 9, since

$$1 + 2 + 3 + 4 + 5 + 4 + 5 = 24 = 3 \times 8.$$

The rule for divisibility by 11 is a little harder to apply, because of the alternate additions and subtractions. As an example consider 1234574; to obviate the difficulty that we cannot take 7 from 4, we start by adding 11 to 4 since this will not affect the question of divisibility by 11, and we obtain in turn $11 + 4 = 15, 15 - 7 = 8$, $8 + 5 = 13, 13 - 4 = 9, 9 + 3 = 12, 12 - 2 = 10, 10 + 1 = 11$, showing that 1234574 is divisible by 11.

Divisibility by 5 (in the scale of 10) is, of course, quite trivially tested, for $d_0 + d_1 10 + d_2 10^2 \ldots$ is divisible by 5 if, and only if,

$d_0 = 0$ or $d_0 = 5$. Similarly $d_0 + d_1 10 + d_2 10^2 + \cdots$ is divisible by 2 if, and only if, d_0 is so divisible, and so if $d_0 = 0$ or d_0 is an even digit. For division by 4, we observe that 10^2, 10^3, ... are all divisible by 4 and therefore $d_0 + d_1 10 + d_2 10^2 + \cdots$ is divisible by 4 if, and only if, $d_0 + d_1 10$ is divisible by 4.

We turn now to a general test for divisibility by a prime number. Let the scale be s, and the prime divisor p. Consider some number N which in the scale of s has at least $2k$ digits. We start by finding the remainder when s^k is divided by p, and denote this remainder by R. As we have already proved, given R we can always find r $(r < p)$ so that

$$Rr = 1 \pmod{p};$$

then since

$$s^k = R \pmod{p}$$

it follows that

$$s^k r = Rr = 1 \pmod{p}.$$

Hence if

$$N = s^k A + B$$

we have

$$rN = r(s^k A + B) = A + rB \pmod{p}.$$

Thus N will be divisible by p if, and only if, $A + rB$ is divisible by p, and $A + rB$ is a (much) smaller number than N.

As a first example test the numbers 123456789, 987654321 and 543219853 for divisibility by 17. We start by determining the values of R, r, for successive powers of 10. On division by 17, 10^2 leaves the remainder 15 and so 10^3 leaves the same remainder as 150, that is, 14, and 10^4 leaves the same remainder as 140, that is 4.

Next we seek r_1, r_2, r_3, so that

$$15r_1 = 1 \pmod{17}$$
$$14r_2 = 1 \pmod{17}$$
$$4r_3 = 1 \pmod{17};$$

we consider the equation $ax - 17y = 1$, for the values 4, 14 and 15 of a. In the first of the rearrangements

	1	2	3	4	5	6	7	8	9	10	11	12	13	14	15	16	17
(i)	16	17	1	2	3	4	5	6	7	8	9	10	11	12	13	14	15
(ii)	15	16	17	1	2	3	4	5	6	7	8	9	10	11	12	13	14
(ii)	5	6	7	8	9	10	11	12	13	14	15	16	17	1	2	3	4

we find the cycle 15, 13, 11, 9, 7, 5, 3, 1 containing 8 terms, so that $r_1 = 8$; in the second arrangement we find the cycle 14, 11, 8, 5, 2, 16, 13, 10, 7, 4, 1 containing 11 terms, so that $r_2 = 11$, and finally in the third arrangement there is the cycle 4, 8, 12, 16, 3, 7, 11, 15, 2, 6, 10, 14, 1, so that $r_3 = 13$.

Now we split 123456789 into $12345 \times 10^4 + 6789$ which shows that 123456789 is divisible by 17 if, and only if,

$$12345 + 13 \times 6789$$

is divisible by 17; to avoid working out 13×6789 we subtract from 17×6789 (which, of course, is divisible by 17) and reach the test number

$$4 \times 6789 - 12345 = 14811.$$

Writing 14811 as $148 \times 10^2 + 11$ we pass to the next test number $148 + 8 \times 11 = 236$, which is not divisible by 17, from which we conclude that 123456789 is not divisible by 17.

To test 987654321 we construct in turn $98765 + 13 \times 4321$, $98765 - 4 \times 4321 = 81481$ (subtracting 17×4312), $814 + 8 \times 81 = 1462$, $14 + 8 \times 62 = 510$ which *is* divisible by 17, showing that 987654321 is divisible by 17.

Finally, to test 543219853 we construct in turn $54321 + 13 \times 9853$, $54321 - 4 \times 9853 = 14909$, $149 + 8 \times 9 = 221$ which is divisible by 17.

A simpler version of this test uses only R; from $10^k = R$ (mod p), and $N = 10^k A + B$ it follows that N is divisible by p if, and only if, $RA + B$ is divisible by p. For example, since $10^2 = 26$ (mod 37), $10^3 = 1$ (mod 37), $10^4 = 10$ (mod 37), $10^5 = 26$ (mod 37), $10^6 = 1$ (mod 37), to find if 11223344556677 is divisible by 37 we construct the test numbers

$$1 \times 11223344 + 556677 = 11780021$$
$$10 \times 1178 + 21 = 11801$$
$$1 \times 11 + 801 = 812$$

and since 812 is not divisible by 37 (the remainder is 35) it follows that 11223344556677 is not divisible by 37.

Another method of testing for divisibility by 37 is based on the congruence $10^3 = 1$ (mod 37), which shows that 999 is divisible by

37 (in fact $999 = 37 \times 27$). Expressing N in the scale of 10^3 we simply add the digits to test for divisibility by $10^3 - 1$. For instance, to test

$$11223344556677 = 11 \times 10^{12} + 223 \times 10^9 + 344 \times 10^6 + 556 \times$$
$$\times 10^3 + 677$$

we add $11 + 223 + 344 + 556 + 677 = 1811$, which is clearly not divisible by 999 (and so not by 37), leaving the remainder 35 on division by 37.

Tests for powers

As a preliminary to the test for powers we remark that for any n, $n(n + 1)$ is divisible by 2, for one of the numbers n and $n + 1$ is even (even and odd numbers follow one another); and $n(n + 1)$ $(n + 2)$ is divisible by 6, for either n itself is divisible by 3 or n leaves the remainder 1 or 2; if n leaves the remainder 1 then $n + 2$ is divisible by 3, and if n leaves the remainder 2 then $n + 1$ is divisible by 3, so that in every case one of the numbers n, $n + 1$, $n + 2$ is divisible by 3, and therefore the product $n(n + 1)(n + 2)$ is divisible by 2 and by 3 and so by 6. The general result is that a product of k consecutive numbers $n(n + 1)(n + 2) \ldots (n + k - 1)$ is divisible by $1 \times 2 \times 3 \times \cdots \times k$ which we prove by induction. We have proved the result for a product of 2 factors; if it is true for a product of k factors, then we must establish the result for a product of $k + 1$ factors, i.e. we must show that

$$n(n + 1) \ldots (n + k)$$

is divisible by $1 \times 2 \times 3 \times \cdots \times (k + 1)$. We proceed by induction over n now; certainly $1 \times 2 \times 3 \times \cdots \times (k + 1)$ is divisible by $1 \times 2 \times \cdots \times (k + 1)$. Let $p(p + 1) \ldots (p + k)$ be divisible by $1 \times 2 \times 3 \times \cdots \times (k + 1)$ for some p. Now

$$(p + 1)(p + 2) \ldots (p + k + 1) - p(p + 1) \ldots (p + k)$$
$$= (p + 1)(p + 2) \ldots (p + k)(p + k + 1 - p)$$
$$= (p + 1)(p + 2) \ldots (p + k)(k + 1).$$

The product of k factors $(p + 1) (p + 2) \ldots (p + k)$ is divisible by $1 \times 2 \times 3 \times \cdots \times k$ and so

$$(p + 1) (p + 2) \cdots (p + k) (k + 1)$$

is divisible by $1 \times 2 \times 3 \times \ldots \times k \times (k + 1)$, and therefore

$$(p + 1) (p + 2) \ldots (p + k + 1)$$

is divisible by $1 \times 2 \times 3 \times \cdots \times (k + 1)$ which completes the proof by induction.

We come now to the tests for powers. We shall prove a few tests which squares and cubes must satisfy. The first is that an *odd* number is a square only if it leaves the remainder 1 on division by 8. For an odd number $2n + 1$ has the square

$$(2n + 1)^2 = 4n^2 + 4n + 1 = 4n(n + 1) + 1;$$

since $n(n + 1)$ is divisible by 2, therefore $4n(n + 1)$ is divisible by 8, showing that $(2n + 1)^2$ leaves the remainder 1 on division by 8.

Thus 1234567 is *not* a square since it leaves the remainder 7 on division by 8. (Of course there are non-squares which leave the remainder 1 on division by 8, for instance 17; observe also that an even number has an even square, since $(2n)^2 = (4n^2)$.) An even square leaves the remainder 0 or 4 since $(2n)^2 = 4n^2$; if n is even, say $n = 2m$, then $4n^2 = 16m^2$ which is divisible by 8, but if n is odd, say $n = 2m + 1$ then $4n^2 = 4(4m^2 + 4m + 1) = 16m(m + 1) + 4$ which leaves the remainder 4 on division by 8.

Another simple test is that a square is either divisible by 3 or leaves the remainder 1; for numbers divisible by 3, (with quotient n say) have the square $(3n)^2 = 9n^2$ which is divisible by 3; numbers with quotient n and remainder 1 have the square $(3n + 1)^2 = 9n^2 + 6n + 1 = 3n(3n + 2) + 1$ which leaves the remainder 1 on division by 3, and finally numbers with quotient n and remainder 2 have the square

$$(3n + 2)^2 = 9n^2 + 12n + 4 = 3(3n^2 + 4n + 1) + 1$$

which also leaves the remainder 1.

The first of these two tests shows that 3784568 *may* be a square for it is divisible by 8, but it leaves the remainder 2 on division by 3, and so, by the second test, it is not a square.

For cubes we prove a test of a rather different kind. We notice first that

$$n^3 - n = n(n^2 - 1) = (n - 1)n(n + 1)$$

which is divisible by 3; if n is an odd number $2m + 1$, say, then $n^3 - n = 2m(2m + 1)(2m + 2) = 4m(m + 1)(2m + 1)$ which is divisible by 8. Thus, if n is odd, $n^3 - n$ is divisible by $3 \times 8 = 24$. If n is even, say $n = 2m$, then we consider

$$n^3 - 4n = n(n^2 - 4) = (n - 2)n(n + 2) = 8(m - 1)m(m + 1)$$

which is divisible by 48.

This test, like those for squares, is a purely negative one. As an instance of its application let us consider whether 12345678 is the cube of 272; we form the difference

$$12345678 - 4 \times 272 = 12344590$$

and since this difference is not divisible by 3 (and so not by 48) it follows that 12345678 is not the cube of 272. As another example we consider whether 19902511 may be the cube of 271; we form the difference

$$19902511 - 271 = 19902240$$

which is readily seen to be divisible by 24 (and in fact $271^3 = 19902511$, but the test does not establish this by itself).

Pascal's Triangle

If we form in turn the successive powers of $1 + x$ an interesting pattern emerges. We find

$$1 + x = 1 + 1x$$
$$(1 + x)^2 = 1 + 2x + x^2$$
$$(1 + x)^3 = 1 + 3x + 3x^2 + x^3$$
$$(1 + x)^4 = 1 + 4x + 6x^2 + 4x^3 + x^4$$
$$(1 + x)^5 = 1 + 5x + 10x^2 + 10x^3 + 5x^4 + x^5$$

and so on; an array which is called Pascal's Triangle, (after the seventeenth century French mathematician and philosopher Blaise Pascal). If we look at the numbers in any row, we see that each number is the sum of the number above it and the number to the left. For instance, in the fourth row we see that 4 (the *coefficient*, that is, the numerical multiplier, of x) is the sum of the 3 above it, and the number 1 to the left of the three; similarly 6, the coefficient of x^2, is the sum of the 3 above it, and the 3 to the left; the next 4, the coefficient of x^3, is the sum of the 1 above it and the 3 to its left. Assuming that this is a general law we write down the sixth row as follows: We start with 1, then comes $6 = 5 + 1$, then $15 = 10 + 5$, then $20 = 10 + 10$, then in turn $15 = 5 + 10$, $6 = 1 + 5$ ending with 1; writing in the powers of x we find

$$(1 + x)^6 = 1 + 6x + 15x^2 + 20x^3 + 15x^4 + 6x^5 + x^6$$

and multiplying the entry in the fifth row by $1 + x$ we readily verify that this holds. To prove the rule, we observe that it holds in the cases so far considered, and show that it necessarily holds in the next row. For, carrying out the multiplication

$$
\begin{array}{l}
1 + 6x + 15x^2 + 20x^3 + 15x^4 + 6x^5 + x^6 \\
1 + x \\
\hline
1 + 6x + 15x^2 + 20x^3 + 15x^4 + 6x^5 + x^6 \\
\quad\ \ x + 6x^2 + 15x^3 + 20x^4 + 15x^5 + 6x^6 + x^7 \\
\hline
1 + (6 + 1)\,x + (15 + 6)x^2 + (20 + 15)x^3 + (15 + 20)x^4 + \\
\qquad\qquad\qquad\qquad + (6 + 15)x^5 + (1 + 6)x^6 + x^7
\end{array}
$$

we see that the rule is of general validity.

The coefficients of successive powers of x in the expansion of $(1 + x)^n$ may also be obtained in the following way. Denoting the coefficient of x^r in the expansion of $(1 + x)^n$ by $\binom{n}{r}$, the upper n referring to the power of $1 + x$, and the lower r referring to the related power of x, the rule we have just verified shows that

$$\binom{n + 1}{r + 1} = \binom{n}{r} + \binom{n}{r + 1}$$

as the following array exhibits (where we write $\binom{n}{0}$ for 1 to complete the notation)

$$\binom{1}{0} \quad \binom{1}{1}$$

$$\binom{2}{0} \quad \binom{2}{1} \quad \binom{2}{2}$$

$$\binom{3}{0} \quad \binom{3}{1} \quad \binom{3}{2} \quad \binom{3}{3}$$

$$\binom{n}{0} \quad \binom{n}{1} \quad \binom{n}{2} \cdots\cdots \binom{n}{r} \quad \binom{n}{r+1} \cdots\cdots \binom{n}{n}$$

$$\binom{n+1}{0} \binom{n+1}{1} \binom{n+1}{2} \cdots \binom{n+1}{r} \binom{n+1}{r+1} \cdots \binom{n+1}{n+1}$$

If we represent the repeated product $1 \times 2 \times 3$ by $3!$, and $1 \times 2 \times \times 3 \times 4$ by $4!$, $1 \times 2 \times 3 \times 4 \times 5$ by $5!$, and so on, (letting $1!$ and $0!$ both stand for 1), then $(k + 1)!$ (read factorial $k + 1$) equals $(k + 1)(k!)$.

We shall prove that

$$\binom{n}{r} = \frac{n!}{r!(n-r)!};$$

(observe that $n!$ is divisible by $r!(n-r)!$, for $n(n-1)\ldots(n-r+1)$ is divisible by $r!$ and so $n! = n(n-1)\ldots(n-r+1)\{(n-r)!\}$ is divisible by $r!(n-r)!$).

This formula is certainly true when $n = 2$, since

$$\binom{2}{0} = 1 = \frac{2!}{0!\,2!}, \quad \binom{2}{1} = 2 = \frac{2!}{1!\,1!}, \quad \binom{2}{2} = 1 = \frac{2!}{2!\,0!},$$

and it certainly holds for the value 0 of r, whatever value n may have; let us suppose that it holds for some value k of n.

Then

$$\binom{k+1}{r+1} = \binom{k}{r} + \binom{k}{r+1}$$

$$= \frac{k!}{r!(k-r)!} + \frac{k!}{(r+1)!(k-r-1)!}$$

$$= \frac{k!}{(r+1)!(k-r)!} \; [(r+1) + (k-r)]$$

$$= \frac{(k+1)!}{(r+1)!(k-r)!}$$

showing that the formula holds also for the value $k + 1$ of n, and so by induction it holds for all values of n.

The numbers $\binom{n}{r}$ have an important significance apart from their role as coefficients.

If we consider, for instance, the product

$$(1 + x)(1 + x)(1 + x),$$

we see that we can obtain x^2 in various ways; we may take x from the first two factors, and not from the third, or from the first and third, but not from the second, or from the second and third, but not the first, showing that the term x^2 can be obtained in 3 ways exactly, that is to say $x^2 + x^2 + x^2 = 3x^2$ is the term in x^2 in the product (as we already know).

Similarly if we consider

$$(1 + x)(1 + x)(1 + x) \ldots (1 + x)$$

with n factors in the product, we see that we can obtain x^r by selecting x from r of the n factors (and the unit from the others) and *therefore* the coefficient of x^r in $(1 + x)^n$ represents *the number of ways of choosing r out of n things*. If we choose r from n things we leave $n - r$ and so the number of ways of choosing r is the same as the number of ways of choosing $n - r$, i.e.

$$\binom{n}{r} = \binom{n}{n - r}$$

as may, of course, readily be verified directly.

The number $n!$ which we met in evaluating $\binom{n}{r}$ itself expresses an important property, for $n!$ is the number of ways of arranging n distinct objects in a row. To see this we observe that the first object may be chosen in n ways (for we choose one from n objects); when the first is chosen $n - 1$ remain, from which the second may be chosen in $n - 1$ ways. Thus the first and second may be chosen in $n(n - 1)$ ways. For example, we may choose the first and second from a, b, c, d, e as follows:

ab	ba	ca	da	ea
ac	bc	cb	db	eb
ad	bd	cd	dc	ec
ae	be	ce	de	ed

that is, in $5 \times 4 = 20$ ways. Notice the difference between choosing two out of five objects, which may be effected in $\binom{5}{2} = 10$ ways, and choosing a first and second from five objects which may be done in $5 \times 4 = 20$ ways; the difference arises from the fact that in one case a, b and b, a are the same pair (when order is irrelevant) and in the second case a, b and b, a are different ways, of choosing a first and second. We may express this by saying that in one case we choose a pair and in the other an *ordered* pair.

To return to the general case, when the first and second have been chosen the third may be selected from $n - 3$, (in $n - 3$ ways of course), the fourth from $n - 4$, and so on, making the total possible number of ways of ordering n objects in a row

$$n(n - 1)(n - 2) \ldots 2 \times 1 = n!.$$

Another way of looking at this result is that if n objects may be arranged in $n!$ ways, then to arrange $n + 1$ objects we may choose the first in $n + 1$ ways, and then order the remaining n in $n!$ ways, making $(n + 1)n! = (n + 1)!$ arrangements in all.

The coefficients $\binom{n}{r}$ arise in connection with finding the number of solutions of an equation. For instance, to find the number of solutions of the equation

$$x + y = n$$

we remark that if we select one from a row of $n + 1$ objects we leave n objects divided into two groups (one of which may be empty), and so we obtain a solution of the equation; thus the number of solutions of the equation is $\binom{n + 1}{1}$.

For the equation

$$x + y + z = n$$

we observe that if we select 2 from $n + 2$ objects in a row we leave n divided into three groups (one or two of which may be empty) which provides a solution, and so the number of solutions is $\binom{n + 2}{2}$.

In the general case

$$x + y + z + u + \cdots = n$$

when there are r unknowns on the left, each solution may be found by selecting $r - 1$ from $n + r - 1$ objects in a row, leaving n ob-

jects separated into r groups, so that the number of solutions is
$$\binom{n + r - 1}{r - 1}.$$

If we seek to choose r from n objects when the *same* object may be chosen more than once, we may reduce the problem to that of finding the number of solutions of an equation. For if the objects are $a, b, c, \ldots$ and if we choose x of the a's, y of the b's, z of the c's and so on, then

$$x + y + z + \cdots = r$$

since r letters are chosen in all, in each selection. The number of solutions, as we have seen, is

$$\binom{n + r - 1}{n - 1} = \binom{n + r - 1}{r}.$$

Of course, if we take account of the order in which the objects are selected the number of ways of choosing r from n is n^r, since the first may be chosen in n ways, the second in n ways again, and so on.

The *binomial* coefficients, as the numbers $\binom{n}{r}$ are called, satisfy many remarkable relations. For instance

$$\binom{n}{0} + \binom{n}{1} + \binom{n}{2} + \cdots + \binom{n}{n} = 2^n;$$

for

$$(1 + x)^n = \binom{n}{0} + \binom{n}{1} x + \binom{n}{2} x^2 + \cdots + \binom{n}{n} x^n$$

and so

$$2^n = (1 + 1)^n = \binom{n}{0} + \binom{n}{1} + \binom{n}{2} + \cdots + \binom{n}{n}.$$

A slightly deeper result is

$$\binom{m + n}{r} = \binom{m}{r} + \binom{m}{r - 1}\binom{n}{1} + \binom{m}{r - 2}\binom{n}{2} + \cdots + \binom{n}{r}$$

which may be obtained by considering the coefficient of x^r in the product

$$(1 + x)^m (1 + x)^n.$$

On the one hand, this coefficient is $\binom{m+n}{r}$, since $(1+x)^m$ $\times (1+x)^n = (1+x)^{m+n}$; on the other hand, if we multiply

$$1 + \binom{m}{1}x + \binom{m}{2}x^2 + \cdots + \binom{m}{m}x^m$$

by

$$1 + \binom{n}{1}x + \binom{n}{2}x^2 + \cdots \cdots \cdots + \binom{n}{n}x^n$$

we see that the term in x^r may be obtained by taking $\binom{m}{r}x^r$ from the first with 1 in the second, or $\binom{m}{r-1}x^{r-1}$ in the first row with $\binom{n}{1}x$ in the second, and so on. The formula remains true even if $r > m$, or $r > n$ provided that we define $\binom{n}{r} = 0$ for $r > n$.

As a final example we give the formula

$$a^{n-1} - \binom{n}{1}(a+b)^{n-1} + \binom{n}{2}(a+2b)^{n-1}$$

$$- \binom{n}{3}(a+3b)^{n-1} + \cdots = 0$$

which was discovered by the great Norwegian mathematician Niels Abel (1802–1829).

An Inequality

The inequality

$$n^4 < 10^n$$

may readily be proved using the binomial theorem. The inequality certainly holds for the values 1, 2 of n. For values of n greater than 2, $n^2 > 4$ and $n^3 > 4$ and so

$$(n+1)^4 = n^4 + 4n^3 + 6n^2 + 4n + 1$$

$$\leqslant n^4 + 2n^4 + 2n^4 + n^4 + n^4 < 10n^4$$

and so, if $n^4 < 10^n$ for some n, then $(n + 1)^4 < 10 \cdot 10^n = 10^{n+1}$, so that, by induction, the inequality holds for all n.

Some numbers are equal to the sum of the digits of their cubes. For instance

$$8^3 = 512, \quad 5 + 1 + 2 = 8$$

$$17^3 = 4913, \quad 4 + 9 + 1 + 3 = 17.$$

Are there infinitely many such numbers?

The inequality we have just proved shows that there are not. For any number of n digits is at least as great as 10^{n-1}, and the sum of n digits cannot exceed $9 + 9 + \cdots + 9 = 9n$, and if $n \geqslant 10 \times 9^3$, then

$$10 \times (9n)^3 = 10 \times 9^3 \times n^3 \leqslant n^4 < 10^n$$

so that

$$(9n)^{3.} < 10^{n-1}$$

and so every number with a cube of more than 10×9^3 digits is greater than the sum of the digits of its cube.

Ordinal numbers

If we seek to specify the position of a letter in a row of letters

$$a, b, c, d, e, f, g, \ldots$$

we may do so by noting the number of letters on its left. For instance, d follows three letters and this fact fixes its position; and similarly g follows six letters. A letter which starts a row is said to be *first* in the row, one that follows a single letter is *second*, one that follows two is third, and so on. The adjectives first, second, third, fourth, and so on, are called *ordinal numbers*, and by contrast the numbers used for counting are called *cardinal numbers*.

The ordinals, first, second, third and so on, suffice for ordering rows with a last element, but are inadequate to describe, for instance, the position of x in the row

$$1, 2, 3, \ldots, x$$

in which we suppose that every (cardinal) number precedes x. To describe the position of x we introduce a new sign ω (Greek letter omega) which denotes the first position after all the finite ordinals. The position after ω is $\omega + 1$, and after that $\omega + 2$ and so on without end. Consider now the position of x in the row

$$1, 3, 5, 7, \ldots 2, 4, 6, \ldots x$$

in which we suppose every odd number precedes every even, and x is preceded by any number; the ordinals of the even numbers are $\omega, \omega + 1, \omega + 2, \ldots$ and so on, and so x has the ordinal $\omega + \omega$, which we write as 2ω. Proceeding in this way we introduce in turn $3\omega, 4\omega, 5\omega$ and so on; consider now the position of x in the row

$$1, 2, 3, \ldots, \quad \omega, \omega + 1, \omega + 2, \ldots, \quad 2\omega, 2\omega + 1, 2\omega + 2, \ldots, \quad 3\omega,$$
$$3\omega + 1, \quad 3\omega + 2, \ldots, \quad x$$

in which we suppose x is preceded by $m\omega + n$ for any numbers m and n. How shall we describe the position of x? The natural extension of the notation is to introduce ω^2 as the first ordinal which follows every ordinal $m\omega + n$. We may then continue from ω^2 to ω^3 to ω^4 and so on, until we have introduced every ordinal

$$a\omega^n + b\omega^{n-1} + \cdots + k.$$

The first ordinal after all of these is denoted by ω^ω and step by step we introduce $\omega^{\omega^\omega}, \omega^{\omega^{\omega^\omega}}$ and so on. After every ordinal of this type has been introduced we have exhausted the possibilities of designating new ordinals by means of ω alone, and we may then introduce a new symbol to start the whole process off again!

The ordinals from ω onwards are called *transfinite* ordinals (because they come after all the finite ordinals). When we pass from finite to transfinite ordinals the form of induction which we have used so far ceases to be adequate. Although it is true for finite ordinals that all ordinals have some property if 1 has the property, and if $n + 1$ has the property provided that n has it, clearly it does not follow that ω has the property, for no amount of adding 1 ever takes us from some finite ordinal n to ω. Instead we must lay down a stronger principle of transfinite induction as follows.

All ordinals have a certain property provided that 1 has the property, and that any ordinal has the property if all the preceding ordinals have the property. As an example of the use of this generalisation of induction we prove that a function $f(m, n)$ depending on two numbers m and n, has its value fixed for every m, n if

$$f(m, 0) = m + 1, \quad f(0, n) = n \quad \ldots \quad \ldots \quad \text{(i)}$$

and

$$f(m + 1, n + 1) = f(m, f(m, n + 1) + m) \quad \ldots \quad \text{(ii)}$$

The first two equations fix the value of $f(m, n)$, if one of m or n is zero. The second equation shows that

$$f(1, n + 1) = f(0, f(0, n + 1)) = f(0, n + 1) = n + 1$$

$$f(2, n + 1) = f(1, f(1, n + 1) + 1) = f(1, n + 2) = n + 2$$

and so on.

To make use of transfinite induction we order the pairs (m, n) in the following way. We take first all the pairs $(0, n)$, then all the pairs $(1, n)$, then all $(2, n)$ and so on, so that the ordinal of the pair (m, n) is $m\omega + n$.

To apply transfinite induction we have to show that the value of $f(m, n)$ for any pair (m, n) is determined provided that the value of $f(m', n')$ is known for all pairs (m', n') such that $m'\omega + n'$ precedes $m\omega + n$. It suffices to consider only pairs $(m + 1, n + 1)$ since the value of $f(m, n)$ when either m or n is zero is given by the two equations (i). Let us suppose then that $f(m', n')$ is known for all m', n' such that $m'\omega + n'$ precedes $(m + 1)\omega + n + 1$. Since $m\omega + f(m, n + 1) + m$ precedes $(m + 1)\omega + n + 1$ whatever value $f(m, n + 1)$ may have, therefore, by assumption, the value of

$$f(m, f(m, n + 1) + m)$$

is known, and so by equation (ii) the value of $f(m + 1, n + 1)$ is known; thus we have shown that when the value of $f(m', n')$ is known for all ordinals $m'\omega + n' < (m + 1)\omega + (n + 1)$, then the value is also known for the ordinal $(m + 1)\omega + (n + 1)$, and hence by transfinite induction $f(m, n)$ is known for all pairs m, n.

Of course, transfinite induction is not really needed to prove this simple result which could have readily been established by ordinary induction. The following result, however, simple though it looks, is one which it is known to be *impossible to prove without transfinite induction*.

Start with any number, represent it in a scale, increase the scale and reduce the number by 1, or more, increase the scale again and reduce the number by 1, or more, and so on. Then whatever number we start from, we come back to zero eventually.

For instance, if we start with the number 4 in the scale of 2, that is with 2^2, and if we increase the scales in turn through 3, 4, 5 and so on, reducing the number each time by 5 say (and then by 1 when less than 5 remains) we obtain in turn the numbers $3^3 - 5 = = 2 \times 3^2 + 1 \times 3 + 1$, 2×4^2, $5^2 + 4 \times 5$, ..., $10^2 + 6$, $11^2 + 1$, ..., $10 \times 16 + 2$, ..., $6 \times 34 + 2$, ..., $5 \times 41 + 2$, ..., $1 \times 72 + 71$, ..., 73, ..., 2, 1, 0. However fast the numbers increase at first, we must reach zero eventually; with enough effort we can convince ourselves of the truth of this for any initial number. but a general proof is possible only by means of transfinite induction over all the ordinals ω, ω^ω, ω^{ω^ω}, ...

Notes on Chapter 1

A proof of the method for placing 0's and 1's round a circle to make all possible arrangements is given in the author's note: "A permutation problem." *Mathematical Gazette*, XL (1956) pp. 46–47.

The counterfeit penny problem: this solution is due to F.J.Dyson, "The problem of the pennies," *Math. Gaz.* XXX (1946) pp. 231–234.

An account of Gauss' theory of constructable polygons may be found in Felix Klein's *Famous Problems of Elementary Geometry*, (Dover, New York).

The measuring problem: this method of solving the measuring problem was found by Eric Goodstein at the age of 15 years. (*Math. Gaz.* XXV (1941) pp. 49–51.)

The digit transformation theorem is due to the same author: "On sums of digits," *Math. Gaz.* XXV (1941) pp. 156–159.

Tests for divisibility: these tests were given by P.J.Clarke. (*Math. Gaz.* XLII (1958) pp. 122–123.)

The problem which cannot be solved without transfinite induction was given in the author's article "On the restricted ordinal theorem," *Journal of Symbolic Logic*, 12 (1947) pp. 123–129.

Semigroups: the results in this section are taken from B.A.Trachtenbrot's *"Wieso können Automaten rechnen"* (VEB Deutscher Verlag der Wissenschaften, Berlin, 1959).

CHAPTER 2

NUMBERS FOR PROFIT AND LOSS
AND NUMBERS FOR SHARING

Positive and negative integers

WE are going to consider a man climbing a stairway. He may climb up or down, any number of steps he likes. We choose a stair which we designate as the landing, which may also be moved up or down. We distinguish between steps *up*, and steps *down* by means of the signs $+$, $-$, writing for instance $+2$ for two steps up, and -2 for two steps down.

If you first climb a stairs, and then b stairs, you have climbed in all $a + b$ stairs and so

$$(+a) + (+b) = +(a + b);$$

if you climb $a + b$ stairs and then descend b stairs, you have ascended a stairs in all, and so

$$+(a + b) + (-b) = +a;$$

similarly if you climb a stairs, and then descend $a + b$ stairs, you are b stairs below the starting level and so

$$(+a) + (-(a + b)) = -b.$$

Since

$$+(a + b) + (-b) = +a$$

therefore

$$(+a) - (-b) = +(a + b)$$

and

$$(+a) - (+(a + b)) = -b.$$

Since

$$(+a) + (+b) = +(a + b)$$

of course

$$+(a + b) - (+b) = +a.$$

For example

$$(+2) + (+3) = +5$$
$$(+5) - (+3) = +2$$
$$(+2) + (-3) = -1$$
$$(-1) - (-3) = +2$$
$$(-1) - (+2) = -3.$$

If a is any natural number, $+a$ and $-a$ are called *integers*, $+a$ being a positive integer, and $-a$ a negative integer.

We interpret multiplication by a positive integer as iteration in the following way. The product $(+2) \times (+3)$ denotes the repetition of the climb $+3$, that is $(+2) \times (+3)$ stands for $(+3) + (+3) = +6$, and similarly $(+2) \times (-3)$ stands for $(-3) + (-3) = -6$. Multiplication by a negative integer, denotes likewise an iteration, but what moves now is the landing, not the climber. Thus $(-2) \times (+3)$ denotes a shift of the landing through $(+3) + (+3) = +6$ steps, i.e. the landing moves up 6 stairs, and $(-2) \times (-3)$ denotes a shift of the landing through $(-3) + (-3) = -6$ stairs, i.e. moving the landing *down* 6 stairs.

Now if the landing moves up 6 stairs, the relation of the man to the landing is the same as if he had descended six stairs, so that we write $(-2) \times (+3) = -6$; similarly, if the landing is moved *down* 6 stairs, the relation between the man and the landing is the same as if he had climbed *up* 6 stairs, and so we write

$$(-2) \times (-3) = +6.$$

Thus the multiplication of integers is summed up in the equations

$$(+a) \times (+b) = +ab$$
$$(+a) \times (-b) = -ab$$
$$(-a) \times (+b) = -ab$$
$$(-a) \times (-b) = +ab.$$

Alternatively, we may regard multiplication by a negative integer as the iteration of a *reversed* step; thus we may take $(-2) \times (+3)$ to mean, not three steps *up* twice, but three steps *down* twice, and $(-2) \times (-3)$ to mean the reverse of three steps down twice, that is, three steps up twice. This interpretation enables us to dispense with movements of the landing, and leads to the same rules of operation.

Of course, the use of integers is not confined to climbing stairs. A positive integer $+a$ is the *relationship* of the number a to the number 0, that is the relationship 'a more', and this is the same as the relationship of $a + 1$ to 1, or $a + 2$ to 2, and so on; similarly the negative integer $-a$ is the relationship of 0 to a, that is the relationship 'a less', and this is the same as the relationship of 1 to $a + 1$, of 2 to $a + 2$ and so on. In business transactions we may use positive and negative integers to denote profit and loss, in physics, to denote rise and fall of temperature, or in history, in place of the familiar A.D., B.C. (which are simply another version of positive and negative in which an oblique reference is made to the landing (or origin) chosen).

The rules for adding, subtracting and multiplying integers may be obtained from the rules for adding, subtracting and multiplying natural numbers in the following simple way. Let x be any number, and consider the equations

$$(x + a) + (x + b) = 2x + (a + b)$$
$$(x + (a + b)) + (x - b) = 2x + a$$
$$(2x + (a + b)) - (x + b) = x + a$$
$$(2x + a) - (x - b) = x + (a + b)$$

$$(x + a)(x + b) = x^2 + (a + b)x + ab$$
$$(x + a)(x - b) = x^2 + (a - b)x - ab$$
$$(x - a)(x + b) = x^2 - (a - b)x - ab$$
$$(x - a)(x - b) = x^2 - (a + b)x + ab:$$

if we now give x the value 0, and interpret $0 + a$ as $+a$, $0 - a$ as $-a$, these equations become

$$(+a) + (+b) = +(a + b), \quad +(a + b) + (-b) = +a,$$
$$+(a + b) - (+b) = +a, \quad (+a) - (-b) = +(a + b),$$
$$(+a) \times (+b) \quad +(ab). \quad (+a)(-b) = -ab,$$
$$(-a)(+b) = -ab, \quad (-a) \times (-b) = +ab,$$

which are precisely the rules for integers which we found before.

Since an integer is simply the relationship of one natural number to another, the arithmetic of integers can also be described in terms of an arithmetic of *pairs* of numbers (a, b).

The rules of this arithmetic are

$$(a + n, b + n) = (a, b)$$
$$(a, b) + (c, d) = (a + c, b + d)$$
$$(a, b) - (c, d) = (a, b) + (d, c)$$
$$(a, b) \times (c, d) = (ac + bd, ad + bc).$$

The integer (a, b) is positive if $a > b$, and negative if $a < b$.

To understand how these results are obtained we think of the pair (a, b) as standing for the difference $a - b$; then for instance

$$(a, b) \times (c, d) = (a - b)(c - d) = ac + bd - (ad + bc)$$
$$= (ac + bd, ad + bc).$$

More precisely, if $a > b$, then $(a, b) = + (a - b)$ and if $a < b$, then $(a, b) = - (b - a)$.

The advantage of this representation is that we do not need to consider separately the cases $a > b$ and $a < b$ when we want to find the sum

$$(+ a) + (- b)$$

since the one sign (a, b) includes both positive and negative integers; one of the disadvantages is that each integer has an unlimited number of representations, for instance $+ 2$ is represented by $(2,0)$, $(3,1)$, $(4,2)$, and so on.

The essential difference between the natural numbers and the integers is that subtraction is always possible for integers. Whereas $3 - 5$ makes no sense (there is no number which added to 5 gives 3), the corresponding difference for integers $(+3) - (+5)$ has the answer -2.

We have remarked that

$$(a + n, b + n) = (a, b),$$

but are there any other circumstances under which two integers are equal? If we agree that two positive integers $+a$, $+b$ are equal if, and only if, $a = b$, and similarly that $-a = -b$ if, and only if, $a = b$, and finally that no positive integer is equal to a negative integer, then

$$(a, b) = (c, d)$$

if, and only if, $a + d = b + c$.

For if (a, b), (c, d) are equal, they are both positive or both negative; if they are positive, then $(a, b) = +(a - b)$ and $(c, d) = +(c - d)$ and from $+(a - b) = +(c - d)$ follows $a - b = c - d$ and therefore $a + d = b + c$; if they are negative, then $(a, b) = -(b - a)$, $(c, d) = -(d - c)$ and so

$$-(b - a) = -(d - c)$$

whence $b - a = d - c$ and therefore $a + d = b + c$. Similarly if $a + d = b + c$, and if $a > c$ so that $a = c + n$ for some n, then $b = d + n$ and therefore $(a, b) = (c + n, d + n) = (c, d)$; and if $a < c$, then $c = a + m$, say, and so $d = b + m$ and therefore $(a, b) = (a + m, b + m) = (c, d)$. (Of course, if $a = c$, then $d = b$ and (a, b) is the same pair as (c, d).)

We draw no distinction between $+0$ and -0, denoting them both by 0, since each stands for the relationship of 0 to itself. In the notation of pairs, $(a, a) = 0$ for any natural number a.

Two integers are equal if, and only if, their difference is 0. $(a, b) = (c, d)$ if, and only if, $a + d = b + c$, and

$$(a, b) - (c, d) = (a, b) + (d, c) = (a + d, b + c) = 0$$

if, and only if, $a + d = b + c$.

The essential property of the integer 0 is that an integer is unchanged by the addition (or subtraction) of 0. We have $(+a) + (+0) = +(a + 0) = +a$, and $(-a) + (+0) = (-a) + (-0) = -(a + 0) = -a$, and the corresponding results for subtraction then follow.

The ring of integers

The integers form a group under addition, with 0 as the neutral element, but do not form a group under multiplication, since division is not always possible (for instance, we cannot divide $+3$ by $+7$ because there is no multiple of 7 between 0 and 7 itself).

Under the two operations of addition and multiplication the integers form a *ring*. To confirm this we must show that the integers form a group under addition, and this we have already observed, and that multiplication is associative, and distributive over addition. The associative property is an immediate consequence of the associative property for natural numbers, since, for instance,

$$\{(+a) \times (-b)\} \times (-c) = +abc = (+a) \times \{(-b) \times (-c)\},$$

and the distributive property is established in the same way. For instance, using the notation of pairs,

$$
\begin{aligned}
(a, b)\, \{(c, d) + (e, f)\} &= (a, b)\,(c + e, d + f) \\
&= (a\,(c + e) + b\,(d + f),\, a\,(d + f) + b\,(c + e)) \\
&= (a, b)\,(c, d) + (a, b)\,(e, f).
\end{aligned}
$$

Inequalities

For natural numbers, we write $a > b$ if, and only if, $a = b + c$ ($c \neq 0$); similarly for integers i, j (using single letters here for integers) we write $i > j$ (and say i is greater than j, j is less than i) if, and only if, there is a positive integer $+d$ such that

$$i = j + (+d).$$

Thus, for instance, $+3 > +1$, since $+3 = +1 + (+2)$, and $+2 > -5$, since $+2 = (-5) + (+7)$, and $-2 > -5$, since $-2 = (-5) + (+3)$.

For two positive integers $+a$, $+b$,

$$+a > +b$$

if, and only if, $a > b$, for if $a = b + c$, then

$$+a = (+b) + (+c)$$

and so

$$+a > +b,$$

and conversely, if

$$+a > +b$$

then there is a positive integer $+c$ so that

$$+a = +b + (+c)$$

whence
$$+a = +(b+c)$$

and so $a = b + c$, and therefore $a > b$.

Any positive integer is greater than 0, and greater than any negative integer. For $+a = 0 + (+a)$, so that $+a > 0$, and $+a = (-b) + (+(a+b))$ so that $+a > -b$.

For negative integers $-a$, $-b$ we have

$$-a > -b$$

if, and only if, $b > a$; for if $-a > -b$, then there is a positive integer $+c$ such that $-a = (-b) + (+c)$ and therefore

$$(-a) + (+(a+b)) = +(a+b) + (-b) + (+c)$$

whence

$$+b = +a + (+c) = +(a+c)$$

and so

$$b = a + c,$$

and therefore

$$b > a.$$

Conversely, if $b > a$, there is a c such that $b = a + c$ and therefore

$$+b = +(a+c)$$

whence, in turn,

$$(+b) + \{-(a+b)\} = +(a+c) + \{-(a+b)\},$$
$$-a = (+c) + (+a) + \{-(a+b)\},$$
$$-a = (+c) + (-b)$$

and so

$$-a > -b.$$

It follows that $-a > -b$ if, and only if, $+b > +a$.

If i, j, k are integers such that $i > j$ and $j > k$, then $i > k$, for if there are positive integers $+d$, $+e$ such that

$$i = j + (+d)$$
$$j = k + (+e)$$

then

$$i = k + (+(d+e))$$

so that $i > k$.

So too if $i > j$, then $i + k > j + k$ (whether k is positive or negative) for from $i = j + (+d)$ follows $i + k = j + k + (+d)$.

An inequality is preserved under multiplication by a positive integer, but reversed under multiplication by a negative integer. For if

$$i = j + (+d),$$

then

$$(+c) \times i = (+c) \times j + (+cd)$$

which shows that if $i > j$, then

$$(+c) \times i > (+c) \times j;$$

but

$$(-c) \times i = (-c) \times j + \{(-c) \times (+d)\} = (-c) \times j - \{+cd\}$$

and so

$$(-c) \times i + (+cd) = (-c) \times j,$$

that is,

$$(-c) \times j > (-c) \times i.$$

The positive integer $+a$ is called the positive value of both the integers $+a, -a$; the positive value of an integer i is denoted by $|i|$.

Thus

$$|+a| = +a, \quad |-a| = +a.$$

In particular

$$|0| = 0.$$

Numbers for sharing

If we share 12 oranges between 3 children, each child receives 4 oranges, *because* $3 \times 4 = 12$, but if we seek to share 13 oranges between 3 children, one orange is left over, and must be divided into *parts* to make an equal share out possible; to represent each child's share we need a sign for one out of three parts into which the orange is divided, and we write $\frac{1}{3}$ to remind us of a quotient. Correspondingly we write $\frac{m}{n}$ to represent m out of n parts; the number $\frac{m}{n}$ is called a *fraction*, m being the *numerator* and n the *denominator* of the fraction.

The arithmetic of fractions is the same as the arithmetic of quotients which we considered on page 32. Let us recall that if $\dfrac{a}{b}$ is the quotient of a divided by b, and $\dfrac{c}{d}$ the quotient of c divided by d, then

$$\frac{a}{b} + \frac{c}{d} = \frac{ad + bc}{bd}$$

$$\frac{a}{b} \times \frac{c}{d} = \frac{ac}{bd}$$

$$\frac{a}{b} \div \frac{c}{d} = \frac{ad}{bc}$$

and if $k \neq 0$,

$$\frac{ka}{kb} = \frac{a}{b}.$$

We observe first that we obtain the same share of a cake if we divide it into n parts, and take m of them, as when we divide it into $2n$ parts, and take $2m$ of them, or divide it into $3n$ parts and take $3m$ of them and so on; suppose, for instance, that we divide a cake into 3 parts, and choose 2 of them; divide each third into two parts, thus dividing the cake into six parts, then we turn the chosen *two* thirds into *four* of the smaller parts, in fact into *four* sixths.

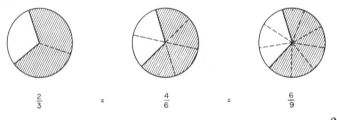

$$\frac{2}{3} \qquad = \qquad \frac{4}{6} \qquad = \qquad \frac{6}{9}$$

Similarly by dividing the thirds into three parts we see that $\dfrac{2}{3}$ is the same share as $\dfrac{6}{9}$, and so on. The general rule is

$$\frac{m}{n} = \frac{km}{kn}, \quad (k \neq 0),$$

exactly as for quotients.

Two fractions $\dfrac{a}{b}$, $\dfrac{c}{d}$ are equal if, and only if,

$$ad = bc,$$

for if

$$\frac{a}{b} = \frac{c}{d},$$

then

$$\frac{ad}{bd} = \frac{a}{b} = \frac{c}{d} = \frac{bc}{bd},$$

that is choosing ad out of bd is the same as choosing bc out of bd, which requires that $ad = bc$.

Conversely, if $ad = bc$ (and neither b nor d is zero) then

$$\frac{ad}{bd} = \frac{bc}{bd}$$

and so

$$\frac{a}{b} = \frac{c}{d}.$$

If we choose m out of n parts and then m' out of n parts, then in all we have chosen $m + m'$ out of n parts so that

$$\frac{m}{n} + \frac{m'}{n} = \frac{m + m'}{n}.$$

To add two fractions $\dfrac{m}{n}$, $\dfrac{p}{q}$ with *different* denominators we first find equivalents of these fractions with the same denominator; for instance

$$\frac{m}{n} = \frac{mq}{nq}, \quad \frac{p}{q} = \frac{np}{nq}$$

and so

$$\frac{m}{n} + \frac{p}{q} = \frac{mq}{nq} + \frac{np}{nq} = \frac{mq + np}{nq}$$

as we found for quotients. Of course, nq is not necessarily the smallest common multiple of n and q; for instance, to add $\dfrac{5}{12}$ and $\dfrac{4}{15}$, we observe that 60 is a common multiple of 12 and 15 (much smaller than 12×15) and so

$$\frac{5}{12} + \frac{4}{15} = \frac{5 \times 5}{12 \times 5} + \frac{4 \times 4}{15 \times 4} = \frac{25 + 16}{60} = \frac{41}{60}.$$

The sum will, of course, be the same whatever common multiple we take; thus

$$\frac{5}{12} + \frac{4}{15} = \frac{5 \times 15}{12 \times 15} + \frac{4 \times 12}{15 \times 12} = \frac{75 + 48}{12 \times 15}$$

$$= \frac{123}{12 \times 15} = \frac{41 \times 3}{60 \times 3} = \frac{41}{60}.$$

To see that this is true generally, let D be the *least* common multiple of n, q with $D = nN$, $D = qQ$, then

$$\frac{m}{n} + \frac{p}{q} = \frac{mN}{D} + \frac{pQ}{D} = \frac{mN + pQ}{D};$$

if D' is any other common multiple of n, q, then D' is a multiple of D, say $D' = kD$, and so

$$D' = knN = kqQ,$$

and therefore

$$\frac{m}{n} + \frac{p}{q} = \frac{kNm}{D'} + \frac{kQp}{D'} = \frac{k(mN + pQ)}{kD}$$

$$= \frac{mN + pQ}{D}$$

as before.

Just as, for instance, 3×7 means three of sevens (that is seven and seven and seven) we take $\frac{3}{4} \times \frac{2}{5}$ to mean (3 out of 4) of (2 out of 5); to bring out the analogy more clearly, we observe that the meaning of multiplication in 3×7 is that we choose 3 objects, when each object is a seven, and the meaning of the multiplication in

$$\frac{3}{4} \times \frac{2}{5}$$

is that we choose three out of four parts, (not of the whole cake, but) of the chosen 5 out of 7 parts. When we divide $\dfrac{2}{5}$ into 4 parts each part is $\dfrac{1}{10}$, and when we choose 3 of these the amount chosen is $\dfrac{3}{10}$, so that $\dfrac{3}{4} \times \dfrac{2}{5} = \dfrac{3}{10}\left(= \dfrac{3 \times 2}{4 \times 5}\right)$. In the general case

$$\frac{m}{n} \times \frac{p}{q}$$

suppose that we are sharing out the trees in an orchard of q rows of n trees. We start by choosing p of the q rows; then we choose m of the n columns (in the chosen rows), so that we end by choosing pm out of qn trees, that is

$$\frac{m}{n} \times \frac{p}{q} = \frac{pm}{nq}.$$

As another example consider the product

$$\frac{3}{5} \times \frac{4}{7};$$

suppose again that we are sharing out the trees in an orchard

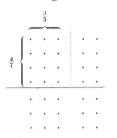

which contains 7 rows of 5 trees. We start by choosing 4 out of the 7 rows, and then we choose 3 out of the 5 columns (in the chosen 4, rows), thus we have selected 3×4 trees out of 5×7 trees which shows that

$$\frac{3}{5} \times \frac{4}{7} = \frac{3 \times 4}{5 \times 7} = \frac{12}{35}.$$

To find the quotient of one fraction by another we proceed as follows. Let the quotient of $\frac{2}{5}$ by $\frac{4}{7}$ be $\frac{a}{b}$, so that

$$\frac{2}{5} \div \frac{4}{7} = \frac{a}{b}$$

and so

$$\frac{2}{5} = \frac{a}{b} \times \frac{4}{7} = \frac{4a}{7b}$$

whence

$$2 \times 7b = 5 \times 4a$$

that is

$$7b = 10a, \dots \dots \dots \dots \quad \text{(i)}$$

one solution of which is $a = 7$, $b = 10$.

Thus

$$\frac{2}{5} \div \frac{4}{7} = \frac{7}{10}.$$

Of course equation (i) has other solutions than $a = 7$, $b = 10$; suppose that $a = A$, $b = B$ is another solution, then

$$\frac{A}{B} = \frac{7}{10}$$

because $7B = 10A$, and we obtain the same quotient whatever solution of equation (i) we use.

Carrying out the same argument in a general case, let the quotient of $\dfrac{p}{q}$ by $\dfrac{r}{s}$ be $\dfrac{a}{b}$, so that

$$\frac{p}{q} = \frac{r}{s} \times \frac{a}{b} = \frac{ar}{bs}$$

and therefore $bps = arq$; a solution of this equation is $b = rq$, $a = ps$ and so

$$\frac{p}{q} \div \frac{r}{s} = \frac{ps}{qr} \, .$$

But

$$\frac{ps}{qr} = \frac{p}{q} \times \frac{s}{r}$$

and therefore

$$\frac{p}{q} \div \frac{r}{s} = \frac{p}{q} \times \frac{s}{r} \, .$$

Thus to divide by a fraction, exchange the numerator and denominator, and then multiply.

We have tacitly assumed that the numerator of a fraction is smaller than the denominator, but, of course, in many sharing problems the shares are not just parts of a whole. For instance, in the first problem we considered, that of sharing 13 oranges amongst 3 boys, each boy receives 4 oranges and one third of an orange, which may simply be denoted by $4\dfrac{1}{3}$ $\left(\text{i.e. } 4 + \dfrac{1}{3} \right)$. What then is the arithmetic of these mixed numbers, partly a natural number, and partly a fraction? If we take $\dfrac{13}{3}$ to stand for

$$\frac{12}{3} + \frac{1}{3} = 4 + \frac{1}{3} = 4\frac{1}{3},$$

then mixed numbers, like fractions, consist of a pair of numbers To add two such pairs, for instance $\dfrac{5}{3}$ and $\dfrac{7}{4}$, we may proceed as follows:

$$\frac{5}{3} + \frac{7}{4} = \left(1 + \frac{2}{3} \right) + \left(1 + \frac{3}{4} \right) = (1 + 1) + \left(\frac{2}{3} + \frac{3}{4} \right)$$

(assuming associativity and commutativity)

$$= 2 + \frac{17}{12} = 2 + 1 + \frac{5}{12} = 3 + \frac{5}{12} = \frac{3 \times 12}{12} + \frac{5}{12} = \frac{41}{12};$$

this result is exactly the same as we should obtain by treating $\frac{5}{3}, \frac{7}{4}$ as fractions, thus,

$$\frac{5}{3} + \frac{7}{4} = \frac{5 \times 4 + 7 \times 3}{12} = \frac{41}{12}.$$

In the general case consider the sum $\frac{B}{b} + \frac{D}{d}$, where $B = pb + a$, $D = qd + c$; this sum is

$$\frac{pb + a}{b} + \frac{qd + c}{d}$$

$$= \left(p + \frac{a}{b} \right) + \left(q + \frac{c}{d} \right)$$

$$= (p + q) + \left(\frac{a}{b} + \frac{c}{d} \right) = (p + q) + \frac{ad + bc}{bd}$$

$$= \frac{(p + q)\, bd + (ad + bc)}{bd}$$

$$= \frac{(pb + a)\, d + (qd + c)\, b}{bd}$$

$$= \frac{Bd + bD}{bd}$$

and this is the same result we should have obtained if B, D had been smaller than b, d respectively. Thus the rule for adding mixed numbers is the same as the rule for fractions.

Multiplication by a natural number being simply iterated addition, it follows that

$$p \times \frac{a}{b} = \frac{a}{b} + \frac{a}{b} + \cdots + \frac{a}{b},$$

with p factors

$$= \frac{a + a + \cdots + a}{b} = \frac{pa}{b}.$$

Hence, if we assume the distributive property for multiplication of mixed numbers we have, for example,

$$\frac{23}{4} \times \frac{17}{5} = \left(5 + \frac{3}{4}\right)\left(3 + \frac{2}{5}\right)$$

$$= (5 \times 3) + \left(5 \times \frac{2}{5}\right) + \left(3 \times \frac{3}{4}\right) + \left(\frac{3}{4} \times \frac{2}{5}\right)$$

$$= 15 + 2 + \frac{9}{4} + \frac{6}{20}$$

$$= 15 + 2 + 2 + \frac{1}{4} + \frac{3}{10}$$

$$= 19 + \frac{5 + 6}{20} = 19\frac{11}{20},$$

and this is the same result that would have been obtained by treating $\frac{23}{4}$ and $\frac{17}{5}$ as fractions; thus

$$\frac{23}{4} \times \frac{17}{5} = \frac{23 \times 17}{4 \times 5} = \frac{391}{20} = 19\frac{11}{20}.$$

In the general case consider the mixed numbers

$$p\frac{a}{b} \quad \text{and} \quad q\frac{c}{d};$$

we have

$$p\frac{a}{b} \times q\frac{c}{d} = \left(p + \frac{a}{b}\right)\left(q + \frac{c}{d}\right)$$

$$= pq + \frac{pc}{d} + \frac{qa}{b} + \left(\frac{a}{b} \times \frac{c}{d}\right)$$

$$= pq + \frac{pbc + qad + ac}{bd}$$

and if we treat $\dfrac{pb + a}{b}, \dfrac{qd + c}{d}$ as *fractions*, then their product is

$$\frac{(pb + a)(qd + c)}{bd} = \frac{pqbd + (pbc + qad + ac)}{bd}$$

$$= pq + \frac{pbc + qad + ac}{bd}$$

as before.

The rules

$$\frac{a}{b} + \frac{c}{d} = \frac{ad + bc}{bd}$$

$$\frac{a}{b} \times \frac{c}{d} = \frac{ac}{bd}$$

are therefore valid, not only for fractions, but also when the numerators exceed the denominators. In practice it is, however, generally simpler to treat mixed numbers as the sum of a natural number and a fraction rather than express them in the form $\dfrac{m}{n}$.

Instead of constructing first an arithmetic of fractions and then extending it to mixed numbers, we can start with a general arithmetic of pairs $\dfrac{m}{n}$, $n \neq 0$, for which we lay down the rules of operation

$$\frac{a}{b} = \frac{c}{d} \qquad\qquad \text{E}$$

if, and only if, $ad = bc$;

$$\frac{a}{b} + \frac{c}{d} = \frac{ad + bc}{bd} \qquad\qquad \text{A}$$

and

$$\frac{a}{b} \times \frac{c}{d} = \frac{ac}{bd}. \qquad\qquad \text{M}$$

If we now consider all the pairs $\dfrac{a}{1}$ we find

$$\frac{a}{1} = \frac{b}{1}$$

if, and only if, $a = b$,

$$\frac{a}{1} + \frac{b}{1} = \frac{a + b}{1}$$

$$\frac{a}{1} \times \frac{b}{1} = \frac{a \times b}{1}$$

which shows that the arithmetic of pairs $\frac{a}{1}$ is *identical* with the arithmetic of natural numbers, and therefore the rules E, A and M make $\frac{a}{1}$ *just another sign for* a. Identifying $\frac{a}{1}$ with a we can now show that the rules E, A and M make $\frac{a}{b}$, with $a < b$, a fraction. For $(b \neq 0)$

$$b \times \frac{a}{b} = \frac{b}{1} \times \frac{a}{b} = \frac{ab}{b} = \frac{a}{1} = a,$$

that is, $\frac{a}{b}$ is what multiplied by b gives a, and this is what we mean by the fraction $\frac{a}{b}$. If a, b have no common factor (greater than unity), then the fraction $\frac{a}{b}$ is said to be in its *lowest terms*.

Inequalities

To decide which of two fractions is the greater we write them with a common denominator. For instance, to decide whether $\frac{17}{35}$ or $\frac{19}{40}$ is the greater we note that 280 is the least common multiple of 35 and 40, and write

$$\frac{17}{35} = \frac{136}{280}, \quad \frac{19}{40} = \frac{133}{280}$$

which shows that $\frac{17}{35}$ is greater than $\frac{19}{40}$.

In the general case, to compare $\frac{a}{b}$ with $\frac{c}{d}$ we write both fractions with the denominator bd, thus

$$\frac{a}{b} = \frac{ad}{bd}, \quad \frac{c}{d} = \frac{bc}{bd}$$

which shows that $\dfrac{a}{b}$ is greater than $\dfrac{c}{d}$ if $ad > bc$, that the fractions are equal if $ad = bc$, and that $\dfrac{a}{b}$ is less than $\dfrac{c}{d}$ if $ad < bc$. To sum up we have

$$\frac{a}{b} \gtreqless \frac{c}{d} \quad \text{according as} \quad ad \gtreqless bc.$$

Between any two natural numbers there is either no number, or a limited number of numbers, for instance between 3 and 4 there is no natural number, and between 3 and 15 there are the 11 numbers $4, 5, 6, 7, 8, 9, 10, 11, 12, 13, 14$; but any two fractions are separated by infinitely many fractions. For instance between $\dfrac{1}{2}$ and $\dfrac{1}{3}$ lies $\dfrac{2}{5}$, between $\dfrac{1}{2}$ and $\dfrac{2}{5}$ lies $\dfrac{3}{7}$, between $\dfrac{2}{5}$ and $\dfrac{1}{3}$ lies $\dfrac{3}{8}$, and so on. We can always write down at once a fraction between two given fractions, just by adding the numerators and denominators, thus between $\dfrac{a}{b}$ and $\dfrac{c}{d}$ lies $\dfrac{a+c}{b+d}$; for suppose that

$$\frac{a}{b} < \frac{c}{d},$$

then $ad < bc$, and therefore

$$ab + ad < ab + bc$$

which proves that

$$\frac{a}{b} < \frac{a+c}{b+d},$$

and further

$$cd + ad < cd + bc$$

so that

$$\frac{a+c}{b+d} < \frac{c}{d},$$

showing that $\dfrac{a+c}{b+d}$ lies between $\dfrac{a}{b}$ and $\dfrac{c}{d}$. A similar proof applies if $\dfrac{c}{d} < \dfrac{a}{b}$.

Thus a fraction has neither an immediate successor, nor an immediate predecessor, no 'next after', or nearest neighbour, in order of magnitude. But this does not mean that we cannot arrange all fractions in a row, provided that we do not arrange them by magnitude. One way of arranging fractions in a row is to collect into 'parcels' the fractions with a common sum of numerator and denominator. Thus in one parcel we should have, for instance $\dfrac{1}{6}$, $\dfrac{2}{5}, \dfrac{3}{4}, \dfrac{4}{3}, \dfrac{5}{2}$ and $\dfrac{6}{1}$, fractions with numerator and denominator adding up to 7. In each 'parcel' we order the fractions by size, as in the example above, and then we order the 'parcels' according to the sum of the numerator and denominator of the fractions in it. In this way we arrive at the following ordering $\left(\text{ignoring} \dfrac{0}{2}, \dfrac{0}{3}, \dfrac{0}{4}, \cdots \right.$ all of which equal $\left. \dfrac{0}{1} \right)$

$$\frac{0}{1}, \frac{1}{1}, \frac{1}{2}, \frac{2}{1}, \frac{1}{3}, \frac{2}{2}, \frac{3}{1}, \frac{1}{4}, \frac{2}{3}, \frac{3}{2}, \frac{4}{1}, \frac{1}{5}, \frac{2}{4}, \frac{3}{3}, \frac{4}{2}, \frac{5}{1}, \frac{1}{6}, \cdots$$

If we write down *in order of magnitude* the fractions $\dfrac{p}{q}$ (in their lowest terms) with $1 \leqslant p \leqslant n$, $1 \leqslant q \leqslant n$ we obtain what is called the *Farey series of order n*. Thus the Farey series of order 3 is

$$\frac{1}{3}, \frac{1}{2}, \frac{2}{3}, \frac{1}{1}$$

and the Farey series of order 5 is

$$\frac{1}{5}, \frac{1}{4}, \frac{1}{3}, \frac{2}{5}, \frac{1}{2}, \frac{3}{5}, \frac{2}{3}, \frac{3}{4}, \frac{4}{5}, \frac{1}{1};$$

that of order 6 is

$$\frac{1}{6}, \frac{1}{5}, \frac{1}{4}, \frac{1}{3}, \frac{2}{5}, \frac{1}{2}, \frac{3}{5}, \frac{2}{3}, \frac{3}{4}, \frac{4}{5}, \frac{5}{6}, \frac{1}{1};$$

and that of order 7 is

$$\frac{1}{7}, \frac{1}{6}, \frac{1}{5}, \frac{1}{4}, \frac{2}{7}, \frac{1}{3}, \frac{2}{5}, \frac{3}{7}, \frac{1}{2}, \frac{4}{7}, \frac{3}{5}, \frac{2}{3}, \frac{5}{7},$$

$$\frac{3}{4}, \frac{4}{5}, \frac{5}{6}, \frac{6}{7}, \frac{1}{1}.$$

We observe that consecutive fractions $\dfrac{p}{q}, \dfrac{r}{s}$ in a Farey series satisfy

$$qr - ps = 1.$$

For instance, in the series of order 7, let us consider the consecutive fractions

$$\frac{1}{3}, \frac{2}{5}, \frac{3}{7}, \frac{1}{2};$$

we observe that $3 \times 2 - 1 \times 5 = 1,\ 5 \times 3 - 2 \times 7 = 1,\ 7 \times 1 - 3 \times 2 = 1$.

It is easy to see why this must be so. First, we remark that we have already shown that, when p, q have no common factor, the equation

$$qx - py = 1$$

has always a solution in x and y, and we can necessarily find a solution in which x and y are both less than some number n, provided that neither p nor q exceeds n; for suppose we have a solution $x = X$, $y = Y$ with $X > n$, then

$$q(X - p) - p(Y - q) = qX - pY = 1$$

so that $x = X - p,\ y = Y - q$ is also a solution (and $Y - q \geqslant 0$ because $p(Y - q) = q(X - p) - 1 \geqslant q - 1 \geqslant 0$), and so by repeatedly subtracting p, we eventually reach a solution in which the value of x is less than n. Now let $\dfrac{p}{q}, \dfrac{r}{s}$ be two fractions which satisfy

$$qr - ps = 1$$

and let $\dfrac{a}{b}$ be a fraction between them, that is

$$\frac{p}{q} < \frac{a}{b} < \frac{r}{s};$$

then $aq > bp$, and so $aq - bp$ is a natural number, not zero, and therefore $aq - bp \geqslant 1$. Similarly $br - as \geqslant 1$.

Hence

$$b = b \times 1 = b(qr - ps) = bqr - bps$$
$$\geqslant aqs + q - bps$$
$$\geqslant bps + s + q - bps = q + s.$$

Thus, if $n < q + s$, there is no fraction in the Farey series of order n lying between $\dfrac{p}{q}$ and $\dfrac{r}{s}$, but in the Farey series of order $p + q$, there is exactly one fraction between

$$\frac{p}{q} \quad \text{and} \quad \frac{r}{s}$$

namely $\dfrac{p+r}{q+s}$ (for $b = q + s$ only if $aq - bp = 1$ and $br - as = 1$ and therefore

$$a = a \times 1 = a(qr - ps) = bpr + r - aps$$
$$= aps + p + r - aps = p + r)$$

and the fractions

$$\frac{p}{q}, \frac{p+r}{q+s}, \frac{r}{s}$$

satisfy

$$q(p + r) - p(q + s) = 1$$
$$r(q + s) - s(p + r) = 1.$$

This gives us the rule for constructing the Farey series of order $n + 1$ from the Farey series of order n. If $\dfrac{p}{q}, \dfrac{r}{s}$ are neighbours in the Farey series of order n, then if $q + s > n + 1$ they are neighbours in the Farey series of order $n + 1$, but if $q + s \leqslant n + 1$ then in the Farey series of order $n + 1$ there is just one fraction between $\dfrac{p}{q}$ and $\dfrac{r}{s}$, namely $\dfrac{p+r}{q+s}$. For example in the Farey series of order 6, $\dfrac{1}{3}$ and $\dfrac{2}{5}$ are neighbours and because $3 + 5 > 7$ they are neighbours again in the Fairey series of order 7, but in the Farey series of order 8 they are separated by the single fraction $\dfrac{1+2}{3+5} = \dfrac{3}{8}$.

Index laws for fractions

The properties of indices which natural numbers have, namely

$$a^m \times a^n = a^{m+n}, \quad (ab)^m = a^m \times b^m, \quad (a^m)^n = a^{mn},$$

hold also for fractions.

Student's Name ....

Category ....

School ....

Subject .... Class ....

Lecturer's Name ....

Date ....

If $\dfrac{p}{q} < \dfrac{x}{y} < \dfrac{r}{s}$ where $p, q, r, s \in N$

and ~~ps~~ $\underline{rq - ps = 1}$,

show that the min. value of
$y = q+s$ i.e. that $y \geq q+s$

$\dfrac{1}{2} - \dfrac{1}{5}$ $\dfrac{1}{4\,c\,14}$ $\dfrac{3}{8} - \dfrac{1}{3} = \dfrac{1}{24}$

$\dfrac{7}{9}$ $< \dfrac{4}{5}$ $\dfrac{35}{45}$ $\dfrac{2c}{45}$

$\tfrac{1}{n}(n+1) - - (n + n - 1) \div n!$

We remark first that

$$\left(\frac{p}{q}\right)^m = \frac{p^m}{q^m},$$

for this is certainly true when m has the value 1, and if it is true for $m = k$, then

$$\left(\frac{p}{q}\right)^{k+1} = \frac{p}{q} \times \left(\frac{p}{q}\right)^k = \frac{p}{q} \times \frac{p^k}{q^k} = \frac{p^{k+1}}{q^{k+1}}$$

which establishes the result for the value $k + 1$ of m, and so for all m.

Hence

$$\left(\frac{p}{q}\right)^m \times \left(\frac{p}{q}\right)^n = \frac{p^m}{q^m} \times \frac{p^n}{q^n} = \frac{p^m \times p^n}{q^m \times q^n} = \frac{p^{m+n}}{q^{m+n}} = \left(\frac{p}{q}\right)^{m+n},$$

$$\left[\left(\frac{p}{q}\right)^m\right]^n = \left[\frac{p^m}{q^m}\right]^n = \frac{(p^m)^n}{(q^m)^n} = \frac{p^{mn}}{q^{mn}} = \left(\frac{p}{q}\right)^{mn},$$

and

$$\left[\frac{p}{q} \times \frac{r}{s}\right]^m = \left[\frac{pr}{qs}\right]^m = \frac{(pr)^m}{(qs)^m} = \frac{p^m r^m}{q^m s^m} = \frac{p^m}{q^m} \times \frac{r^m}{s^m}$$

$$= \left[\frac{p}{q}\right]^m \times \left[\frac{r}{s}\right]^m.$$

The field of rational numbers

We have seen that for natural numbers, addition and multiplication are always possible, but both subtraction and division may fail (which is perhaps what makes the natural numbers so interesting); for integers only division may fail; for fractions division never fails, but subtraction may fail, for instance we cannot take $\frac{2}{3}$ from $\frac{1}{3}$. To obtain a system of numbers in which neither subtraction nor division may fail, we combine the ideas underlying fractions and integers to form the so-called *rational numbers*.

Writing now single letters for integers (one of the ways in which mathematics evolves is by writing single letters for pairs, triples, and so on, even for an unending succession) we set up an arithmetic of pairs of integers i/j, $j \neq 0$, as follows:

$$i/j = i'/j'$$

if, and only if, $ij' = i'j$;

$$i/j + i'/j' = (ij' + i'j)/jj'$$

and

$$i/j \times i'/j' = ii'/jj'.$$

Subtraction is defined as usual in terms of addition so that the difference between i/j and i'/j' is what must be added to i'/j' to give i/j, that is

$$i'/j' + (i/j - i'/j') = i/j;$$

writing I/J for the difference we have

$$i'/j' + I/J = i/j$$

and so

$$(i'J + Ij')/Jj' = i/j$$

and therefore

$$Ijj' = J(ij' - i'j)$$

one solution of which is

$$I = ij' - i'j, \quad J = jj',$$

giving

$$i/j - i'/j' = (ij' - i'j)/jj'.$$

If I', J' is another solution, so that

$$I'jj' = J'(ij' - i'j)$$

it follows that

$$I'/J' = (ij' - i'j)/jj'$$

which shows that the difference is *unique*.

To find the quotient of i/j divided by i'/j' ($i' \neq 0$) we denote the quotient by I/J and observe that

$$I/J \times i'/j' = i/j$$

and so

$$Ii'/Jj' = i/j$$

which holds if, and only if,

$$Ii'j = Jij';$$

thus one solution is $I = ij'$, $J = i'j$ giving

$$i/j \div i'/j' = ij'/i'j = i/j \times j'/i'$$

(the familiar rule for fractions). The quotient is unique because a second solution

$$I', J' \quad \text{of the equation} \quad Ii'j = Jij'$$

of course satisfies

$$I'i'j = J'ij'$$

which ensures that

$$I'/J' = ij'/i'j.$$

It is important to observe that if $i/j = i'/j'$ and $I/J = I'/J'$, then

$$i/j + I/J = i'/j' + I'/J'$$

and

$$i/j \times I/J = i'/j' \times I'/J'.$$

We leave the proofs of these equivalences to the reader.

The pair $0/j$ which we have had to exclude in division, is the zero of the rational numbers; we remark first that

$$0/j = 0/j'$$

since

$$0 \times j' = 0 \times j.$$

Then

$$i/j + 0/j = (i + 0)/j = i/j$$

showing that $0/j$ is the zero.

The rational numbers form a system in which subtraction is always possible and division is always possible (except by zero); as we remarked before, when we considered the arithmetic of remainders to a prime divisor, such a system is called a *field*. The rational numbers are the first example we have met of a field with an unlimited number of elements. Fields may therefore be finite or infinite.

The rational numbers contain all the previously considered systems, natural numbers, fractions and integers. We shall show first that the rational numbers $+a/+1$ have the same arithmetic as the natural number a (or the positive integer $+a$). For $+a/+1 =$ $= +b/+1$ if, and only if, $+a = +b$, that is $a = b$; $(+a/+1) +$ $+ (+b/+1) = +(a+b)/+1$ and $(+a/+1) \times (+b/+1) =$ $+ ab/+1$, showing that $+a/+1$ is just another way of writing a, and that the arithmetic of the rational number $+a/+1$ is exactly the same as the arithmetic of the natural number a. (In fact $-a/-1$ has also the same arithmetic as the natural number a.) The rational number $-a/+1$ has the same arithmetic as the negative integer $-a$, and the rational number $+a/+b$ has the same arithmetic as the fraction $\dfrac{a}{b}$. To prove only the second of these we observe

$$+ a/+ b = +c/+ d$$

if, and only if, $+ ad = + bc$, that is, if, and only if, $ad = bc$, $\left(\text{and therefore } \dfrac{a}{b} = \dfrac{c}{d}\right)$;

$$(+ a/+ b) + (+ c/+ d) = +(ad + bc)/+ bd$$

and

$$\frac{a}{b} + \frac{c}{d} = \frac{ad + bc}{bd};$$

$$(+ a/+ b) \times (+ c/+ d) = +ac/+ bd.$$

$$\frac{a}{b} \times \frac{c}{d} = \frac{ac}{bd}$$

which confirms that $\dfrac{a}{b}$ and $+a/+b$ have the same arithmetic.

As we have already noted, the rational numbers $+p/+q$, $-p/-q$ are equal; we denote their common value by $+\dfrac{p}{q}$. So too the rational numbers $+p/-q$, $-p/+q$ are equal, and we denote their common value by $-\dfrac{p}{q}$ $\left(\text{notice that } +\dfrac{p}{q}, -\dfrac{p}{q} \text{ are related to}\right.$ the *fraction* $\dfrac{p}{q}$, as the integers $+n$, $-n$ are related to the natural number n).

In this new notation the arithmetic of rationals takes a more familiar form: for instance

$$+ \frac{p}{q} = + \frac{r}{s}$$

if, and only if,

$$\frac{p}{q} = \frac{r}{s},$$

since

$$+\frac{p}{q} = +p/+q, \quad +\frac{r}{s} = +r/+s$$

and

$$+p/+q = +r/+s$$

if, and only if, $\frac{p}{q} = \frac{r}{s}$ as we have observed.

Similarly $-\frac{p}{q} = -\frac{r}{s}$ if, and only if, $\frac{p}{q} = \frac{r}{s}$. Since $\frac{+p}{+q} > \frac{0}{+1}$, that is $+\frac{p}{q} > 0$, we call $+\frac{p}{q}$ a positive rational (or positive fraction), and since $\frac{-p}{+q} < \frac{0}{+1}$, that is $-\frac{p}{q} < 0$, we call $-\frac{p}{q}$ a negative rational number (or negative fraction). The product of a positive and a negative fraction is a negative fraction, for

$$\left(+\frac{p}{q}\right) \times \left(-\frac{r}{s}\right)$$

$$= (+p/+q) \times (-r/+s) = -pr/+qs$$

$$= -\frac{pr}{qs} = -\left(\frac{p}{q} \times \frac{r}{s}\right),$$

and the product of two negative fractions is a positive fraction, since

$$\left(-\frac{p}{q}\right) \times \left(-\frac{r}{s}\right)$$

$$= (-p/+q) \times (-r/+s) = +pr/+qs$$

$$= +\frac{pr}{qs} = +\left(\frac{p}{q} \times \frac{r}{s}\right).$$

The positive fractions $+\frac{p}{q}$ and the fraction $\frac{p}{q}$ have the same arithmetic, as we have already remarked. We may therefore omit the $+$ in front of a positive fraction, writing simply $\frac{p}{q}$ for $+\frac{p}{q}$.

Negative indices

We shall now consider the question whether any meaning can be found for *negative* indices. Let us start by considering the index -1. If we require this new index to satisfy the same rules of operation as positive indices, we have for instance

$$a^2 \times a^{-1} = a^{2-1} = a^1$$

and therefore

$$a^{-1} = \frac{a^1}{a^2} = \frac{1}{a}, \quad (a \neq 0).$$

Assuming that $(a^{-1})^m = a^{-m}$, by analogy with $(a^n)^m = a^{n\,m}$, it follows that

$$a^{-m} = \left(\frac{1}{a}\right)^m = \frac{1}{a^m}.$$

Accordingly we *define*

$$a^{-m} = \frac{1}{a^m} = 1 \div a^m, \quad a \neq 0,$$

where a may be either a natural number or a fraction. It is easily verified that the three laws of indices

$$a^m \times a^n = a^{m+n}, \ (ab)^n = a^n b^n, \ (a^m)^n = a^{m\,n}$$

hold also for negative indices. For instance

$$(a^{-m})^{-n} = \left(\frac{1}{a^m}\right)^{-n} = 1 \div \left(\frac{1}{a^m}\right)^n = 1 \div \frac{1}{a^{m\,n}} = a^{m\,n} = a^{(-m) \times (-n)}.$$

It follows that $a^0 = 1$, for $a^0 = a^{1-1} = a \times \frac{1}{a} = 1, a \neq 0$.

Fractional indices

If we seek to pass from negative to fractional indices in the same way we meet a difficulty. Let us first consider $9^{\frac{1}{2}}$. Assuming fractional indices obey the index law we should have

$$9^{\frac{1}{2}} \times 9^{\frac{1}{2}} = 9^{\frac{1}{2}+\frac{1}{2}} = 9^1 = 9;$$

since 9 can be expressed as a product of equal factors in only one way (confining our attention now to natural numbers), namely as 3×3, it follows that $9^{\frac{1}{2}} = 3$. But if we carry through the same operation for $2^{\frac{1}{2}}$, we find

$$2^{\frac{1}{2}} \times 2^{\frac{1}{2}} = 2,$$

even though 2 cannot be expressed as a product of two equal factors. Thus $2^{\frac{1}{2}}$ does not represent a natural number, and we shall show shortly that it does not even represent a fraction.

Similarly, since

$$8^{\frac{1}{3}} \times 8^{\frac{1}{3}} \times 8^{\frac{1}{3}} = 8^{\frac{1}{3} + \frac{1}{3} + \frac{1}{3}} = 8$$

and $8 = 2 \times 2 \times 2$, therefore $8^{\frac{1}{3}} = 2$, but $7^{\frac{1}{3}}$ does not represent a natural number (nor a fraction).

It is clear that if we are to make use of fractional indices we must find a further extension of the number concept. Let us confine our attention in the first instance to the index $\frac{1}{2}$. We remarked before that there is no fraction whose square is 2. To prove this consider the difference

$$2p^2 - q^2$$

where p, q have no common factor; if q is divisible by 2 let $q = 2Q$, and let $p = 2P + 1$, since p and q are not both divisible by 2.

Then $2p^2 - q^2 = 2\{(2P + 1)^2 - 2Q^2\}$, and the difference in brackets cannot be zero since $(2P + 1)^2 - 2Q^2 = 2(2P^2 + 2P - Q^2) + 1$ which leaves the remainder 1 on division by 2. On the other hand, if q is not divisible by 2, then $q = 2Q + 1$, where Q is the quotient when q is divided by 2, and so

$$2p^2 - q^2 = 2(p^2 - 2Q^2 - 2Q) - 1$$

which also leaves the remainder 1 on division by 2, and is therefore not zero. It follows that

$$2p^2 - q^2$$

is never zero, and so its positive value is at least 1; that is

$$|2p^2 - q^2| \geqslant 1.$$

Dividing by p^2, we find

$$\left| 2 - \frac{q^2}{p^2} \right| \geqslant \frac{1}{p^2}$$

which shows that the square of *any* fraction $\dfrac{q}{p}$ differs from 2 by at least $\dfrac{1}{p^2}$, and so there is no fraction whose square is 2. Can we then find a meaning for $2^{\frac{1}{2}}$? In other words, can we construct an arithmetic for $2^{\frac{1}{2}}$?

Once more we construct an arithmetic of pairs $\{x, y\}$, where x, y are now rational numbers. We lay down the properties

$$\{x, y\} = \{x', y'\}$$

if, and only if, $x = x'$, $y = y'$.

$$\{x, y\} + \{x', y'\} = \{x + x', y + y'\}$$

and

$$\{x, y\} \times \{x', y'\} = \{xx' + 2yy', xy' + x'y\}.$$

These rules have not, of course, been chosen at random but on the following plan. We consider the numbers $x + yt$ for all rational values of x and y. Then $(x + yt) + (x' + y't) = (x + x') + (y + y')t$, and

$$(x + yt)(x' + y't) = xx' + yy't^2 + (xy' + x'y)t;$$

if in the product we replace t^2 by 2 (remember we are looking for a 'number' with square 2) we obtain

$$(x + yt)(x' + y't) = xx' + 2yy' + (xy' + x'y)t$$

which corresponds to the rule of multiplication we gave for the pairs $\{x, y\}$, $\{x', y'\}$.

Next we observe that the arithmetic of the pairs $\{x, 0\}$ with zero second term is precisely the arithmetic of rationals, for $\{x, 0\} = \{x', 0\}$ if, and only if, $x = x'$, and

$$\{x, 0\} + \{x', 0\} = \{x + x', 0\}, \ \{x, 0\} \times \{x', 0\} = \{xx', 0\}$$

so that we may write just x for the pair $\{x, 0\}$; since

$$\{x, 0\} \times \{x', y'\} = \{xx', xy'\}$$

we have

$$x \times \{x', y'\} = \{xx', xy'\}.$$

In particular

$$\{x, y\} = \{x, 0\} + \{y, 0\} \times \{0, 1\}$$
$$= x + y \times \{0, 1\}$$

where
$$\{0, 1\} \times \{0, 1\} = 2$$

(this is what we secured by replacing t^2 by 2 above). Writing $\sqrt{2}$ for $\{0,1\}$ (the sign $\sqrt{2}$ is called the *square root* of 2) we reach the representation of the pair $\{x, y\}$ in the form

$$\{x, y\} = x + y\sqrt{2}$$

where $\sqrt{2}$ has the property

$$\sqrt{2} \times \sqrt{2} = 2.$$

In fact $-\sqrt{2}$, that is $-1 \times \sqrt{2} (= -1 \times \{0,1\} = \{0, -1\})$ has the same property, namely

$$(-\sqrt{2}) \times (-\sqrt{2}) = 2$$

for $\{0, -1\} \times \{0, -1\} = \{+2,0\} = 2$, and so we may identify $2^{\frac{1}{2}}$ with either $\sqrt{2}$, or with $-\sqrt{2}$.

This method of constructing a number with a desired property is a particular case of a general method which we shall describe later.

The numbers $x + y\sqrt{2}$ form a *field*; to find the difference between $x + y\sqrt{2}$, and $x' + y'\sqrt{2}$, denote the difference by $u + v\sqrt{2}$, then we have

$$(x' + y'\sqrt{2}) + (u + v\sqrt{2}) = x + y\sqrt{2}$$

and therefore

$$x' + u = x$$
$$y' + v = y$$

whence

$$u = x - x', \ v = y - y'.$$

proving that

$$(x - x') + (y - y')\sqrt{2}$$

is the difference between $x + y\sqrt{2}$ and $x' + y'\sqrt{2}$. To find the quotient of $x + y\sqrt{2}$ divided by $x' + y'\sqrt{2}$ (when x', y' are not both 0), let $p + q\sqrt{2}$ be the quotient, then

$$(x' + y'\sqrt{2}) \times (p + q\sqrt{2}) = (x + y\sqrt{2})$$

whence we find

$$px' + 2qy' = x$$
$$py' + qx' = y.$$

Multiplying the first equation by y' and the second by x' (to make the terms in p the same in both equations) we find

$$px'y' + 2qy'^2 = xy'$$
$$px'y' + qx'^2 = x'y.$$

From the first equation, we see that

$$px'y' = xy' - 2qy'^2$$

and from the second that

$$px'y' = x'y - qx'^2$$

which shows that

$$xy' - 2qy'^2 = x'y - qx'^2$$

and therefore

$$q(x'^2 - 2y'^2) = x'y - xy'$$

from which it follows that

$$q = \frac{x'y - xy'}{x'^2 - 2y'^2}$$

(observe that $x'^2 - 2y'^2$ is never zero, so that the division is sound). Similarly we may show that

$$p = \frac{xx' - 2yy'}{x'^2 - 2y'^2}.$$

The procedure through which we have passed makes division seem very difficult, but in fact once we have shown that division is possible there is a nice short cut for finding the quotient. We notice first that

$$(x' + y'\sqrt{2}) \times (x' - y'\sqrt{2}) = x'^2 - 2y'^2;$$

then, treating

$$\frac{x + y\sqrt{2}}{x' + y'\sqrt{2}}$$

like a fraction we have

$$\frac{x + y\sqrt{2}}{x' + y'\sqrt{2}} = \frac{x + y\sqrt{2}}{x' + y'\sqrt{2}} \times \frac{x' - y'\sqrt{2}}{x' - y'\sqrt{2}}$$
$$= \frac{xx' - 2yy' + (x'y - xy')\sqrt{2}}{x'^2 - 2y'^2}$$

as before. We could obviously apply the method we have just used to construct $\sqrt{2}$ to construct for instance $3^{\frac{1}{2}}$, that is a number x satisfying $x^2 = 3$, or $2^{\frac{1}{3}}$, that is a number x satisfying $x^3 = 2$. What is more interesting is that after each extension, to construct number pairs, we can use not just the rationals but any new numbers already constructed. For instance, having constructed the numbers $x + y\sqrt{2}$, with x, y rational we may use single letters to denote these numbers, for instance capital letters A, B, C, ..., and then consider an arithmetic of pairs $[A, B]$ with the rules

$$[A, B] = [A', B'] \quad \text{if, and only if,} \quad A = A', B = B'$$
$$[A, B] + [A', B'] = [A + A', B + B']$$
$$[A, B] \times [A', B'] = [AA' + 3BB', AB' + A'B],$$

and these pairs may in turn be written simply as

$$A + B\sqrt{3}$$

where $\sqrt{3}$ satisfies $\sqrt{3} \times \sqrt{3} = 3$; remembering that A, B are themselves of the form $x + y\sqrt{2}$, our new number takes the form

$$a + b\sqrt{2} + c\sqrt{3} + d(\sqrt{2})(\sqrt{3}).$$

It is instructive to see what happens if we seek to apply this process to a number like 4 which already has a square root 2, (by which we mean, of course, just that $2 \times 2 = 4$). We proceed to construct an arithmetic of pairs of rationals (x, y) such that

$$(x, y) = (x', y')$$

if, and only if,

$$x = x', \quad y = y',$$
$$(x, y) + (x', y') = (x + x', y + y')$$
$$(x, y) \times (x', y') = (xx' + 4yy', xy' + x'y).$$

Exactly as before we find that we may identify $(x, 0)$ with x itself, and we arrive at the representation

$$(x, y) = x + y \times (0, 1).$$

Subtraction proceeds exactly as before, but if we attempt division, we meet a difficulty. Let us suppose that division is possible and that

$$(x, y) \div (x', y') = (p, q),$$

then

$$(x, y) = (x', y') \times (p, q)$$

and so

$$px' + 4qy' = x$$

$$py' + qx' = y$$

whence, as before,

$$q(x'^2 - 4y'^2) = xy' - x'y;$$

now, however, we cannot proceed to divide by $x'^2 - 4y'^2$ since there are values of x' and y' for which $x'^2 - 4y'^2$ vanish, for instance $x' = 2$, $y' = 1$. Because 4 has a rational square root, the extension now does *not* form a field.

In the same way we can show that if we extend the rationals first to $\sqrt{2}$ and $\sqrt{3}$ and then seek a further extension to $\sqrt{6}$, again we fail to obtain a field; this is because

$$(\sqrt{2} \times \sqrt{3}) \times (\sqrt{2} \times \sqrt{3}) = (\sqrt{2} \times \sqrt{2}) \times (\sqrt{3} \times \sqrt{3}) = 2 \times 3 = 6,$$

that is

$$2^{\frac{1}{2}} \times 3^{\frac{1}{2}} = (2 \times 3)^{\frac{1}{2}}$$

verifying one of the index laws for the fractional index $\frac{1}{2}$.

Polynomials

Starting with any field, for instance, the rational field to make it definite, we proceed now to construct new numbers by using the rationals as 'digits' and some letter as 'base' symbol. We shall denote the rationals by a, b, c, ... and the 'base' symbol by x. The new numbers, called *polynomials*, are of the forms

$$ax + b, \quad ax^2 + bx + c, \quad ax^3 + bx^2 + cx + d,$$

and so on, according to the number of 'digits'. In fact $ax + b$ is merely a convenient way of recording a *pair* of rationals, $ax^2 + bx + c$ of recording a triple and so on. The elements x, x^2, x^3, ... are mere place holders, separating the components of the pair, triple and so on. In $ax + b$, a is called the *coefficient* of x, in $ax^2 + bx + c$, a is the coefficient of x^2, and so on. Of course, if in any polynomial we replaced x by an element from the field to which $a, b, c, \ldots$ belong, we obtain another element of the field. Alternatively we may think of x as belonging to a 'higher' field which contains the field of the coefficients, so that the polynomials are simply elements of this higher field. From this point of view it is easy to see how polynomials add and multiply; for instance

$$(ax^2 + bx + c) + (a'x^2 + b'x + c')$$
$$= (a + a')x^2 + (b + b')x + c + c'$$

using the associative and distributive laws (in the higher field) and

$$(ax^2 + bx + c) \times (a'x^3 + b'x^2 + c'x + d') =$$
$$aa'x^5 + (ab' + a'b)x^4 + (ac' + bb' + ca')x^3 +$$
$$+ (ad' + bc' + cb')x^2 + (bd' + cc')x + cd'.$$

The index of the highest power of x in a polynomial is called the *degree* of the polynomial. Polynomials form a ring with 0 and 1 as zero and unit (polynomial); the polynomial ring is without divisors of zero, for the product of a polynomial of degree m with one of degree n is of degree $m + n$, so that the product of two polynomials is of degree not less than the degrees of the factors of the product.

Given two polynomials, say $A(x)$ of degree m, and $B(x)$ of degree, n, where $m \geqslant n$, by subtracting a suitable multiple of $B(x)$ from $A(x)$ we may obtain a remainder polynomial of degree less than n. For instance, given the polynomials $x^2 + 2x + 3$ and $x^5 + 4x^4 + x^3 + 2x^2 + x + 1$ we may proceed as follows:

$$
\begin{array}{r}
x^2 + 2x + 3)\overline{\smash{)}x^5 + 4x^4 + x^3 + 2x^2 + x + 1}(x^3 + 2x^2 - 6x + 8 \\
\underline{x^5 + 2x^4 + 3x^3} \\
2x^4 - 2x^3 + 2x^2 \\
\underline{2x^4 + 4x^3 + 6x^2} \\
-6x^3 - 4x^2 + x \\
\underline{-6x^3 - 12x^2 - 18x} \\
8x^2 + 19x + 1 \\
\underline{8x^2 + 16x + 24} \\
3x - 23
\end{array}
$$

Step by step we subtract multiples of $x^2 + 2x + 3$, first multiplying $x^2 + 2x + 3$ by x^3, then by $+2x^2$, then by $-6x$ and finally by $+8$, so that in all we subtract $x^3 + 2x^2 - 6x + 8$ times $x^2 + 2x + 3$ from $x^5 + 4x^4 + x^3 + 2x^2 + x + 1$, leaving the remainder $3x - 23$. This process is, of course, the exact parallel of long division for integers. Since

$$x^5 + 4x^4 + x^3 + 2x^2 + x + 1 -$$
$$- (x^2 + 2x + 3)(x^3 + 2x^2 - 6x + 8) = 3x - 23$$

we have

$$x^5 + 4x^4 + x^3 + 2x^2 + x + 1$$
$$= (x^2 + 2x + 3)(x^3 + 2x^2 - 6x + 8) + (3x - 23)$$

so that $x^3 + 2x^2 - 6x + 8$ is the quotient, and $3x - 23$ the remainder, when $x^5 + 4x^4 + x^3 + 2x^2 + x + 1$ is divided by $x^2 + 2x + 3$.

In the same way, starting with polynomials $A(x)$, $B(x)$, by repeatedly subtracting multiples of $B(x)$ from $A(x)$ we obtain a quotient $Q(x)$, and remainder $R(x)$, so that

$$A(x) = B(x) \times Q(x) + R(x).$$

Two polynomials are equal if, and only if, they are of the same degree, and their corresponding coefficients are equal, for their difference is the zero polynomial in which all coefficients are zero; thus, for instance

$$ax^2 + bx + c = a'x^2 + b'x + c'$$

if, and only if,

$$(a - a')x^2 + (b - b')x + (c - c') = 0$$

that is, if, and only if,

$$a - a' = 0, \quad b - b' = 0, \quad c - c' = 0,$$

and so

$$a = a', \quad b = b', \quad c = c'.$$

It follows that if two polynomials are equal, then they yield the same element if we substitute in each for x an element from the field of the coefficients. Consider now the quotient of a polynomial $P(x)$ on division by the polynomial $x - a$; let $Q(x)$ be the quotient and R the remainder (which is of degree zero and so does not contain x), then

$$P(x) = (x - a) Q(x) + R;$$

substitute a for x and we find

$$P(a) = 0 \times Q(a) + R = R$$

showing that the remainder when $P(x)$ is divided by $x - a$ is $P(a)$; $P(a)$, of course, is an element of the coefficient field, not a polynomial.

If $R = 0$ we have

$$P(x) = (x - a) Q(x)$$

showing that $x - a$ is a factor of $P(x)$; thus the condition for $P(x)$ to be divisible by $x - a$ is that $P(a) = 0$, a result which is known as the *Remainder Theorem*.

We shall now consider a famous process for finding the highest common factor of two elements of a polynomial ring; let the elements be a, b and let the quotient and remainder when a is divided by b be q_1, r_1 respectively, so that

$$a = bq_1 + r_1;$$

next divide b by r_1 yielding a quotient q_2 and remainder r_2;

$$b = r_1q_2 + r_2;$$

then divide r_1 by r_2 with quotient q_2, remainder r_3;

$$r_1 = r_2q_3 + r_3,$$

and so on. The degrees of b, r_1, r_2, r_3, ... are steadily decreasing and so we must reach a remainder r_{n+1} which is zero where

$$r_{n-2} = r_{n-1}q_n + r_n$$

and

$$r_{n-1} = r_nq_{n+1}.$$

We remark first that any factor of a and of b is a factor of r_1, (from the first equation) and hence in turn a factor of r_2, r_3, ..., r_n. Conversely, running through the equations backwards we see that a factor of r_n is a factor of r_{n-1} and hence of r_{n-2} and so on up to

r_1, b and a. Thus every common factor of a and b is a factor of r_n (the last non-zero remainder) and every factor of r_n is a common factor of a, b showing that r_n is itself the highest common factor of a, b. (This process applies equally to the ring of integers where instead of the *degree* of the remainders decreasing, we find that the positive values of the remainders necessarily decrease, leading again to a zero remainder.)

Let us exhibit the process by finding the highest common factor of the polynomials $x^3 + 6x^2 + 11x + 6$ and $x^4 + 8x^3 + 20x^2 + 19x + 6$.

$$x^3 + 6x^2 + 11x + 6 \overline{)x^4 + 8x^3 + 20x^2 + 19x + 6}\,(x + 2$$
$$\underline{x^4 + 6x^3 + 11x^2 + 6x}$$
$$2x^3 + 9x^2 + 13x + 6$$
$$\underline{2x^3 + 12x^2 + 22x + 12}$$
$$-3x^2 - 9x - 6\,\overline{)x^3 + 6x^2 + 11x + 6}\,(-\tfrac{1}{3}x - 1$$
$$\underline{x^3 + 3x^2 + 2x}$$
$$3x^2 + 9x + 6$$
$$3x^2 + 9x + 6$$

The highest common factor is therefore $-3(x^2 + 3x + 2)$; we may ignore the factor -3 for if a polynomial $A(x)$ has a factor $F(x)$, and if

$$A(x) = F(x) \times Q(x),$$

then, of course,

$$A(x) = fF(x) \times \frac{1}{f} Q(x)$$

where f is any non-zero polynomial of degree zero (for the co-efficients belong to a field, so that $\frac{1}{f}$ is an element of this field and therefore $\frac{1}{f} Q(x)$ is a polynomial).

The highest common factor process yields another very important property. Suppose that polynomials a, b are without common factor (of degree greater than zero, that is, for as we have just remarked, any two polynomials have a common factor of degree zero); then the last non-zero remainder r_n in the highest common factor process is simply one element of the coefficient field.

Let us say that a polynomial p is *linearly dependent* on polynomials, a, b if there are polynomials A, B such that

$$p = Aa + Bb.$$

Then the highest common factor process shows, in turn, that r_1 is linearly dependent on a, b; thence that r_2 is linearly dependent on a, b and so on, until finally we see that r_n is linearly dependent on a, b. Hence there are poylnomials A', B' such that

$$r_n = A'a + B'b$$

or dividing by the non-zero element r_n we have

$$Aa + Bb = 1$$

where we have written A, B for the polynomials $\dfrac{1}{r_n} A'$, $\dfrac{1}{r_n} B'$ respectively.

Remainder fields

We remarked earlier that the process by which we constructed a field with an element $\sqrt{2}$ is a particular case of the process by which we constructed the fields of remainders on division by a prime natural number, and we are now in a position to justify this remark. Consider the ring of polynomials over some field F (that is, with coefficients in F), and let p be a prime polynomial (that is, p cannot be expressed as a product of two polynomials with coefficients in F). We shall show that the remainders when polynomials are divided by p form a field. Let us denote the remainder when a is divided by p by $[a]$. In the arithmetic of remainders the sum of two remainders $[r]$, $[s]$ say, is defined as the remainder $[r + s]$ when $r + s$ is divided by p, and the product of $[r]$ and $[s]$ as the remainder $[r \times s]$ when the product $r \times s$ is divided by p. Since

$$s + (r - s) = r$$

it follows that, on division by p, the remainder when $r - s$ is divided by p added to the remainder when s is divided by p, leaves the same remainder on division by p as r; for if $r - s = pa + b$, and $s = pc + d$, then $r = p(a + c) + b + d$. Thus

$$[s] + [r - s] = [r].$$

Consider now two polynomials a, b with $[b] \neq 0$. We shall show that $[a]$ is divisible by $[b]$, that is to say, that there is a polynomial $[c]$ such that

$$[a] = [b] \times [c].$$

Since $[b] \neq 0$, therefore b is not a multiple of p, and therefore, since p is prime, b and p have no common factor. It follows that there are polynomials B, P such that

$$Bb + Pp = 1$$

and therefore the remainder when aBb is divided by p is the same as the remainder when a is divided by p, that is

$$[a] = [b] \times [aB]$$

showing that $[a]$ is divisible by $[b]$ with quotient $[aB]$. *This proves that the remainders on division by a prime p form a field.*

For instance, if the field of the coefficients is the rational field, then $x^2 - 2$ is prime for as we have seen $x^2 - 2$ is divisible by $x - a$ only if $a^2 - 2 = 0$, and we know that there is no rational a such that $a^2 - 2 = 0$. Hence the remainders on division by $x^2 - 2$ form a field. These remainders are of the form $ax + b$ where a, b are rationals. The sum of $ax + b$, $a'x + b'$ is simply $(a + a') x + (b + b')$ because this is a degree less than 2, but the product of $ax + b$, $a'x + b'$, in the arithmetic of remainders, is not simply

$$aa'x^2 + (ab' + a'b) x + bb'$$

but the remainder when this is divided by $x^2 - 2$, which is

$$(ab' + a'b) x + bb' + 2aa'$$

(which it will be observed can be obtained by writing 2 for x^2, since $x^2 = (x^2 - 2) + 2$ showing that x^2 and 2 leave the same remainder on division by $x^2 - 2$). This is precisely the value for the product we obtained before (with x standing for $\sqrt{2}$).

It is instructive to apply the same process in the case when the field of the coefficients is a finite field. Consider, for instance, the field (of remainders) with elements 0,1 and the arithmetic $1 + 1 = 0$. In this field the polynomial $x^2 + x + 1$ is prime (for neither $1^2 + 1 + 1$ nor $0^2 + 0 + 1$ is equal to 0) and the remainders when polynomials are divided by $x^2 + x + 1$ are

$$x, \quad x + 1, \quad 0, \quad 1.$$

These four elements constitute a field. The addition table is:

+	x	$x+1$	0	1
x	0	1	x	$x+1$
$x+1$	1	0	$x+1$	x
0	x	$x+1$	0	1
1	$x+1$	x	1	0

and the multiplication table (for the non-zero elements) is

$\times$	x	$x+1$	1
x	$x+1$	1	x
$x+1$	1	x	$x+1$
1	x	$x+1$	1

Similarly, taking the field of the coefficients to be the field of remainders modulo 3, with elements $0, 1, 2$, we observe that, for instance, $x^2 + x + 2$ is a prime polynomial (for none of $0^2 + 0 + 2$, $1^2 + 1 + 2$, $2^2 + 2 + 2$ is equal to 0 modulo 3); the remainders modulo $x^2 + x + 2$ are $0, 1, 2, x, x + 1, x + 2, 2x, 2x + 1$, $2x + 2$ and these form a field of nine elements; their addition table is:

+	0	1	2	x	$x+1$	$x+2$	$2x$	$2x+1$	$2x+2$
0	0	1	2	x	$x+1$	$x+2$	$2x$	$2x+1$	$2x+2$
1	1	2	0	$x+1$	$x+2$	x	$2x+1$	$2x+2$	$2x$
2	2	0	1	$x+2$	x	$x+1$	$2x+2$	$2x$	$2x+1$

+	0	1	2	x	$x+1$	$x+2$	$2x$	$2x+1$	$2x+2$
x	x	$x+1$	$x+2$	$2x$	$2x+1$	$2x+2$	0	1	2
$x+1$	$x+1$	$x+2$	x	$2x+1$	$2x+2$	$2x$	1	2	0
$x+2$	$x+2$	x	$x+1$	$2x+2$	$2x$	$2x+1$	2	0	1
$2x$	$2x$	$2x+1$	$2x+2$	0	1	2	x	$x+1$	$x+2$
$2x+1$	$2x+1$	$2x+2$	$2x$	1	2	0	$x+1$	$x+2$	x
$2x+2$	$2x+2$	$2x$	$2x+1$	2	0	1	$x+2$	x	$x+1$

The fact that every element occurs in every row confirms that subtraction is always possible.

The multiplication table for the non-zero elements is:

×	1	2	x	$x+1$	$x+2$	$2x$	$2x+1$	$2x+2$
1	1	2	x	$x+1$	$x+2$	$2x$	$2x+1$	$2x+2$
2	2	1	$2x$	$2x+2$	$2x+1$	x	$x+2$	$x+1$
x	x	$2x$	$2x+1$	1	$x+1$	$x+2$	$2x+2$	2
$x+1$	$x+1$	$2x+2$	1	$x+2$	$2x$	2	x	$2x+1$
$x+2$	$x+2$	$2x+1$	$x+1$	$2x$	2	$2x+2$	1	x
$2x$	$2x$	x	$x+2$	2	$2x+2$	$2x+1$	$x+1$	1
$2x+1$	$2x+1$	$x+2$	$2x+2$	x	1	$x+1$	2	$2x$
$2x+2$	$2x+2$	$x+1$	$x+1$	2	$2x+1$	x	1	$2x$	$x+2$

Once again the fact that every element appears in every row (or just that a 1 appears in every row) confirms that division is always possible.

Sequence of polynomials

If the elements of the field of the coefficients can be arranged in a simple sequence $f_0, f_1, f_2, f_3, \ldots$, then all the polynomials over this field can also be arranged in a simple sequence. For we may first identify the polynomial by the suffixes of its coefficients, so that each polynomial is uniquely associated with an ordered set of integers; for instance the polynomial $f_p x^2 + f_q x + f_r$ is uniquely associated with the triple (p, q, r). It remains only to enumerate all possible ordered sets of integers, and this we do as follows:

Let $p_0 = 2, p_1, p_2, p_3, \ldots$ be the prime numbers in increasing order, so that $p_1 = 3$, $p_2 = 5$, $p_3 = 7$ and so on, and p_k is the k-th odd prime. Then we associate the ordered set of integers

$$n_0, n_1, n_2, n_3, \ldots, n_k$$

with the integer

$$N = 2^{n_0} \times p_1^{n_1} \times p_2^{n_2} \times \cdots \times p_k^{n_k}$$

Thus each polynomial is assigned its position N in the sequence Conversely, given N, we can reconstruct the polynomial; for N can be expressed in only one way as a product of primes, say

$$N = p_0^{n_0} \times p_1^{n_1} \times \cdots \times p_k^{n_k},$$

and the N-th polynomial is therefore

$$f_{n_k} x^k + f_{n_{k-1}} x^{k-1} + \cdots + f_{n_1} x + f_{n_0}.$$

But the class of all simple sequences, even of 0's and 1's, *cannot* be numbered off. For if $s_n = a_1^n, a_2^n, a_3^n, \ldots$ is the n-th sequence in an enumeration of *all* sequences of 0's und 1's, let $b_n = a_n^n + 1$ (modulo 2), then the sequence $b_1, b_2, b_3, \ldots$ of 0's and 1's does not appear in the enumeration since it differs from the sequence s_n at the n-th term, for each n.

Notes on Chapter 2

Fields of residues were first introduced by A. L. Cauchy (1789–1857) and E. Galois (1811–1832); Galois was also the originator of the theory of groups, and yet he was killed in a duel before his 21st birthday. The general notions of ring and field were developed by R. Dedekind (1831–1916). D. Hilbert (1863–1942), the greatest mathematician of his age, and E. Steinitz (1871–1928) who also initiated the definition of rationals as ordered pairs. The first systematic account of this work, and later developments, appeared in B. L. van der Waerden's *Moderne Algebra*, 1930.

CHAPTER 3

NUMBERS UNENDING

Decimal fractions

WE have met many kinds of numbers, natural numbers for counting, positive and negative integers for recording profit and loss, fractions for sharing, and algebraic irrational numbers, like $\sqrt{2}$ for solving the equation $x^2 - 2 = 0$; but we have by no means exhausted the varieties of numbers found useful in mathematics. It has been known for over a hundred years that the numbers so far described represent only a negligible proportion of all numbers. Since polynomials may be numbered, the class of algebraic numbers, the class which contains all solutions of polynomial equations with integral coefficients (and this, of course, includes integers and rationals as well as irrationals like $\sqrt{2}$) may be numbered off in a simple succession; we have also seen that the totality of simple sequences cannot itself be numbered off. We shall use this result to show that the algebraic numbers do not exhaust the class of numbers.

We start by considering the decimal notation for fractions. In the scale of 10, a symbol like 345 represents 3 hundreds, 4 tens and 5 units. To represent fractions in a similar way, we introduce a positional notation for tenths, hundredths, thousandths and so on, and write for instance

$$\cdot345$$

to denote 3 tenths, 4 hundredths and 5 thousandths (or 345 thousandths which is the same thing), the dot before the figures serving to distinguish 345 thousandths from three hundred and forty-five; this dot is called the decimal point and ·345 is read as 'point three four five'.

Some fractions may be expressed in decimal notation without difficulty. For instance

$$\frac{1}{4} = \frac{25}{100} = \frac{20}{100} + \frac{5}{100} = \frac{2}{10} + \frac{5}{100} = \cdot 25$$

and $\quad \dfrac{3}{16} = \dfrac{3 \times 625}{16 \times 625} = \dfrac{1875}{10000} = \cdot 1875,$

but if we seek to express the fraction $\dfrac{1}{3}$ in decimal notation we run into a difficulty, for in converting $\dfrac{1}{4}$ and $\dfrac{3}{16}$ we used the fact that both 4 and 16 divide exactly into some power of 10, whereas no power of 10 is divisible by 3 (since the sum of the digits of 10^n is 1, whatever value n may have, but the sum of the digits of a multiple of 3 is divisible by 3). In fact since $10 = 2 \times 5$, powers of 10 are divisible only by numbers of the form $2^a \times 5^b$.

Although $\dfrac{1}{3}$ cannot be expressed as a decimal, we can *approximate* to $\dfrac{1}{3}$ as closely as we please by decimals. Thus $\cdot 3 = \dfrac{3}{10}$ differs from $\dfrac{1}{3}$ by $\dfrac{1}{10}$ of $\dfrac{1}{3}$; $\cdot 33 = \dfrac{33}{100}$ differs from $\dfrac{1}{3}$ by $\dfrac{1}{100}$ of $\dfrac{1}{3}$; $\cdot 333 = \dfrac{333}{1000}$ differs from $\dfrac{1}{3}$ by $\dfrac{1}{1000}$ of $\dfrac{1}{3}$ and so on. Thus the decimals $\cdot 3$, $\cdot 33$, $\cdot 333$, ... approach $\dfrac{1}{3}$ as closely as we please, and we take this sequence itself as the representative of $\dfrac{1}{3}$, writing the sequence for short in the form

$$\cdot 3333 \ldots$$

To distinguish it from an ordinary decimal we call $\cdot 333 \ldots$ an *infinite* (or endless) decimal; more specifically $\cdot 333 \ldots$ is an infinite recurring decimal since the same digit repeats.

A more interesting example of a recurring decimal is the decimal representation of $\dfrac{1}{7}$. Since $10^6 - 1$ is divisible by 7, 10^6 leaves the remainder 1 on division by 7; thus

$$\frac{10^6}{7} = 142857 + \frac{1}{7}$$

and so

$$\frac{1}{7} = \cdot142857 + \frac{1}{7} \times \frac{1}{10^6} = \cdot142857142857 + \frac{1}{7} \times \frac{1}{10^{12}}$$

and so on. It follows that the decimals $\cdot142857$, $\cdot142857142857$, $\cdot142857142857142857$, ... approach $\frac{1}{7}$ as closely as we please, so that

$$\cdot142857142857 \ldots$$

is the decimal representation of the fraction $\frac{1}{7}$; here a block of digits 142857 recurs, not just a single digit. A rather interesting fact emerges if we seek for the representations of the fractions $\frac{2}{7}, \frac{3}{7}$ and so on up to $\frac{6}{7}$. We readily find

$$\frac{2}{7} = \cdot285714\ 285714 \ldots$$

$$\frac{3}{7} = \cdot428571\ 428571 \ldots$$

$$\frac{4}{7} = \cdot571428\ 571428 \ldots$$

$$\frac{5}{7} = \cdot714285\ 714285 \ldots$$

$$\frac{6}{7} = \cdot857142\ 857142 \ldots$$

and observe that the same block of digits recurs each time, thinking of the block as running round a circle thus,

$$7 \quad 1 \quad 4$$
$$5 \quad 8 \quad 2$$

although the starting digit (round the circle) changes from one fraction to the next. It is easy to see why this is so. When we divide a large power of 10 by 7 all the six remainders $1, 2, 3, 4, 5, 6$ occur (but not in this order, the remainder 1 coming last) and when the remainder 1 occurs we run through the same sequence of remainders again, in the same order. Thus

$$7\,)10000 \ldots \quad (142857\;142857$$

$$\frac{30}{}$$
$$\frac{20}{}$$
$$\frac{60}{}$$
$$\frac{40}{}$$
$$\frac{50}{}$$
$$\frac{10}{}$$
$$\frac{30}{}$$
$$\frac{20}{}$$
$$\frac{60}{}$$
$$\frac{40}{}$$
$$\frac{50}{}$$
$$1$$

From the stage when the remainder 2 occurs we are in effect working out the decimal representation of $\frac{2}{7}$, from the stage when the remainder 3 occurs we are working out the decimal representation of $\frac{3}{7}$, and so on. This shows that all the decimals will contain the same digits, but will start the cycle in a different position.

Some fractions, however, do not have a full cycle, that is to say, not all remainders will occur; for example $\frac{1}{11} = \cdot090909 \ldots$, and so the decimal representations of $\frac{2}{11}, \frac{3}{11}, \ldots, \frac{10}{11}$ do not exhibit the same property as the representations of multiples of $\frac{1}{7}$.

Terminating decimals also have a representation as an infinite decimal. The decimal 1·5 for instance has the representation 1·4999 ...; for the difference between 1·5 and 1·49 is $1/10^2$, between 1·5 and 1·499 is $1/10^3$, between 1·5 and 1·4999 is $1/10^4$, and so on, showing that the numbers 1·49, 1·499, 1·4999, and so on, approach 1·5 as closely as we please. This result is not, of course peculiar to 1·5. If we take any terminating decimal, say

$$a \cdot a_1 a_2 \ldots a_k$$

(where the digit $a_k \neq 0$), and if $a'_k = a_k - 1$, then

$$a \cdot a_1 a_2 \ldots a_{k-1} a'_k 999 \ldots$$

is a representation of $a \cdot a_1 a_2 \ldots a_k$ as an infinite decimal; for the difference between $a \cdot a_1 a_2 \ldots a_k$ and $a \cdot a_1 a_2 a_3 \ldots a_{k-1} a'_k 99 \ldots 9$ with n nines, is $1/10^{k+n}$, and so can be made as small as we please by taking n large enough.

Addition, subtraction and multiplication of decimals follow the same rules exactly as these operations for natural numbers. For instance, to add $2\frac{1}{4}$ and $5\frac{3}{8}$ in decimal notation we proced as follows:

$$2\tfrac{1}{4} = 2 \cdot 25$$
$$5\tfrac{3}{8} = 5 \cdot 375$$
$$\overline{7 \cdot 625}$$

Notice that we keep the decimal point in its own column, and treat a missing digit (on the right of 2·25) as a zero. To see why this is so, we observe that

$$2\tfrac{1}{4} = 2\,\frac{250}{1000}, \quad 5\tfrac{3}{8} = 5\,\frac{375}{1000}$$

and so in adding the fractions we have to add 250 and 375 thousandths, and this is precisely what the decimal notation achieves. Subtraction proceeds in the same way:

$$5\tfrac{3}{8} = 5 \cdot 375$$
$$-\ 2\tfrac{1}{4} = 2 \cdot 25$$
$$\overline{3 \cdot 125}$$

In multiplication we have only to keep the decimal point in its column. For instance, to multiply $2\frac{1}{4} \times 5\frac{3}{8}$

$$5 \cdot 375$$
$$2 \cdot 25$$
$$\overline{\cdot 26875}$$
$$1 \cdot 0750$$
$$10 \cdot 750$$
$$\overline{12 \cdot 09375}$$

Alternatively we can ignore the decimal point, multiply 5375 by 225 and then count $3 + 2 = 5$ digits from the end of the product. The explanation of both methods is to be found in the fact that

$$5\cdot375 \times 2\cdot25 = \frac{5375}{10^3} \times \frac{225}{10^2} = \frac{5375 \times 225}{10^5}.$$

Division may present a difficulty to which we shall return later. We have seen that some fractions cannot be represented by a terminating decimal, but have for their representation an infinite decimal. What is an infinite decimal? Simply a succession of terminating decimals each of which is a section of the one which follows. Thus $2\frac{1}{3} = 2\cdot3333\ldots$, that is the sequence of decimals,

$$2\cdot3, \quad 2\cdot33, \quad 2\cdot333, \quad \ldots$$

Consider now the class of all infinite decimals

$$a_0 \cdot a_1 a_2 a_3 \ldots.$$

This class contains all possible sequences of digits

$$a_1, a_2, a_3, \ldots$$

and we already know that there are more sequences than there are algebraic numbers. Thus there are *more* infinite decimals than algebraic numbers.

The infinite decimal constitutes a further extension of the class of numbers.

Irrational decimals

We have seen how the decimal representation of a fraction is obtained. To find the representation of an irrational, like $\sqrt{2}$, we may proceed as follows: The largest integer whose square does not exceed 2 is 1. The largest number with one decimal digit whose square does not exceed 2 is $1\cdot4$ ($1\cdot4^2 = 1\cdot96$, $1\cdot5^2 = 2\cdot25$), the largest with two decimal digits is $1\cdot41$, and so on. Thus the decimal representation of $\sqrt{2}$ is $1\cdot414\ldots.$ Observe that $2 - 1^2 = 1$, $2 - 1\cdot4^2 = \cdot04$, $2 - 1\cdot41^2 = \cdot0119$ and so on, so that 1^2, $1\cdot4^2$, $1\cdot41^2$, $\ldots$ approach 2 as closely as we please. The point of choosing the largest decimal at each stage is this. Let $1 \cdot a_1 a_2 \ldots a_n$ be the largest decimal of n digits whose square does not exceed 2, then

$$(1 \cdot a_1 a_2 \ldots a_n)^2 < 2 < \left(1 \cdot a_1 a_2 \ldots a_n + \frac{1}{10^n}\right)^2,$$

or writing

$$b = 1 \cdot a_1 a_2 \ldots a_n,$$

$$b^2 < 2 < \left(b + \frac{1}{10^n}\right)^2$$

and so

$$b^2 + \frac{2b}{10^n} + \frac{1}{10^{2n}} > 2$$

whence

$$0 < 2 - b^2 < \frac{2b}{10^n} + \frac{1}{10^{2n}} < \frac{3}{10^n} + \frac{1}{10^{2n}} < \frac{1}{10^{n-1}}$$

which shows that the difference between b^2 and 2 can be made as small as we please by taking n large enough.

In school arithmetic books this process is generally given an abbreviated form which conceals the fundamental simplicity of the process. For finding the square root of 2, for instance, the steps are set out as follows:

$$
\begin{array}{r|l}
 & 1{\cdot}414 \ldots \\
\hline
1 & 200000 \ldots \\
 & 1 \\
\hline
24 & 100 \\
 & 96 \\
\hline
281 & 400 \\
 & 281 \\
\hline
2824 & 11900 \\
 & 11296 \\
\hline
 & 604 \\
\end{array}
$$

The first step picks 1 as the largest integer whose square does not exceed 2, then (instead of trying $1{\cdot}0^2$, $1{\cdot}1^2$, $1{\cdot}2^2$, $1{\cdot}3^2$, ..., $1{\cdot}9^2$ in turn) the second step seeks for the largest integer x so that $20 \times 1 + x$ multiplied by x does not exceed 100. The idea behind this step is that since

$$x(x + 20 \times 1) + (10 \times 1)^2 = (10 \times 1 + x)^2$$

therefore

$$200 - (10 + x)^2 = 200 - \{x(x + 20 \times 1) + 100\}$$
$$= 100 - x(x + 20).$$

At the next stage we rely on the equation

$$(10 \times 14)^2 + x(x + 20 \times 14) = (10 \times 14 + x)^2$$

from which we find

$$20000 - (10 \times 14 + x)^2 = 20000 - (10 \times 14)^2 - x(x + 20 \times 14)$$
$$= 400 - x(x + 20 \times 14)$$

and so on.

A far more practical method of evaluating the square root (and one which lends itself well to computation on a hand operated calculating machine) involves a succession of averaging and division. To consider again the problem of finding the square root of 2, we start with the approximation $1\frac{1}{2}$ which we divide into 2 giving the quotient $4/3$; the average of the first approximation and this quotient is $\frac{1}{2}\left(\frac{3}{2} + \frac{4}{3}\right) = \frac{17}{12} = 1 \cdot 416 \ldots$; divide 2 by the second approximation $\frac{17}{12}$ giving the quotient $\frac{24}{17}$; the average of $\frac{17}{12}$ and $\frac{24}{17}$ is $\frac{577}{408} = 1 \cdot 4142 \ldots$, and so on.

To see why the method works, let N be the number whose square root is required and a the first approximation (which we suppose not less than unity), then the second approximation a' is given by

$$a' = \frac{1}{2}\left(\frac{N}{a} + a\right)$$

so that

$$a' - \sqrt{N} = \frac{1}{2a}(a^2 - 2a\sqrt{N} + N)$$

$$= \frac{(a - \sqrt{N})^2}{2a} < (a - \sqrt{N})^2,$$

thus if a differs from $\sqrt{N}$ by less than $1/10$, a' differs from $\sqrt{N}$ by less than $1/10^2$, and the next approximation will differ from $\sqrt{N}$ by less than $1/10^4$, and the next by less than $1/10^8$ and so on.

Addition of infinite decimals

The addition of two infinite decimals can not, of course, be carried out exactly as the addition of two terminating decimals, because there is no last right-hand digit with which to start the addition. Instead we proceed as follows. To add, for instance, the decimals

$$17 \cdot 123123123123 \ldots$$

and

$$5 \cdot 987698769876 \ldots$$

we take in turn the sums

17·1	17·12	17·123
5·9	5·98	5·987
23·0	23·10	23·110

17·1231	17·12312	17·123123
5·9876	5·98769	5·987698
23·1107	23·11081	23·110821

and so on.

We observe that the whole number 23 settles down from the start; the first decimal digit 1 settles down from the second sum onwards, the second and third digits, 10, settle down from the third sum onwards, the fourth digit 8 from the fifth sum onwards, and so on, forming the answer

$$23 \cdot 11082 \ldots$$

Why do the digits settle down? Well, all the numbers we add together lie, for instance, between 17·1231 and 17·1232 (because $17 \cdot 1231 \, abc \ldots < 17 \cdot 1232$ whatever the digits a, b, c may be, since $171231 \, abc < 171232000$) and between 5·9876 and 5·9877; we have already seen that the sum of 17·1231 and 5·9876 is 23·1107, and since the sum of 17·1232 and 5·9877 is 23·1109 it follows that *all* the sums lie between 23·1107 and 23·1109 and therefore the part of the answer 23·110 is *fixed*. A difficulty may arise when we meet a run of 9's in the answers. For instance, if we seek to add 1·445544 ... to 1·554455 we obtain the succession of sums

$$2 \cdot 9, \quad 2 \cdot 99, \quad 2 \cdot 999, \quad 2 \cdot 9999, \quad 2 \cdot 99999, \quad 2 \cdot 999999, \ldots$$

but we cannot be certain that even the initial 2 has settled down, for if the next digits are, say, 5 and 6 in the two numbers to be added, the sum taken to seven places of decimals is

$$1\cdot 4455445$$
$$1\cdot 5544556$$
$$\overline{3\cdot 0000001}$$

but if the next digits are 2 and 3 the sum is

$$2\cdot 9999995$$

and the whole run of 9's is secure. However, either the run of 9's continues indefinitely, or we eventually reach a sum which decides the issue, as in the above cases. As far as the partial answer is concerned it is of little significance whether we write $2\cdot 999999$ or $3\cdot 000000$ since these differ by only $1/10^6$ (and the difference can be made as small as we please by continuing the calculation).

Multiplication of infinite decimals

Multiplication of infinite decimals is likewise performed by multiplying a succession of finite decimals. Thus to multiply $2\cdot 71417 \ldots$ by $1\cdot 20102010 \ldots$ we consider the products

2·7	2·71	2·714	2·7141
× 1·2	× 1·20	× 1·201	× 1·2010
3·24	2·252	3·254714	3·25892 ...

which show the digits 3 and 2 have settled down (but perhaps not the next 5). However all the products are less than

$$2\cdot 71418 \times 1\cdot 20103 \;=\; 3\cdot 2598116054$$

which shows that the third digit of the product is in fact 5.

Subtraction of infinite decimals

Subtraction presents no new difficulty. For instance, to find the difference between 3·714281 ... and 1·852197 ... we consider the differences

3·7	3·71	3·714	3·7142	3·71428
− 1·8	− 1·85	− 1·852	− 1·8521	− 1·85219
1·9	1·86	1·862	1·8621	1·86209

after which all differences lie between 1·86209 and 3·71428 − − 1·85220 = 1·86208 showing that the digits 1·8620 have settled down.

Division of infinite decimals

Division of infinite decimals is a little more complicated, and we start by considering the special case of finding $1/d$ for an infinite decimal d; in particular let us consider $1/1·4142$ ... We divide 1 in turn by 1·4, 1·41, 1·414, 1·4142 ...

Now
$$\frac{1}{1·4} = \frac{10}{14} = ·714 \dots$$

$$\frac{1}{1·41} = \frac{100}{141} = ·7092 \dots$$

$$\frac{1}{1·414} = \frac{1000}{1414} = ·7072 \dots$$

$$\frac{1}{1·4142} = \frac{10000}{14142} = ·7071 \dots$$

All subsequent quotients lie between ·7071 and $1/1·4143 = ·707 \dots$ showing that the digits ·707 have settled down.

Finally to divide an infinite decimal a by an infinite decimal b we may divide b into 1 and multiply the result by a, or we may proceed as follows.

To divide $1\cdot7328\ldots$ by $1\cdot4142\ldots$ we consider in turn the quotients

$$\frac{1\cdot7}{1\cdot4} = \frac{17}{14} = 1\cdot214\ldots$$

$$\frac{1\cdot73}{1\cdot41} = \frac{173}{141} = 1\cdot226\ldots$$

$$\frac{1\cdot732}{1\cdot414} = \frac{1732}{1414} = 1\cdot224\ldots$$

$$\frac{1\cdot7328}{1\cdot4142} = \frac{17328}{14142} = 1\cdot225\ldots$$

Since all quotients from this stage onwards lie between

$$\frac{1\cdot7328}{1\cdot4143} = 1\cdot2251\ldots$$

and

$$\frac{1\cdot7329}{1\cdot4142} = 1\cdot2253\ldots$$

it follows that the digits $1\cdot225$ of the quotient have settled down.

To see in a general setting why the digits in a quotient settle down, consider the division of $(10a + r)/10^n$ by $(10b + s)/10^n$ where r and s are digits and a and b are numbers of $m + 1$ digits say. We have

$$\frac{10a + r}{10b + s} \leqslant \frac{10(a + 1)}{10b} = \frac{a + 1}{b}$$

and

$$\frac{10a + r}{10b + s} \geqslant \frac{10a}{10(b + 1)} = \frac{a}{b + 1}$$

and the difference

$$\frac{a + 1}{b} - \frac{a}{b + 1} = \frac{a + b + 1}{b(b + 1)} \leqslant \frac{2 \times 10^{m+1}}{10^{2m}} < \frac{1}{10^{m-2}}$$

showing that $(10a + r)/(10b + s)$ lies between two numbers whose difference is less than $1/10^{m-2}$, so that (apart from the complication of recurring 9's) $(a + 1)/b$ and $a/(b + 1)$ have $m - 2$ decimal digits in common, and these digits are common to all the quotients of the decimals $\dfrac{a}{10^{n-1}} + \dfrac{r}{10^n} + \cdots$ and $\dfrac{b}{10^{n-1}} + \dfrac{s}{10^n} + \cdots$ no matter what digits follow r and s.

Positive and negative decimals

We shall take for granted the further extension of the number system from decimals to positive and negative decimals. This extension may be effected in exactly the same way as the extension from natural numbers to integers, or we may simply define a negative decimal $-a_0 \cdot a_1 a_2 a_3 \ldots$ to be a sequence of negative rationals

$$-a_0, \quad -a_0 \cdot a_1, \quad -a_0 \cdot a_1 a_2, \ldots$$

Whichever way we proceed the arithmetic of positive and negative decimals follows a familiar pattern. The product of two positive, or two negative decimals is a positive decimal, but the product of a positive and a negative decimal is a negative decimal. If we define inequality between *unequal* endless decimals

$$A = a_0 \cdot a_1 a_2 \ldots, \quad B = b_0 \cdot b_1 b_2 \ldots$$

so that $A < B$ if, and only if, $a_0 \cdot a_1 a_2 \ldots a_n < b_0 \cdot b_1 b_2 \ldots b_n$ for some n, then we can formulate the rules for adding and subtracting positive and negative decimals exactly as for integers; thus

$$
\begin{aligned}
(+A) + (+B) &= +(A + B) \\
(+A) - (+B) &= +(A - B) \quad \text{if} \quad A > B, \\
&= -(B - A) \quad \text{if} \quad B > A, \\
(+A) + (-B) &= (+A) - (+B) \\
(-A) + (-B) &= -(A + B) \\
(-A) - (+B) &= -(A + B) \\
(-A) - (-B) &= (+B) + (-A) \\
(-A) + (+B) &= (+B) + (-A) \\
(+A) - (-B) &= +(A + B).
\end{aligned}
$$

Convergence

A sequence of endless decimals s_1, s_2, s_3, ... is said to *converge*, or to be convergent, if the digits of the decimals s_1, s_2, s_3 and so on, settle down. That is to say, if from some term, say s_p onwards all s_p, s_{p+1}, s_{p+2}, ... have the same whole part and first decimal digit, from some (later) s_q onwards, all s_q, s_{q+1}, s_{q+2}, ... have the same first two decimal digits, and so on.
For example, the sequence

$$2, \quad 1\cdot5, \quad 1\cdot42, \quad 1\cdot415, \quad 1\cdot4143, \quad 1\cdot41426, \ldots$$

converges, and so does the sequence

$$4, \quad 3\cdot6, \quad 3\cdot59, \quad 3\cdot573, \quad 3\cdot5736, \quad 3\cdot57359, \quad 3\cdot573573, \ldots.$$

The decimal formed by the digits which settle down in a convergent sequence is called the *limit* of the sequence. For instance the limit of the sequence

$$4, \quad 3\cdot6, \quad 3\cdot59, \quad 3\cdot573, \quad 3\cdot5736, \quad 3\cdot57359, \quad 3\cdot573573, \quad 3\cdot5735736$$

is $3\cdot57357357\ldots$.
A recurrence of 9's in the terms of a sequence may cause a slight complication. For instance, we accept the sequence $1\cdot4$, $1\cdot49$, $1\cdot5$, $1\cdot499$, $1\cdot5$, $1\cdot4999$, $1\cdot5$, ... as convergent, with limit $1\cdot5$, even though the digits do not completely settle down, just because $1\cdot4999\ldots$ is another representation of $1\cdot5$.
If s is the limit of a convergent sequence s_1, s_2, s_3, ... we write $s_n \to s$.
We may express the condition for convergence in another way which does not make a direct reference to the decimal digits. A sequence

$$s_1, s_2, s_3, \ldots$$

converges if the terms pack tighter and tighter together. More precisely, the sequence converges if all the terms from some term s_p (say) onwards differ by less than $\frac{1}{10}$, and all the terms from some s_q onwards differ by less than $\frac{1}{10^2}$, and all the terms from some s_r onwards differ by less than $\frac{1}{10^3}$, and so on.

To see why this condition ensures convergence consider the example in which $s_p = 3 \cdot 572 \ldots$, $s_q = 3 \cdot 628 \ldots$, $s_r = 3 \cdot 627 \ldots$. all s_n from s_p onwards differ from $3 \cdot 572$ by less than $\dfrac{1}{10}$, and so all such s_n lie between $3 \cdot 4$ and $3 \cdot 6$ and so all have the whole part 3. Next all s_n from s_q onwards differ from $3 \cdot 628 \ldots$ by less than $\dfrac{1}{10^2}$ and so all lie between $3 \cdot 61$ and $3 \cdot 63$ showing that all have the first digit 6. Then, all from s_r onwards differ from $3 \cdot 627$ by less than $\dfrac{1}{10^3}$ and so all lie between $3 \cdot 626$ and $3 \cdot 628$, showing that all have the figures $3 \cdot 62$ in common, and so on.

Of course, recurring 9's or recurring 0's may cause complications. For instance, if $s_p = 3$ we do not know if all subsequent s_n have whole part 3 or 2; we must therefore look further along the sequence to decide the question; for instance, if $s_q = 3 \cdot 1$, then all subsequent s_n lie between $3 \cdot 09$ and $3 \cdot 11$ and so have whole part 3, and if $s_q = 2 \cdot 97$, then all subsequent s_n lie between $2 \cdot 96$ and $2 \cdot 98$ and have whole part 2. But if $s_q = 3$ (or $2 \cdot 99$) we still cannot tell, and must look further along the sequence. We shall either reach a term which decides the whole part for us or there are 3's (or $2 \cdot 99 \ldots 9$ with arbitrary long runs of 9's) without end in the sequence, in which case the sequence converges with limit 3. If it can be shown in advance that the sequence has no *rational* limit, then this complication is ruled out.

We may also express the connection between a convergent sequence and its limit without directly referring to the decimal digits. A number l is the limit of the sequence $s_1, s_2, s_3, \ldots$ if from some s_p onwards all s_n lie between $l - 1/10$ and $l + 1/10$, from some q_q onwards, between $l - 1/10^2$, $l + 1/10^2$, from some s_r onwards between $l - 1/10^3$, $l + 1/10^3$ and so on. These conditions ensure that the further we go along the sequence the more digits has l in common with the terms of the sequence (apart again from possible complications about recurring 9's).

Some important limits

A very important convergent sequence is the sequence

$$1, \quad 1 + a, \quad 1 + a + a^2, \quad 1 + a + a^2 + a^3,$$
$$1 + a + a^2 + a^3 + a^4, \ldots$$

To discuss the convergence of this sequence we start by noting that

$$1 + a = \frac{1 - a^2}{1 - a}$$

$$1 + a + a^2 = \frac{1 - a^3}{1 - a}$$

$$1 + a + a^2 + a^3 = \frac{1 - a^4}{1 - a}$$

and so on.

For if we multiply

$$1 + a + a^2 + \cdots + a^n$$

by $1 - a$ we obtain

$$(1 + a + a^2 + \cdots + a^n) - (a + a^2 + \cdots + a^n + a^{n+1})$$
$$= 1 - a^{n+1}$$

and so

$$1 + a + a^2 + \cdots + a^n = \frac{1 - a^{n+1}}{1 - a}.$$

This famous result holds for all numbers $a \neq$ (and all positive exponents n).

Suppose now that $0 < a < 1$. Then $a^2 = a \times a < 1 \times a = a$, $a^3 = a \times a^2 < 1 \times a^2 = a^2$ and so on, so that the numbers $1, a, a^2, a^3, \ldots$ steadily decrease.

Thus

$$1 + a + a^2 + \cdots + a^n > na^n;$$

but

$$\frac{1 - a^{n+1}}{1 - a} < \frac{1}{1 - a}$$

and so

$$na^n < \frac{1}{1 - a}$$

that is

$$a^n < \frac{1}{n(1-a)}$$

which shows that a^n may be made as small as we please by taking n large enough. For instance, to make a^n less than $1/10^3$ it suffices to take $n \geqslant 10^3/(1-a)$. In other words a^n differs from zero by as little as we please, if n is large enough, so that 0 is the limit of the sequence a, a^2, a^3, ...

Since, as we have already seen

$$1 + a + a^2 + \cdots + a^n$$

differs from $1/(1-a)$ by $a^{n+1}/(1-a)$, and since $a^{n+1}/(1-a)$ can be made as small as we please by taking n large enough, (if $0 < a < < 1$) it follows that the sequence

$$1, \quad 1 + a, \quad 1 + a + a^2, \ldots$$

converges with limit $1/(1-a)$.

Suppose next that $-1 < a \leqslant 0$; let $b = -a$, so that b is positive and less than 1, then $a^n = \pm b^n$, according as n is even or odd. But b^n can be brought as close to 0 as we please by taking n great enough, and so a^n can be brought as close to 0 as we please (since the *positive* difference between 0 and b^n is the same as the *positive* difference between 0 and a^n) which proves that $a^n \to 0$. Since

$$1 + a + a^2 + \cdots + a^n = \frac{1}{1-a} - \frac{a^{n+1}}{1-a}$$

whether a is positive or negative, it follows that the limit of the series

$$1 + a + a^2 + \cdots$$

is $1/(1-a)$ also in the case $-1 < a \leqslant 0$.

It is convenient to write a sequence like $1, 1+a, 1+a+a^2, \ldots$ in the abbreviated form

$$1 + a + a^2 + a^3 + \cdots;$$

when a sequence u_1, $u_1 + u_2$, $u_1 + u_2 + u_3$, ... is written in the form

$$u_1 + u_2 + u_3 + \cdots$$

the numbers u_1, u_2, u_3, ... are called the *terms* of the *series* $u_1 +$ $+ u_2 + u_3 + \cdots$, and the terms of the sequence u_1, $u_1 + u_2$, $u_1 +$ $+ u_2 + u_3$, ... are called the *partial sums* of the series. When the sequence u_1, $u_1 + u_2$, $u_1 + u_2 + u_3$, ... converges, then $u_1 + u_2 +$ $+ u_3 + \cdots$ denotes its limit.

If $a \geqslant 1$ the series

$$1 + a + a^2 + \cdots$$

does *not* converge because the difference between *any* partial sum $1 + a + a^2 + \cdots + a^k$, and the next partial sum $1 + a + a^2 +$ $+ \cdots + a^k + a^{k+1}$ is a^{k+1} which exceeds 1, so that the partial sums do *not* pack together, and so the series does not converge.

Another important example of a convergent series is

$$1 + \frac{1}{1} + \frac{1}{1 \times 2} + \frac{1}{1 \times 2 \times 3} + \frac{1}{1 \times 2 \times 3 \times 4} +$$

$$+ \frac{1}{1 \times 2 \times 3 \times 4 \times 5} + \cdots.$$

We start by introducing the abbreviation $n!$ (read factorial n) for the product $1 \times 2 \times 3 \times \cdots \times n$, and s_n for the partial sum

$$1 + \frac{1}{1!} + \frac{1}{2!} + \frac{1}{3!} + \cdots + \frac{1}{n!}.$$

Then the difference between s_n and any s_N (with $N > n$) is

$$\frac{1}{(n+1)!} + \frac{1}{(n+2)!} + \cdots + \frac{1}{N!}$$

$$= \frac{1}{(n+1)!} \left[1 + \frac{1}{n+2} + \frac{1}{(n+2)(n+3)} + \cdots \right].$$

But

$$1 + \frac{1}{n+2} + \frac{1}{(n+2)(n+3)} + \cdots$$

$$< 1 + \frac{1}{n+2} + \frac{1}{(n+2)^2} + \frac{1}{(n+2)^3} + \cdots$$

$$< \frac{1}{1 - \frac{1}{n+2}} = \frac{n+2}{n+1} < 2, \quad \text{if} \quad n \geqslant 1,$$

and $n! > 2^{n+2}$, for $n \geqslant 6$, since this inequality certainly holds with $n = 6$ ($6! = 720 > 256 = 2^8$) and if

$$k! > 2^{k+2} \quad \text{for some} \quad k \geqslant 6,$$

then

$$(k + 1)! = (k + 1)\, k! > 2 \times k! > 2^{k+3}$$

whence, by induction, $n! > 2^{n+2}$ holds for all n. It follows therefore that the difference between s_n and s_N is *less* than

$$\frac{1}{2^{n+2}} \times 2 = \frac{1}{2^{n+1}}$$

and since $a^n < 1/n\,(1 - a)$ therefore

$$\frac{1}{2^n} < \frac{1}{n\,(1 - 1/2)} = \frac{2}{n}$$

and so

$$\frac{1}{2^{n+1}} < \frac{1}{n}$$

Thus, finally we see that the difference between s_n and s_N is less than $1/n$, and may therefore be made as small as we please by choosing n large enough, proving that the sequence $s_1, s_2, s_3, \ldots$ is convergent. To determine the limit of this important sequence we observe that

$$s_1 = 1 + 1 = 2$$

$$s_2 = s_1 + \frac{1}{2!} = 2 \cdot 5$$

$$s_3 = s_2 + \frac{1}{3!} = 2 \cdot 6666 \ldots$$

$$s_4 = s_3 + \frac{1}{4!} = 2 \cdot 70833 \ldots$$

$$s_5 = s_4 + \frac{1}{5!} = 2 \cdot 71666 \ldots$$

$$s_6 = s_5 + \frac{1}{6!} = 2 \cdot 71805 \ldots.$$

The difference between s_6 and any subsequent term s_N is less than

$$\frac{1}{7!}\left(1 + \frac{1}{8} + \frac{1}{8 \times 9} + \cdots\right) < \frac{1}{7!} \times \frac{1}{1 - 1/8}$$

$$= \frac{8}{7 \times 7!} = \frac{1}{4410} < \cdot00025$$

so that all s_n from $n = 6$ onwards lie between $2\cdot71805\ldots$ and $2\cdot7183\ldots$ proving that the limit is

$$2\cdot718\ldots.$$

This number plays a very important part in mathematics and is denoted by e.

It is easy to show that the number e is not rational. Certainly e is not an integer because

$$\frac{1}{2!} + \frac{1}{3!} + \cdots + \frac{1}{n!}$$

$$= \frac{1}{2} + \frac{1}{6}\left[1 + \frac{1}{4} + \frac{1}{4 \times 5} + \cdots + \frac{1}{4 \times 5 \times \cdots \times n}\right]$$

$$< \frac{1}{2} + \frac{1}{6}\left[1 + \frac{1}{4} + \frac{1}{4^2} + \frac{1}{4^3} + \cdots\right]$$

$$< \frac{1}{2} + \frac{1}{6}\left[\frac{1}{1 - 1/4}\right] = \frac{1}{2} + \frac{1}{6} \times \frac{4}{3} = \frac{13}{18}$$

so that e lies between 2 and $2^{13}/_{18}$.

Consider now any fraction p/q, $q \geqslant 2$; the difference

$$1 + \frac{1}{1} + \frac{1}{2!} + \frac{1}{3!} + \cdots + \frac{1}{q!} - \frac{p}{q}$$

is a fraction with denominator $q!$, and therefore, multiplying by $q!$, we obtain an integer Q, say. Thus

$$q!\left[1 + \frac{1}{1} + \frac{1}{2!} + \cdots + \frac{1}{q!} + \cdots + \frac{1}{n!} - \frac{p}{q}\right]$$

$$= Q + \frac{1}{q + 1} + \frac{1}{(q + 1)(q + 2)} + \cdots + \frac{1}{(q + 1)(q + 2)\ldots n};$$

but

$$\frac{1}{q+1} + \frac{1}{(q+1)(q+2)} + \cdots < \frac{1}{q+1} + \frac{1}{(q+1)^2} +$$

$$+ \frac{1}{(q+1)^3} + \cdots < \frac{1}{q+1}\left[\frac{1}{1 - 1/(q+1)}\right] = \frac{1}{q}$$

which proves that $\left(1 + \frac{1}{1!} + \frac{1}{2!} + \cdots + \frac{1}{n!} - \frac{p}{q}\right)q! = D_q$, say,

lies between $Q + \dfrac{1}{q+1}$ and $Q + \dfrac{1}{q}$.

If $Q \geqslant 0$ then D_q is positive and not less than $1/(q+1)$; if $Q < 0$, then since Q is an integer, $-Q \geqslant 1$, and therefore

$$-D_q \geqslant -Q - \frac{1}{q} \geqslant 1 - \frac{1}{q} = \frac{q-1}{q} > \frac{1}{q+1}$$

(since $q(q-1) > 1$ as $q \geqslant 2$) which proves that the positive value of D_q is never less than $1/(q+1)$ and therefore e cannot be equal to p/q.

We have seen that if $-1 < a < 1$, then $a^n \to 0$; we can, however, prove a much stronger result. In fact, if $-1 < a < 1$,

$$n^r a^n \to 0$$

for any (fixed) integer r. It suffices to consider only values of a such that $0 < a < 1$, for if a is negative (so that $-a$ is positive), then $n^r a^n = \pm n^r(-a)^n$ and so the limit of $n^r a^n$ is also 0 if the limit of $n^r(-a)^n$ is 0. With $r = 0$, $n^r a^n = a^n$ and we already know that $a^n \to 0$. If $n^{k-1}a^n \to 0$ for some k, then since

$$na^n < \frac{1}{1-a}$$

we have $n^k a^{2n} < \dfrac{n^{k-1}a^n}{1-a}$; but $\dfrac{n^{k-1}a^n}{1-a}$ may be made as small as we please and so $n^k a^{2n}$ may be made as small as we please, choosing n large enough. Since 2^k is constant, it follows that $(2n)^k a^{2n}$ can be made as small as we please, choosing n large enough. Finally we note that $(2n+1)^k a^{2n+1} < (2(n+1))^k a^{2(n+1)}/a$ which can be made as small as we please. Thus we have shown that $n^k a^n$ can be made as small as we please whether n is odd or even, which completes the proof by induction that $n^r a^n \to 0$. Since $n + k \leqslant (k + 1)n$, for $n \geqslant 1$ and $k \geqslant 1$, it follows that

$$\frac{n(n + 1)(n + 2)\dots(n + r - 1)}{r!} \leqslant \frac{n \times 2n \times 3n \times \cdots \times rn}{r!} = n^r$$

and therefore

$$\frac{n(n + 1)(n + 2)\dots(n + r - 1)}{r!} a^n \to 0.$$

Generalized binomial theorem

We come now to a generalization of the binomial theorem. For a positive integer n

$$(1 + x)^n = 1 + nx + \frac{n(n - 1)}{2!} x^2 +$$

$$+ \frac{n(n - 1)(n - 2)}{3!} x^3 + \cdots + x^n$$

as we have already seen*. The corresponding result for a negative exponent is that, if $-1 < x < 1$, the *limit* of the series

$$1 + nx + \frac{n(n + 1)}{2!} x^2 + \frac{n(n + 1)(n + 2)}{3!} x^3 +$$

$$+ \frac{n(n + 1)(n + 2)(n + 3)}{4!} x^4 + \cdots$$

is $(1 - x)^{-n}$, as we shall now show.

First we notice that

$$\frac{(n + 1)(n + 2)\dots(n + r)}{r!} - \frac{(n + 1)(n + 2)\dots(n + r - 1)}{(r - 1)!}$$

$$= \frac{(n + 1)(n + 2)\dots(n + r - 1)}{r!}\{n + r - r\}$$

$$= \frac{n(n + 1)(n + 2)\dots(n + r - 1)}{r!}$$

* The proof of the binomial theorem (with positive integral exponents) when x is an infinite decimal is exactly the same as the proof for integral values of x.

If we write $\left\{ \begin{matrix} n \\ r \end{matrix} \right\}$ as an abbreviation for

$$\frac{n(n + 1)(n + 2) \ldots (n + r - 1)}{r!}$$

this result takes the form

$$\left\{ \begin{matrix} n + 1 \\ r \end{matrix} \right\} - \left\{ \begin{matrix} n + 1 \\ r - 1 \end{matrix} \right\} = \left\{ \begin{matrix} n \\ r \end{matrix} \right\}.$$

We have to prove that $(1 - x)^{-n}$ is the limit of the series

$$1 + \left\{ \begin{matrix} n \\ 1 \end{matrix} \right\} x + \left\{ \begin{matrix} n \\ 2 \end{matrix} \right\} x^2 + \left\{ \begin{matrix} n \\ 3 \end{matrix} \right\} x^3 + \cdots;$$

call this assertion P_n.

With $n = 1$,

$$\left\{ \begin{matrix} n \\ r \end{matrix} \right\} = \frac{1 \times 2 \times 3 \times \cdots \times r}{r!} = 1$$

and $(1 - x)^{-1} = 1/(1 - x)$ is the limit of

$$1 + x + x^2 + x^3 + \cdots$$

when x lies between -1 and $+1$, which shows that P_1 holds. We proceed by induction.

Let P_k hold for some k, and consider the product

$$(1 - x)\left[1 + \left\{ \begin{matrix} k + 1 \\ 1 \end{matrix} \right\} x + \left\{ \begin{matrix} k + 1 \\ 2 \end{matrix} \right\} x^2 + \cdots + \left\{ \begin{matrix} k + 1 \\ n \end{matrix} \right\} x^n \right]$$

$$= 1 + \left(\left\{ \begin{matrix} k + 1 \\ 1 \end{matrix} \right\} - 1 \right) x + \left(\left\{ \begin{matrix} k + 1 \\ 2 \end{matrix} \right\} - \left\{ \begin{matrix} k + 1 \\ 1 \end{matrix} \right\} \right) x^2 + \cdots$$

$$\cdots + \left(\left\{ \begin{matrix} k + 1 \\ n \end{matrix} \right\} - \left\{ \begin{matrix} k + 1 \\ n - 1 \end{matrix} \right\} \right) x^n - \left\{ \begin{matrix} k + 1 \\ n \end{matrix} \right\} x^{n+1}$$

$$= 1 + \left\{ \begin{matrix} k \\ 1 \end{matrix} \right\} x + \left\{ \begin{matrix} k \\ 2 \end{matrix} \right\} x^2 + \cdots + \left\{ \begin{matrix} k \\ n \end{matrix} \right\} x^n - \left\{ \begin{matrix} k + 1 \\ n \end{matrix} \right\} x^{n+1}$$

By hypothesis

$$1 + \left\{ \begin{matrix} k \\ 1 \end{matrix} \right\} x + \left\{ \begin{matrix} k \\ 2 \end{matrix} \right\} x^2 + \cdots + \left\{ \begin{matrix} k \\ n \end{matrix} \right\} x^n \to (1 - x)^{-k}$$

and

$$\left\{ \begin{matrix} k+1 \\ n \end{matrix} \right\} x^{n+1} = \frac{(k+1)(k+2)\ldots(k+n)}{n!} x^{n+1}$$

$$= \frac{(k+n)!}{n!\,k!} x^{n+1}$$

$$= \frac{(k+n)(k+n-1)\ldots(n+1)}{k!} x^{n+1}$$

$$\leqslant (n+1)^k x^{n+1} \to 0$$

and therefore

$$(1-x)\left[1 + \left\{ \begin{matrix} k+1 \\ 1 \end{matrix} \right\} x + \left\{ \begin{matrix} k+1 \\ 2 \end{matrix} \right\} x^2 + \cdots + \left\{ \begin{matrix} k+1 \\ n \end{matrix} \right\} x^n \right]$$

$$\to (1-x)^{-k},$$

and so, dividing by $(1-x)$, the limit of the series

$$1 + \left\{ \begin{matrix} k+1 \\ 1 \end{matrix} \right\} x + \left\{ \begin{matrix} k+1 \\ 2 \end{matrix} \right\} x^2 + \cdots$$

is $(1-x)^{-(k+1)}$, proving P_{k+1}, so that by induction P_n holds for all n.

The binomial theorem for both positive and negative exponents (and, in fact, for fractional exponents, but we have not proved this) is given by the single formula

$$(1+x)^n = 1 + \binom{n}{1} x + \binom{n}{2} x^2 + \binom{n}{3} x^3 + \cdots$$

where $-1 < x < 1$ and

$$\binom{n}{r} = \frac{n(n-1)(n-2)\ldots(n-r+1)}{r!}$$

The binomial theorem was discovered by Isaac Newton, the greatest mathematician of his time (1643–1727) and perhaps the greatest of all time.

By means of the binomial theorem we shall obtain another sequence for e. We shall prove that both the sequences $\left(1 + \dfrac{1}{n}\right)^n$ and $\left(1 - \dfrac{1}{n}\right)^{-n}$ converge with limit e.

We start by observing that, for a positive integer n,

$$\left(1 + \frac{1}{n}\right)^n = 1 + n \times \frac{1}{n} + \frac{n(n-1)}{2!} \times \frac{1}{n^2} + \frac{n(n-1)(n-2)}{3!} \times$$

$$\times \frac{1}{n^3} + \cdots = 1 + 1 + \left(1 - \frac{1}{n}\right)\frac{1}{2!} +$$

$$+ \left(1 - \frac{1}{n}\right)\left(1 - \frac{2}{n}\right)\frac{1}{3!} + \cdots +$$

$$+ \left(1 - \frac{1}{n}\right)\left(1 - \frac{2}{n}\right)\cdots\left(1 - \frac{n-1}{n}\right)\frac{1}{n!};$$

as n increases each term $1 - \frac{r}{n}$ increases, and the number of terms in the expansion of $\left(1 + \frac{1}{n}\right)^n$, being $n + 1$, also increases with n. Thus $\left(1 + \frac{1}{n}\right)^n$ itself increases with n, and furthermore, since $1 - \frac{r}{n} < 1$,

$$\left(1 + \frac{1}{n}\right)^n < 1 + \frac{1}{1} + \frac{1}{2!} + \frac{1}{3!} + \cdots + \frac{1}{n!} < e.$$

Similarly

$$\left(1 - \frac{1}{n}\right)^{-n} = \left(\frac{n-1}{n}\right)^{-n} = \left(\frac{n}{n-1}\right)^n = \left(1 + \frac{1}{n-1}\right)^n$$

$$= \left(1 + \frac{1}{n-1}\right)\left(1 + \frac{1}{n-1}\right)^{n-1} < e\left(1 + \frac{1}{n-1}\right);$$

but, by the binomial theorem

$$\left(1 - \frac{1}{n}\right)^{-n} = 1 + n \times \frac{1}{n} + \frac{n(n+1)}{2!}\frac{1}{n^2} + \frac{n(n+1)(n+2)}{3!}\frac{1}{n^3} + \cdots$$

$$= 1 + 1 + \left(1 + \frac{1}{n}\right)\cdot\frac{1}{2!} + \left(1 + \frac{1}{n}\right)\left(1 + \frac{2}{n}\right)\frac{1}{3!} + \cdots$$

$$\geqslant 1 + 1 + \frac{1}{2!} + \frac{1}{3!} + \cdots = e.$$

Thus

$$e \leqslant \left(1 - \frac{1}{n}\right)^{-n} < e\left(1 + \frac{1}{n-1}\right)$$

and since $1 + \dfrac{1}{n-1} \to 1$ it follows that $\left(1 - \dfrac{1}{n}\right)^{-n} \to e$, as was to be shown.

Moreover, since $\left(1 + \dfrac{1}{n}\right)^{n}$ increases with n,

$$e > \left(1 + \frac{1}{n}\right)^{n} > \left(1 + \frac{1}{n-1}\right)^{n-1} = \left(\frac{n}{n-1}\right)^{n-1} = \left(\frac{n-1}{n}\right)^{-n+1}$$

$$= \left(1 - \frac{1}{n}\right)^{-n} \times \left(1 - \frac{1}{n}\right);$$

but, as we have seen,

$$\left(1 - \frac{1}{n}\right)^{-n} \to e, \quad \text{and so} \quad \left(1 - \frac{1}{n}\right)^{-n} \times \left(1 - \frac{1}{n}\right) \to e$$

therefore $\left(1 + \dfrac{1}{n}\right)^{n}$ lies between e and a number which may be made as close to e as we please by taking n large enough, which proves that

$$\left(1 + \frac{1}{n}\right)^{n} \to e.$$

The exponential series

In preparation for the next result we prove that, for all decimals x,

$$\frac{x^{n}}{n!} \to 0.$$

It suffices to consider positive values of x for as we have already remarked, if $\dfrac{x^{n}}{n!} \to 0$ for positive x, then also $\pm \dfrac{x^{n}}{n!} \to 0$.

Choose $p \geqslant 2x$, and write

$$u_{n} = \frac{x^{n+p}}{(n+p)!};$$

then

$$u_{n+1} = \frac{x}{n+p+1} u_{n} \leqslant \tfrac{1}{2} u_{n}$$

and therefore

$$(n+1) u_{n+1} \leqslant \tfrac{1}{2} (n+1) u_{n} \leqslant n u_{n}$$

showing that $n u_n$ steadily decreases, that is to say the numbers

$$u_1, \quad 2u_2, \quad 3u_3, \quad 4u_4, \; \ldots$$

steadily decrease and therefore

$$n u_n \leqslant u_1$$

so that, finally, $u_n \leqslant u_1/n$ which proves that u_n may be made as small as we please by choosing n large enough, and therefore $u_n \to 0$, and so $\dfrac{x^n}{n!} \to 0$.

We may now show that the series

$$1 + x + \frac{x^2}{2!} + \frac{x^3}{3!} + \cdots$$

converges for all decimals x.

Write

$$s_n = 1 + x + \frac{x^2}{2!} + \frac{x^3}{3!} + \cdots + \frac{x^{n-1}}{(n-1)!},$$

then the difference between s_n and any later s_N is

$$\frac{x^n}{n!} \left[1 + \frac{x}{n+1} + \frac{x^2}{(n+1)(n+2)} + \cdots \right];$$

now $1 + \dfrac{x}{n+1} + \dfrac{x^2}{(n+1)(n+2)} + \cdots$ is greatest when x is positive and for positive x, and $n \geqslant 2x$ (so that $x/(n+1) < 1/2$) we have

$$1 + \frac{x}{(n+1)} + \frac{x^2}{(n+1)(n+2)} + \cdots < 1 + \tfrac{1}{2} + (\tfrac{1}{2})^2 + \\ + (\tfrac{1}{2})^3 + \cdots < 2$$

which shows that the positive difference between s_n and s_N is less than $2x^n/n!$, and this, as we have seen, may be made as small as we please by taking n large enough. For a reason we shall later discover, this series is called the exponential series.

Decimal collision

Two sequences of decimals s_n and t_n which approach one another from left and right, respectively, have a common limit. To be more precise, if s_n steadily increases, that is $s_{n+1} > s_n$, and t_n steadily decreases, $t_{n+1} < t_n$, and if $t_n > s_n$ and $t_n - s_n \to 0$, then there is a decimal l such that

$$s_n \to l, \quad t_n \to l.$$

For if $N > n$, then

$$s_n < s_N < t_N < t_n$$

and since $t_n - s_n$ can be made as small as we please by choosing n large enough, therefore $s_N - s_n$ can be made as small as we please, which proves that s_n converges, with limit s say, and since s_n increases, therefore $s_n \leqslant s$. Similar considerations show that t_n decreases to a limit t, and it remains to show that $s = t$. If $s < t$ then $t_n - s_n \geqslant t - s > 0$ and so $t_n - s_n$ does not tend to zero, which rules out this possibility. And if $s > t$, since we can find an s_n nearer to s than $\frac{1}{2}(s - t)$ and a t_m nearer to t than $\frac{1}{2}(s - t)$

$$\begin{array}{ccccc} | & | & | & | & | \\ t & t_m & & s_n & s \end{array}$$

and fo rthese terms necessarily $s_n > t_m$, which rules out this possibility, proving that $s = t$.

Continuity

Some functions change their values in jumps, for instance 'the whole part of the decimal x' which has the value 2 for any x lying between 2 and 3 but jumps to 3 when $x = 3$; others like x^2 vary smoothly and are said to be continuous. Thus

$$x^2 - 2^2 = (x - 2)(x + 2)$$

and so if x lies between 2 and 3 (so that $x + 2 < 5$)

$$0 < x^2 - 2^2 < 5(x - 2)$$

and if x lies between 1 and 2

$$0 < 2^2 - x^2 < 4(2 - x)$$

which shows that x^2 differs by as little as we please from 2^2 if x is taken near enough to 2, or in other words if x moves only a little way from the value 2, then x^2 moves only a little way from its value 2^2 at $x = 2$. A similar argument applies to any other value of x. Amongst the continuous functions are all the powers of x, x^2, x^3, x^4, x^5 and so on; also fractional powers. Let us show for instance that $x^{\frac{1}{2}} = \sqrt{x}$ is continuous at $x = 2$. We have

$$\sqrt{x} - \sqrt{2} = \frac{(\sqrt{x} - \sqrt{2})(\sqrt{x} + \sqrt{2})}{\sqrt{x} + \sqrt{2}} = \frac{x - 2}{\sqrt{x} + \sqrt{2}}$$

and so if x is greater than 2 we have

$$0 < \sqrt{x} - \sqrt{2} < \frac{x - 2}{2\sqrt{2}} < \tfrac{1}{2}(x - 2)$$

and if x is less than 2 (but greater than 1, say)

$$0 < \sqrt{2} - \sqrt{x} < \frac{2 - x}{1 + \sqrt{2}} < \tfrac{1}{2}(2 - x)$$

so that $\sqrt{x}$ is even nearer to $\sqrt{2}$ than x is 2.

It is quite easy to show that the sum (or difference) and product of two continuous functions is continuous; in particular any polynomial

$$a + bx + cx^2 + \cdots + px^2$$

is continuous.

Another example of a continuous function is the exponential function

$$E(x) = 1 + x + \frac{x^2}{2!} + \frac{x^3}{3!} + \cdots .$$

For we have, writing

$$E_n(x) = 1 + x + \frac{x^2}{2!} + \cdots + \frac{x^{n-1}}{(n-1)!} ,$$

$$R_n(x) = \frac{x^n}{n!} + \frac{x^{n+1}}{(n+1)!} + \cdots$$

$$E(x) - E(a) = E_n(x) - E_n(a) + R_n(x) - R_n(a)$$

and

$$|R_n(x)| < \frac{2\,|x^n|}{n!} , \quad |R_n(a)| < \frac{2\,|a^n|}{n!} .$$

For an x not too far from a, for instance one lying between $\frac{1}{2}a$ and $2a$ $(a > 0)$, we have

$$\frac{x^n}{n!} < \frac{(2a)^n}{n!}$$

and we can make $\dfrac{(2a)^n}{n!}$ as small as we please by choosing n large enough; for this value of n, $E_n(x)$ is continuous (it is a polynomial) and so $E_n(x) - E_n(a)$ can be made as small as we please by choosing x near enough to a. Thus for such values of x, we can make $E(x) - E(a)$ as small as we like, showing that $E(x)$ is continuous. A similar argument may be used to show that any *convergent* power series

$$a_0 + a_1 x + a_2 x^2 + \cdots$$

is continuous.

INTEGRATION

THE *graph* of the function x^2, for values of x between $x = -3$ and $x = +3$ looks like this

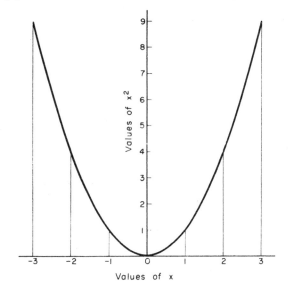

Values of x

We are going to determine the area under the curve, or rather of that piece of the curve for which x lies between 0 and 3. The method we shall use is to divide the area up into narrow strips by drawing a lot of parallel lines:

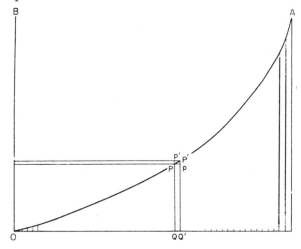

Let us start by drawing 16 strips, of equal breadth, and let $PQQ'P'$ be a typical strip. The area under the arc PP' is more than the area of the rectangle $PQQ'p$, but the excess is less than the area of the rectangle $PpP'p'$.

Now the sum of all such rectangles as $PpP'p'$ is equal to

$$OB \times QQ'.$$

For the area of $PpP'p'$ is $Pp' \times QQ'$; all the rectangles have the same *breadth* (QQ') and the sum of the heights Pp' is OB. But $OB = 9$ and $QQ' = \dfrac{3}{16}$, so that $OB \times QQ' = \dfrac{27}{16}$. The sum of the rectangles $PQQ'p$ is

$$\frac{3}{16} \times \left(\frac{3}{16}\right)^2 + \frac{3}{16} \times \left(\frac{2 \times 3}{16}\right)^2 + \frac{3}{16} \times \left(\frac{3 \times 3}{16}\right)^2 + \cdots +$$

$$\frac{3}{16} \times \left(\frac{15 \times 3}{16}\right)^2 = \frac{3^3}{16^3}(1^2 + 2^2 + 3^2 + \cdots + 15^2)$$

$$= \frac{3^3}{16^3} \times 15 \times 16 \times 31 \times \frac{1}{6} = 8,$$

approximately; for the area of the rectangle $PQQ'p$ is $PQ \times QQ' =$

$$= \frac{3}{16} \times PQ \text{ and } PQ = OQ^2, \text{ making}$$

$$PQ \times QQ' = \frac{3}{16} OQ^2,$$

so that if we give OQ in turn the values $\dfrac{3}{16}, \dfrac{2 \times 3}{16}, \dfrac{3 \times 3}{16}, \dots$ we obtain the areas

$$\frac{3}{16} \times \left(\frac{3}{16}\right)^2, \frac{3}{16} \times \left(\frac{2 \times 3}{16}\right)^2, \frac{3}{16} \times \left(\frac{3 \times 3}{16}\right)^2,$$

and so on. If instead of drawing 16 strips we consider the result of drawing any number n of strips, then the area of a typical rectangle $PQQ'p$ is $PQ \times QQ' = \dfrac{3}{n} \times OQ^2$, and the successive values of OQ are $\dfrac{3}{n}, \dfrac{2 \times 3}{n}, \dfrac{3 \times 3}{n}, \dots, \dfrac{(n-1) \times 3}{n}$, so that the sum of the rectangles is

$$\left(\frac{3}{n}\right)^3 [1^2 + 2^2 + 3^2 + \dots + (n-1)^2] = \frac{27}{n^3} \times \frac{(n-1)(n)(2n-1)}{6}$$

$$= \frac{9}{2} \left[2 - \frac{3}{n} + \frac{1}{n^2}\right].$$

The sum of the rectangles $PpP'p'$ is $OB \times QQ' = 3^2 \times \dfrac{3}{n} = \dfrac{27}{n}$ showing that the area under the curve x^2 lies between

$$9 - \frac{27}{2n} + \frac{9}{2n^2} \quad \text{and} \quad 9 + \frac{27}{2n} + \frac{9}{2n^2}$$

and both the sequences

$$9 - \frac{27}{2n} + \frac{9}{2n^2}, \quad 9 + \frac{27}{2n} + \frac{9}{2n^2}$$

approach the common limit 9, which is the value of the area under the curve.

If we repeat the calculation with a general value of x, say $x = a$, instead of $x = 3$, we find that the area lies between

$$\frac{a^3}{6}\left(2 - \frac{3}{n} + \frac{1}{n^2}\right) \quad \text{and} \quad \frac{a^3}{6}\left(2 + \frac{3}{n} + \frac{1}{n^2}\right)$$

and these sequences have the common limit $\dfrac{a^3}{3}$, the area under x^2 from $x = 0$ to $x = a$.

Let us now repeat the calculation, using this time not a particular function x^2, but any increasing function $f(x)$. The notation $f(x)$ for an arbitrary function is intended to express the dependence upon x, the "f" being the unspecified name of the function, by analogy with 'square x' for x^2, 'cube x' for x^3, and so on.

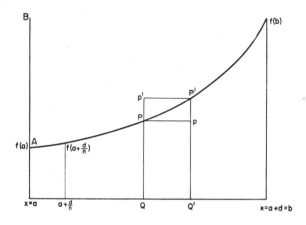

Divide the interval $x = a$ to $x = a + d = b$ into n parts. Then the area of the rectangles under the curve is

$$A_n = \frac{d}{n}\left[f(a) + f\left(a + \frac{d}{n}\right) + f\left(a + \frac{2d}{n}\right) + \cdots + \right.$$
$$\left. + f\left(a + (n-1)\frac{d}{n}\right)\right]$$

and the area under the curve exceeds this by less than the sum of the areas of the rectangles $P p P' p'$, which is equal to

$$\frac{d}{n}\left\{\left[f\left(a + \frac{d}{n}\right) - f(a)\right] + \left[f\left(a + \frac{2d}{n}\right) - f\left(a + \frac{d}{n}\right)\right] + \cdots + \right.$$
$$\left. + \left[f(b) - f\left(a + (n-1)\frac{d}{n}\right)\right]\right\} = \{f(b) - f(a)\}\frac{d}{n}.$$

In this general case we cannot of course directly evaluate the sum A_n as we could when 'f' was the function 'square'. But we shall nevertheless show that A_n tends to a limit which is the area under the curve of $f(x)$ from $x = a$ to $x = a + d$. We start by observing that if we split a strip into two strips we increase the area of the rectangles under the curve

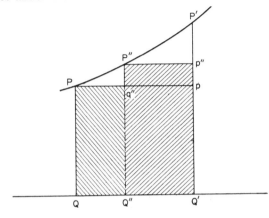

for the area of the rectangle $PQQ'p$ is less than the sum of the rectangles $PQQ''q''$, $P''Q''Q'p''$.

Thus the sequence

$$A_2, A_4, A_8, A_{16}, \ldots$$

is steadily increasing (the successive sums being formed by halving the previous strips).

Similarly if B_n denotes the sum of the rectangles $p'QQ'P'$, the sequence

$$B_2, B_4, B_8, B_{16}, \ldots$$

decreases, for the area of the rectangle $p'QQ'P'$ is *greater* than the sum of the rectangles $qQQ''P''$, $q'Q''Q'P'$.

Now $B_n > A_n$ and

$$B_n - A_n < AB \times QQ' = \{f(b) - f(a)\}\frac{d}{n}$$

so that $B_n - A_n \to 0$.

It follows that both these sequences

$$A_2, A_4, A_6, \ldots, \quad B_2, B_4, B_6, \ldots$$

tend to a common limit, A say.

Consider now any two corresponding pairs of sums A_N, B_N and A_{2^n}, B_{2^n}. Divide the interval (a, b) up by *all* the points of sub-

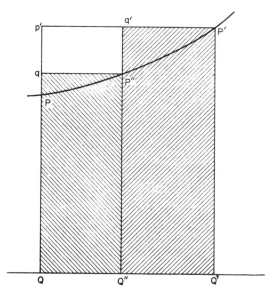

division on which *both* the sum A_N and the sum A_{2^n} are formed, and on this combined subdivision form the sums of areas of the rectangles below and above the curve, as usual; denote these sums by A_n^*, B_n^*.

Then because we form A_n^* by *adding* points of subdivision to the subdivision on which A_N is formed, it follows that

$$B_N > B_n^* > A_n^* > A_N$$

and similarly that

$$B_{2^n} > B_n^* > A_n^* > A_{2^n};$$

this latter set of inequalities shows that B_n^*, A_n^* both tend to the common limit A of A_{2^n} and B_{2^n}.

But $A_n^* - A_N < B_N - A_N$, and $B_N - A_N \to 0$ and therefore $A_n^* - A_N \to 0$ as N increases. Hence since $A_n^* - A_N = (A_n^* - A) + (A - A_N)$ and since $A_n^* - A \to 0$, it follows finally that $A_N - A \to 0$. In other words, the sums

$$\frac{d}{n}\left[f(a) + f\left(a + \frac{d}{n}\right) + f\left(a + \frac{2d}{n}\right) + \cdots + f\left(a + (n-1)\frac{d}{n}\right)\right]$$

tend to the limit A.

This limit represents the area under the curve of $f(x)$ from $x = a$ to $x = b$ and is also known as the *integral* of $f(x)$ from $x = a$ to $x = b$, denoted by

$$I_a^b f(x).$$

In particular, as we have seen, $I_0^a x^2 = \frac{1}{3} a^3$.

We have shown that the integral of an *increasing* function exists; a similar argument shows that a *decreasing* function has an integral. It is also true that a *continuous* function has an integral, but we shall take this for granted without venturing upon the details of the proof.

We note in passing that the integrals of x, x^2, x^3, x^4, ... have the following values:

$$I_0^a x = \frac{1}{2} a^2, \; I_0^a x^2 = \frac{1}{3} a^3, \; I_0^a x^3 = \frac{1}{4} a^4, \; I_0^a x^4 = \frac{1}{5} a^5,$$

showing that the general law is

$$I_0^b x^n = \frac{b^{n+1}}{n+1}.$$

If $f(x)$ is just a constant c, its graph will be a line parallel to the base line

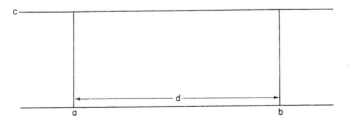

and the area under the graph, from $x = a$, to $x = b$, is the area of a rectangle of sides $b - a$, c, that is

$$I_0^a c = (b - a) c = cd.$$

Note however that if $f(x)$ is a negative constant $-c$, the limit of the sum

$$\frac{d}{n}\left(f(a) + f\left(a + \frac{d}{n}\right) + f\left(a + \frac{2d}{n}\right) + f\left(a + \frac{3d}{n}\right) + \cdots + \right.$$

$$\left. + f\left(a + \frac{(n-1)d}{n}\right)\right)$$

is $-cd$, because we must add n terms each equal to $-c$ giving a sum

$$-nc\frac{d}{n} = -cd.$$

It follows from the definition of the integral as the limit of a sum that the integral of a sum of two functions is the sum of the integrals of the functions. For instance

$$I_0^a (x^2 + x^3) = I_0^a x^2 + I_0^a x^3$$

$$= \frac{a^3}{3} + \frac{a^4}{4}.$$

For a similar reason

$$I_0^a \, cf(x) = c I_0^a \, f(x)$$

so that for instance

$$I_0^a (x^3 + 4x^2 + 7x - 5) = I_0^a x^3 + 4 I_0^a x^2 + 7 I_0^a x - 5a$$

$$= \frac{a^4}{4} + \frac{4a^3}{3} + \frac{7a^2}{2} - 5a.$$

Thus the integral of a polynomial is a polynomial.

If one curve lies above another its integral is greater because the area beneath is greater:

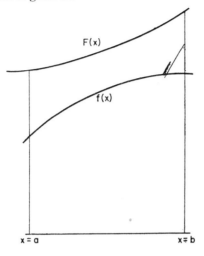

Without using the figure we see that, if $f(x) < F(x)$, since

$$f(a) < F(a),\ f\left(a + \frac{d}{n}\right) < F\left(a + \frac{d}{n}\right),\ f\left(a + \frac{2d}{n}\right) < F\left(a + \frac{2d}{n}\right), \cdots$$

therefore

$$\frac{d}{n}\left\{f(a) + f\left(a + \frac{d}{n}\right) + f\left(a + \frac{2d}{n}\right) + \cdots\right\}$$

$$< \frac{d}{n}\left\{F(a) + F\left(a + \frac{d}{n}\right) + F\left(a + \frac{2d}{n}\right) + \cdots\right\}$$

and so

$$I_a^b f(x) \leqslant I_a^b F(x),$$

(the limits may be equal, since for instance

$$1 - \frac{2}{n} < 1 - \frac{1}{n}$$

but each of $1 - \frac{2}{n}$, $1 - \frac{1}{n}$ has the limit 1).

If we appeal to a diagram

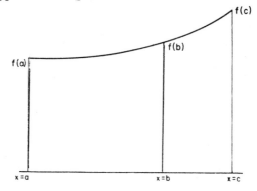

we see immediately that the area under the curve of $f(x)$ from $x = a$ to $x = c$ is the sum of the area under the curve from $x = a$ to $x = b$, and the area from $x = b$ to $x = c$, so that

$$I_a^c f(x) = I_a^b f(x) + I_b^c f(x).$$

If we wish to avoid making an appeal to a figure to prove this result (and it is only an assumption that the integral has *all* the properties of the figure) we must take a closer look at the construction of an integral.

We shall show that in determining the integral it is *not* necessary to divide the interval into *equal* parts; any method of successive divisions will do, provided that the lengths of the parts into which the interval is divided tend to zero. Thus for instance a succession of subdivisions of the interval $(0, 1)$ first by the point $\frac{1}{2}$; then by $\frac{1}{2}, \frac{1}{3}$; then by $\frac{1}{2}, \frac{1}{3}, \frac{1}{4}$ and so on, will not do since the part $\left(0, \frac{1}{2}\right)$ remains undivided. But a succession of subdivisions of $(0,1)$ like the following is acceptable:

Divide $(0,1)$ into 3 parts in the proportion $1:2:3$

$$0 \quad \frac{1}{6} \quad \frac{1}{2} \quad 1$$

at the points $\dfrac{1}{6}, \dfrac{1}{2}$. Divide each part in the same proportion and so on indefinitely

$$0 \quad \frac{1}{36} \quad \frac{1}{12} \quad \frac{1}{6} \quad \frac{2}{9} \quad \frac{1}{3} \qquad \frac{1}{2} \quad \frac{7}{12} \quad \frac{3}{4}$$

After n subdivisions the length of the largest part is $\dfrac{1}{2^n}$ which tends to zero as n increases indefinitely. Consider now any subdivision of the interval (a, b) by the points

$$a = a_0, a_1, a_2, \ldots, a_p, a_{p+1} = b,$$

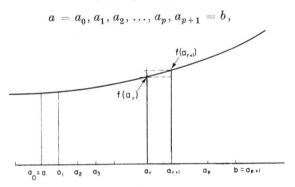

and let $d_r = a_{r+1} - a_r$ be the length of the part (a_r, a_{r+1}). Then the area under the curve, from $x = a_r$ to $x = a_{r+1}$, lies between $f(a_r)d_r$ and $f(a_{r+1})d_r$, and therefore the area under the curve from $x = a$ to $x = b$ lies between

$$s_p = f(a_0)\, d_0 + f(a_1)\, d_1 + \cdots + f(a_p)\, d_p$$

(called the *lower sum* on the subdivision) and

$$S_p = f(a_1)\, d_0 + f(a_2)\, d_1 + \cdots + f(a_{p+1})\, d_p$$

(called the *upper sum* on the subdivision).

Now combine the points of subdivision $a_0, a_1, \ldots, a_p, a_{p+1}$ with the points of *equal* subdivision of (a, b) into n parts and let the corresponding sums formed on these combined subdivisions be

$$s_p^* \quad \text{and} \quad S_p^*.$$

Since the sums s_p^*, S_p^* are formed on subdivisions which contain the points a_0, a_1, ..., a_p, a_{p+1} and perhaps *extra* points therefore

$$s_p \leqslant s_p^* \leqslant S_p^* \leqslant S_p;$$

similarly, remembering the relationship of the sums, A_n, B_n (on the equal subdivision) to s_p^*, S_p^*, we have

$$A_n \leqslant s_p^* \leqslant S_p^* \leqslant B_n.$$

Let d be the length of the *greatest* subinterval (a_r, a_{r+1}), that is, let d be the greatest of d_0, d_1, d_2, ... d_p. Then,

$$\begin{aligned}
S_p - s_p &= \{f(a_1) - f(a_0)\} d_0 + \{f(a_2) - f(a_1)\} d_1 + \cdots \\
&\leqslant \{f(a_1) - f(a_0) + f(a_2) - f(a_1) + \cdots + f(b) - f(a_p)\} d \\
&= \{f(b) - f(a)\} d.
\end{aligned}$$

We know that both A_n and B_n tend to A, the integral of $f(x)$ from a to b, and so, if we take n large enough we can make $B_n - A_n$ as small as we like, say less than $1/k$. Then, since s_p^* and A both lie between A_n and B_n their positive difference is less than $B_n - A_n < \dfrac{1}{k}$. But

$$s_p^* - s_p \leqslant S_p - s_p \leqslant \frac{1}{k}$$

if we take

$$d = 1/k\,(f(b) - f(a))$$

and so the positive difference between s_p and A is less than $\dfrac{2}{k}$

$$s_p - \frac{1}{k} \qquad s_p \qquad s_p + \frac{1}{k}$$

$\left(\text{for both } A \text{ and } s_p^* \text{ lie between } s_p - \dfrac{1}{k} \text{ and } s_p + \dfrac{1}{k}\right)$. Thus by taking d small enough we can bring s_p as near to the integral as we please.

With this result we can easily prove that

$$I_a^b f(x) + I_b^c f(x) = I_a^c f(x).$$

For take subdivisions of the intervals (a, b) and (b, c) in which the length of the greatest subinterval is d; these two subdivisions together form a subdivision of the whole interval (a, c). Form the lower sums s_1 and s_2 on the subdivisions of the intervals (a, b), (b, c)

and the lower sum s on the resulting subdivision of (a, c) so that, by their nature as sums

$$s_1 + s_2 = s.$$

Now, if d is small enough, s_1 and s_2 differ from $I_a^b f(x)$ and $I_b^c f(x)$ respectively by as little as we please, and s differs from $I_a^c f(x)$ by as little as we please. Hence since the difference $I_a^c f(x) - I_a^b f(x) - I_b^c f(x)$ is a *fixed* amount and its positive value can be made as small as we please, it follows that this difference is zero.

THE DERIVATIVE

EVEN a cursory examination of the values of x^2 shows that, if we vary the value of x, the values of x^2 change more rapidly than the values of x. For instance, when x changes from 1 to 2, x^2 changes from 1 to 4. To obtain a more precise idea of this behaviour, let us consider two arbitrary values of x, say x and a, and compare the change in value of x^2 with the change in x. The ratio of these changes is

$$\frac{x^2 - a^2}{x - a}$$

and since $x^2 - a^2 = (x - a)(x + a)$, and since x and a are not equal, we may divide numerator and denominator by $x - a$, giving

$$\frac{x^2 - a^2}{x - a} = x + a = 2a + (x - a).$$

Thus the nearer we bring x to a the closer does the ratio $(x^2 - a^2)/(x - a)$ approach the value $2a$. The value approached is called the *rate of change* at a. Thus the rate of change of x^2 at a is $2a$. Instead of 'rate of change' we shall generally use the term *derivative*, calling $2a$ the derivative of x^2 at a.

To find the derivative of x^3 at a we consider the ratio

$$\frac{x^3 - a^3}{x - a}$$

Since $x^3 - a^3 = (x - a)(x^2 + ax + a^2)$, as we may readily verify, and

$$x^2 + ax + a^2 = 3a^2 + ax - a^2 + x^2 - a^2$$
$$= 3a^2 + a(x - a) + (x - a)(2a + x - a)$$
$$= 3a^2 + 3a(x - a) + (x - a)^2$$

therefore

$$\frac{x^3 - a^3}{x - a} = 3a^2 + 3a(x - a) + (x - a)^2.$$

It follows that the smaller we make the difference $x - a$, that is the nearer we bring x to a, the closer the ratio approaches $3a^2$ (for instance, if $a = 4$ and $x - a = 1/100$, then $\dfrac{x^3 - 4^3}{x - 4}$ differs from $3 \times 16 = 48$ by less than $12/100 + 1/10,000$, that is, by less than $\cdot13$; and if $x - a = 1/1000$, the ratio differs from 48 by less than $\cdot013$, and so on).

Thus the derivative of x^3 at a is $3a^2$.

The derivatives of $x^4, x^5, x^6, \ldots, x^n$ at a are respectively $4a^3$, $5a^4, 6a^5, \ldots, na^{n-1}$.

If we interchange the roles which x and a have played in this discussion we see that the derivative of a^2 at x is $2x$, that of a^3 at x is $3x^2$ and so on. The *notation* in which we express the function in question is irrelevant; if the function is *square*, then we may represent it equally by x^2 or a^2—this is not to say that x^2 is equal to a^2, only that if we give x and a the same value, then x^2 and a^2 take the same value.

In fact, by a slight abuse of the notation, we may call $2x$ the derivative of x^2 at x, $3x^2$ the derivative of x^3 at x, $4x^3$ the derivative of x^4 at x, and so on, and we write,

$$Dx^2 = 2x, \quad Dx^3 = 3x^2, \quad Dx^4 = 4x^3,$$

and so on, 'D' standing for derivative.

Derivative of an integral

These results indicate a connection between the integral and the derivative. We have

$$I_0^a\, 2x = a^2, \quad Da^2 = 2a$$

$$I_0^a\, 3x^2 = a^3, \quad Da^3 = 3a^2$$

$$I_0^a\, 4x^3 = a^4, \quad Da^4 = 4a^3$$

and so on, suggesting the general result

$$DI_0^a\, f(x) = f(a)$$

which we now proceed to prove.

We confine the proof to the case when $f(x)$ is steadily increasing and continuous, but the result is also true for any continuous function.

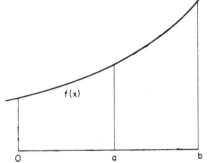

Let us denote $I_0^a\, f(x)$ by $F(a)$, for brevity. Then, as we have already remarked,

$$F(b) - F(a) = I_a^b\, f(x).$$

But when x lies between a and b, $f(x)$ lies between $f(a)$ and $f(b)$ and so

$$I_a^b\, f(x) < I_a^b\, f(b) = (b - a)\, f(b)$$

and

$$I_a^b\, f(x) > I_a^b\, f(a) = (b - a)\, f(a).$$

Hence

$$\frac{F(b) - F(a)}{b - a}$$

lies between $f(a)$ and $f(b)$; but since $f(x)$ is continuous, $f(b)$ approaches $f(a)$ as b approaches a, and therefore the derivative of $F(x)$, at $x = a$, that is the value

$$\frac{F(b) - F(a)}{b - a}$$

approaches as b approaches a, is $f(a)$ which proves that

$$D I_0^a f(x) = f(a).$$

Derivative of a sum

If $h(x) = f(x) + g(x)$, then since

$$\frac{f(x) - f(a)}{x - a} + \frac{g(x) - g(a)}{x - a} = \frac{h(x) - h(a)}{x - a}$$

it follows that

$$Dh(x) = Df(x) + Dg(x).$$

Similarly

$$Dcf(x) = cDf(x).$$

To find the derivative of a product we consider first the derivative of a square. We have

$$\frac{\{f(x)\}^2 - \{f(a)\}^2}{x - a} = \left| \frac{f(x) - f(a)}{x - a} \right| \{f(x) + f(a)\}$$

and since $\dfrac{f(x) - f(a)}{x - a}$ approaches $Df(a)$, and $f(x)$ approaches $f(a)$, as x approaches a, therefore

$$D\{f(x)\}^2 = 2f(x) \, D f(x).$$

Hence, since

$$f(x) \times g(x) = \left| \frac{f(x) + g(x)}{2} \right|^2 - \left| \frac{f(x) - g(x)}{2} \right|^2$$

it follows that

$$\begin{aligned} D f(x) g(x) &= \{f(x) + g(x)\} \{Df(x) + Dg(x)\} \\ &\quad - \{f(x) - g(x)\} \{Df(x) - Dg(x)\} \\ &= f(x) \, Dg(x) + g(x) \, Df(x). \end{aligned}$$

Provided that $f(a) \neq 0$ (and so, by continuity $f(x) \neq 0$ when x is near enough to a) we have

$$\left\{ \frac{1}{f(x)} - \frac{1}{f(a)} \right\} \Big/ (x - a) = - \frac{f(x) - f(a)}{x - a} \times \frac{1}{f(x) f(a)}$$

which approaches

$$\frac{- Df(a)}{\{f(a)\}^2}$$

as x approaches a, proving that

$$D\{1/f(x)\} = - \frac{Df(x)}{\{f(x)\}^2}$$

provided that $f(x) \neq 0$.

Finally, if $g(x) \neq 0$, we have

$$D \frac{f(x)}{g(x)} = D \left\{ f(x) \times \frac{1}{g(x)} \right\} = \frac{Df(x)}{g(x)} - \frac{f(x) Dg(x)}{\{g(x)\}^2}$$

$$= \frac{g(x) Df(x) - f(x) Dg(x)}{\{g(x)\}^2}.$$

We may summarise these results by writing

$$D(f + g) = Df + Dg, \quad D(fg) = (Df) g + f(Dg)$$

$$D\left(\frac{f}{g} \right) = \frac{(Df)g - f(Dg)}{g^2}.$$

The formula for the derivative of a composite function $f(g(x))$ is

$$D\{f(g(x))\} = Df(g(x)) \times Dg(x),$$

that is to say, to find the derivative of $f(g(x))$ we take the derivative of $f(t)$, $Df(t)$, and then multiply the value of this derivative for the value $g(x)$ of t, by the derivative of $g(x)$. In proving this result we consider first the case when $g(x) - g(a)$ does not take the value 0 for values of x arbitrarily near to a.

Writing $X = g(x)$, $A = g(a)$, $h(x) = f(g(x))$, we see that when

$x \neq a$ then $X \neq A$, (by assumption) and when x approaches a, X approaches A, and so

$$\frac{h(x) - h(a)}{x - a} = \frac{f(g(x)) - f(g(a))}{x - a} = \frac{f(X) - f(A)}{X - A} \times \frac{X - A}{x - a}$$

which approaches $Df(A) \times Dg(a)$ as x approaches a, showing that the derivative of $f(g(x))$ at $x = a$ is

$$Df(A) \times Dg(a).$$

If $g(x) - g(a) = 0$ for values of x as near a as we please, then $Dg(a) = 0$, and since $h(x) - h(a) = 0$ when $g(x) = g(a)$, the derivative $Dh(a) = 0$, and therefore once again

$$Dh(a) = Df(A) \times Dg(a)$$

since both sides of the equation are equal to zero. Thus whether $g(x) - g(a)$ vanishes for x arbitrarily near to a or not

$$Dh(a) = Df(A) \times Dg(a).$$

If a function $f(x)$ is constant for all values of x in an interval $a < x < b$, then the derivative of the function is zero for all x such that $a < x < b$, for if x, X lie between a and b, then

$$\frac{f(X) - f(x)}{X - x} = 0$$

and so the derivative has the value 0. It can also be shown that *a constant function is the only kind of function with derivative* 0 *throughout an interval*, but we shall not attempt to prove this. One consequence of this result is that, if $f(x)$ is the derivative of $F(x)$ for all x, then

$$I_a^b f(x) = F(b) - F(a);$$

for *regarded as functions of* b, the left- and right-hand sides of this equation have derivative $f(b)$ (note that $F(a)$ is a constant), so that their difference has derivative zero, and is therefore independent of b. But $F(b) - F(a)$ and $I_a^b f(x)$ can both be made as small as we please by taking b near enough to a (for $F(b) - F(a)$ is approximately equal to $(b - a) f(a)$, and $I_a^b f(x)$ is the area under the curve of $f(x)$ from $x = a$ to $x = b$), and so the constant difference between $I_a^b f(x)$ and $F(b) - F(a)$ must be 0.

It follows that if the derivative $f(x)$ of $F(x)$ satisfies $f(x) \geqslant 0$ for all x between a and b, then $F(b) \geqslant F(a)$, for $I_a^b f(x) \geqslant 0$ when $f(x) \geqslant 0$.

Another important consequence is that if f' and g' are the derivatives of f and g and if

$$f'(g(x)) = 1/g'(x)$$

and

$$f(g(0)) = 0,$$

then

$$f(g(x)) = x,$$

which we express by saying that if

$$y = g(x),$$

then

$$x = f(y).$$

For $f'(g(x))\, g'(x) - 1$ is the derivative of $f(g(x)) - x$ so that

$$f(g(x)) - x$$

is independent of x (does not change when x changes) and its value when $x = 0$ is 0, so that

$$f(g(x)) - x = 0$$

for *all* values of x.

Let us now return to the exponential function

$$E(x) = 1 + x + \frac{x^2}{2!} + \frac{x^3}{3!} + \cdots$$

which we met earlier.

Since for $x > 0$ and $n > x$

$$\frac{x^n}{n!} + \frac{x^{n+1}}{(n+1)!} + \cdots$$

$$= \frac{x^n}{n!} \left\{ 1 + \frac{x}{n+1} + \frac{x^2}{(n+1)(n+2)} + \cdots \right\}$$

$$< \frac{x^n}{n!} \left\{ 1 + \frac{1}{2} + \frac{1}{2^2} + \cdots \right\} = \frac{2x^n}{n!},$$

therefore, if x is positive, and $n > x$,

$$1 + x + \frac{x^2}{2!} + \cdots + \frac{x^n}{n!} < E(x) < 1 + x + \frac{x^2}{2!} + \cdots +$$

$$+ \frac{x^{n-1}}{(n-1)!} + \frac{2x^n}{n!}$$

and therefore, integrating from $x = 0$ to $x = a$,

$$a + \frac{a^2}{2!} + \frac{a^3}{3!} + \cdots + \frac{a^{n+1}}{(n+1)!} < I_0^a E(x) < a +$$

$$+ \frac{a^2}{2!} + \cdots + \frac{a^n}{n!} + \frac{a^{n+1}}{(n+1)!} + \frac{a^{n+1}}{(n+1)!} \, .$$

Since

$$\frac{a^{n+1}}{(n+1)!} \to 0, \quad \text{and} \quad a + \frac{a^2}{2!} + \cdots + \frac{a^{n+1}}{(n+1)!} \to E(a) - 1$$

therefore

$$I_0^a E(x) = E(a) - 1,$$

and taking the derivative of both sides we find

$$E(a) = DE(a),$$

proving the remarkable fact that the function $E(x)$ *is its own derivative*. We have so far supposed that x is positive, and we now complete the picture by showing that $E(x)$ is its own derivative also for negative values of x. We consider the product

$$\left\{ 1 - x + \frac{x^2}{2!} - \frac{x^3}{3!} + \cdots + \frac{(-x)^n}{n!} \right\} E(x)$$

for positive values of x.

The derivative of this product is

$$\left\{ 1 - x + \frac{x^2}{2!} - \frac{x^3}{3!} + \cdots + \frac{(-x)^n}{n!} \right\} E(x) -$$

$$- \left\{ 1 - x + \frac{x^2}{2!} - \cdots + \frac{(-x)^{n-1}}{(n-1)!} \right\} E(x) = \frac{(-x)^n}{n!} E(x)$$

which is positive if n is even and negative if n is odd and so the product is increasing for n even, and decreasing for n odd, from which it follows that, comparing the values of the product at $x = a > 0$ and at $x = 0$,

$$\left\{ 1 - a + \frac{a^2}{2!} - \cdots + \frac{a^{2n}}{(2n)!} \right\} E(a) \geqslant 1$$

and

$$\left\{ 1 - a + \frac{a^2}{2!} - \cdots - \frac{a^{2n+1}}{(2n+1)!} \right\} E(a) \leqslant 1$$

so that $1/E(a)$ lies between

$$1 - a + \frac{a^2}{2!} - \cdots + \frac{a^{2n}}{(2n)!}$$

and

$$1 - a + \frac{a^2}{2!} - \cdots + \frac{a^{2n}}{(2n)!} - \frac{a^{2n+1}}{(2n+1)!},$$

and since $\dfrac{a^n}{n!} \to 0$ it follows that

$$\frac{1}{E(a)} = 1 - a + \frac{a^2}{2!} - \frac{a^3}{3!} + \cdots = E(-a).$$

Hence, for negative values of x, the derivative of $E(x)$ is the derivative of $1/E(-x)$, which is

$$\frac{-E(-x)}{\{E(-x)\}^2} \times -1 = + \frac{1}{E(-x)} = E(x)$$

(since $-x$ is positive when x is negative).

We have seen that $E(-x) = 1/E(x)$. This is a particular case of the property

$$E(x + y) = E(x) \times E(y)$$

which gives the function $E(x)$ its name, the exponential function (because we add exponents when we multiply, for instance $a^m \times \times a^n = a^{m+n}$). To prove the exponential property of the function $E(x)$ we consider the derivative of the product

$$E(x) \times E(a - x);$$

this derivative is

$$E(x) \times E(a-x) - E(x) E(a-x) = 0$$

(since the derivative of

$$E(a-x) = E(a-x) \times D(a-x) = -E(a-x)),$$

showing that the product is constant, and therefore

$$E(x) \times E(a-x) = E(0) E(a-0) = E(a).$$

This equation is true for any values of a and x, in particular when a has the value $x + y$, giving

$$E(x) \times E(y) = E(x + y)$$

as required.

Since

$$E(1) = 1 + \frac{1}{1!} + \frac{1}{2!} + \cdots = e$$

it follows that

$$E(2) = E(1) \times E(1) = e \times e = e^2$$

$$E(3) = E(1) \times E(2) = e \times e^2 = e^3$$

and so on, giving

$$E(n) = e^n.$$

It follows that $e^{-n} = 1/E(n) = E(-n)$.

Similarly,

$$E\left(\frac{1}{n}\right) \times E\left(\frac{1}{n}\right) \times \cdots \times E\left(\frac{1}{n}\right) = E\left(\frac{1}{n} + \frac{1}{n} + \cdots + \frac{1}{n}\right)$$

$$= E(1) = e,$$

(the product containing n factors) and so

$$E\left(\frac{1}{n}\right) = e^{\frac{1}{n}}.$$

Hence

$$e^{\frac{m}{n}} = E\left(\frac{1}{n}\right) \times E\left(\frac{1}{n}\right) \times \cdots \times E\left(\frac{1}{n}\right),$$

with m factors,

$$= E\left(\frac{1}{n} + \frac{1}{n} + \cdots + \frac{1}{n}\right) = E\left(\frac{m}{n}\right).$$

Thus

$$E(x) = e^x$$

for any integer or fraction x.

If x is an endless decimal $a_0 \cdot a_1 a_2 a_3 \ldots$, then by continuity, since $a_0 \cdot a_1 a_2 \ldots a_n \to x$

$$E(a_0 \cdot a_1 a_2 \ldots a_n) \to E(x)$$

whence

$$e^{a_0 \cdot a_1 a_2 \cdots a_n} \to E(x).$$

Hence, if we *define* e^x as the limit of $e^{a_0 \cdot a_1 a_2 \cdots a_n}$ it follows that

$$e^x = E(x)$$

also when x is an infinite decimal.

The logarithmic function

The function $\dfrac{1}{x}$ is steadily decreasing for positive values of x and so the integral

$$I_1^a \frac{1}{x}$$

exists for positive $a \geqslant 1$, and the integral

$$I_a^1 \frac{1}{x}$$

exists for $0 < a < 1$.

We join these integrals together by defining

$$I_1^a \frac{1}{x} = -I_a^1 \frac{1}{x}$$

when $0 < a < 1$. It can readily be verified that this definition preserves the property

$$I_a^b f(x) + I_b^c f(x) = I_a^c f(x)$$

for *all* values of a, b and c.

The integral $I_1^a \dfrac{1}{x}$ is called the *logarithm* of a, denoted by $\log a$.

Thus log a is defined for all positive values of a, and

$$D \log a = \frac{1}{a}.$$

Consider now the function log e^x; the derivative of this function is

$$\frac{1}{e^x} \times e^x = 1$$

and

$$\log E(0) = \log 1 = I_1^1 \frac{1}{x} = 0,$$

and therefore

$$\log e^x = x.$$

In particular

$$\log e = 1.$$

Since log x has a positive derivative $1/x$ (log x is defined only for positive values of x) it follows that if $a > b$, then log $a >$ log b. Hence if log $x =$ log a, then $x = a$.

But from

$$\log e^x = x$$

it follows that

$$\log \{e^{\log a}\} = \log a,$$

by giving x the value log a, which proves that

$$e^{\log a} = a.$$

Thus log a *is the power to which the number* e *must be raised to give the number* a.

For positive values of x, e^x being a sum of positive terms, is positive, and since $e^{-x} = 1/e^x$, therefore e^{-x} is positive; but $De^x = e^x$ and therefore e^x is *increasing* for all values of x. It follows that if $e^a = e^b$, then $a = b$.

Hence, from

$$e^{\log a + \log b} = e^{\log a} \times e^{\log b} = ab = e^{\log ab}$$

it follows that

$$\log ab = \log a + \log b.$$

For positive b, and any decimal a, we have

$$b^a = e^{a \log b}.$$

We start by considering the case when a is a positive integer. We have, if n is a positive integer,

$$b^n = b \times b \times \cdots \times b = e^{\log b} \times e^{\log b} \times \cdots \times e^{\log b}$$

$$= e^{\log b + \log b + \cdots + \log b} = e^{n \log b}$$

and

$$b^{-n} = 1/b^n = 1/e^{n \log b} = e^{-n \log b};$$

furthermore

$$\left\{ e^{\frac{1}{n} \log b} \right\}^n = e^{\frac{1}{n} \log b + \frac{1}{n} \log b + \cdots + \frac{1}{n} \log b} = e^{\log b} = b$$

so that

$$e^{\frac{1}{n} \log b} = b^{\frac{1}{n}}$$

and finally

$$b^{\frac{m}{n}} = \left(b^{\frac{1}{n}} \right)^m = \left\{ e^{\frac{1}{n} \log b} \right\}^m = e^{\frac{m}{n} \log b}$$

showing that

$$b^a = e^{a \log b}$$

for integral and rational values of a.

For a decimal $a = a_0 \cdot a_1 a_2 a_3 \ldots$ we *define*

$$b^a = \lim b^{a_0 \cdot a_1 a_2 \ldots a_n};$$

it follows, by continuity, that

$$e^{a \log b} = \lim e^{(a_0 \cdot a_1 a_2 \ldots a_n) \log b} = \lim b^{a_0 \cdot a_1 a_2 \ldots a_n}$$

and therefore

$$e^{a \log b} = b^a$$

for *any* decimal a.

In terms of $\log x$ we may now find the power to which any positive number b must be raised to give a positive number a.

Since

$$\left\{ \frac{\log a}{\log b} \right\} \times \log b = \log a$$

therefore,

$$e^{\{\log a / \log b\} \log b} = e^{\log a} = a$$

and so

$$b^{\{\log a / \log b\}} = a$$

showing that $\dfrac{\log a}{\log b}$ is the power to which b must be raised to give a.

We write

$$\log_b a = \frac{\log a}{\log b}$$

and call $\log_b a$ *the logarithm of a to the base b.* In particular, since $\log e = 1$, we have $\log_e a = \log a$, that is, the logarithm to the base e is just $\log a$. It follows immediately from the definition that

$$\log_b a_1 a_2 = \frac{\log a_1 a_2}{\log b} = \frac{\log a_1}{\log b} + \frac{\log a_2}{\log b} = \log_b a_1 + \log_b a_2$$

and

$$\log_b a_1{}^{a_2} = \frac{\log a_1{}^{a_2}}{\log b} = \frac{a_2 \log a_1}{\log b} = a_2 \log_b a_1.$$

An elegant relation between logarithms to different bases is

$$\log_b a \times \log_c b \times \log_a c = 1:$$

this follows immediately from the definition.

The logarithmic series

To find a series for the logarithm function we proceed as follows. We know that

$$\frac{1}{1+x} = 1 - x + x^2 - \cdots + (-x)^n + \frac{(-x)^{n+1}}{1+x}$$

therefore

$$I_0^a \frac{1}{1+x} = a - \frac{a^2}{2} + \frac{a^3}{3} - \cdots - \frac{(-a)^{n+1}}{n+1} +$$

$$+ (-1)^{n+1} I_0^a \frac{x^{n+1}}{1+x};$$

since $D \log (1+x) = 1 + x$ we have

$$\log (1 + a) = a - \frac{a^2}{2} + \frac{a^3}{3} - \cdots - \frac{(-a)^{n+1}}{n+1} + (-1)^{n+1} R$$

where

$$R = I_0^a \frac{x^{n+1}}{1+x}.$$

If $1 \geqslant a > 0$, and $0 \leqslant x \leqslant a$, then $1 + x \geqslant 1$ and therefore

$$I_0^a \frac{x^{n+1}}{1+x} \leqslant I_0^a x^{n+1} = \frac{a^{n+2}}{n+2} \leqslant \frac{1}{n+2}$$

and since $1/(n+2) \to 0$ therefore

$$\log(1+a) = a - \frac{a^2}{2} + \frac{a^3}{3} \cdots$$

for $0 \leqslant a \leqslant 1$.

Similarly from

$$\frac{1}{1-x} = 1 + x + x^2 + \cdots + x^n + \frac{x^{n+1}}{1-x}$$

we find

$$-\log(1-a) = a + \frac{a^2}{2} + \cdots + \frac{a^{n+1}}{n+1} + I_0^a \frac{x^{n+1}}{1-x};$$

but, if $0 < x < 1$,

$$n x^{n+1} < 1 + x + x^2 + \cdots + x^n < \frac{1}{1-x}$$

and so, for $0 < a < 1$,

$$I_0^a \frac{x^{n+1}}{1-x} < \frac{1}{n} I_0^a \frac{1}{(1-x)^2} = \frac{1}{n} \left\{ \frac{1}{1-a} - 1 \right\} = \frac{1}{n} \frac{a}{1-a}.$$

Since $\dfrac{1}{n} \dfrac{a}{1-a} \to 0$, therefore

$$-\log(1-a) = a + \frac{a^2}{2} + \frac{a^3}{3} + \cdots.$$

It follows that

$$\log(1+x) = x - \frac{x^2}{2} + \frac{x^3}{3} - \cdots$$

for all decimals x which satisfy $-1 < x \leqslant 1$.

If $t > 1$, then since

$$t = \left(1 + \frac{t-1}{t+1}\right) \Big/ \left(1 - \frac{t-1}{t+1}\right)$$

and

$$0 < \frac{t-1}{t+1} < 1$$

we have

$$\log t = \log\left(1 + \frac{t-1}{t+1}\right) - \log\left(1 - \frac{t-1}{t+1}\right)$$

$$= 2\left\{\frac{t-1}{t+1} + \frac{1}{3}\left(\frac{t-1}{t+1}\right)^3 + \frac{1}{5}\left(\frac{t-1}{t+1}\right)^5 + \cdots\right\}.$$

By methods quite like those we have applied to the series

$$1 + x + \frac{x^2}{2!} + \frac{x^3}{3!} + \cdots$$

we may study the functions

$$\sin x = x - \frac{x^3}{3!} + \frac{x^5}{5!} - \frac{x^7}{7!} + \cdots$$

and

$$\cos x = 1 - \frac{x^2}{2!} + \frac{x^4}{4!} - \frac{x^6}{6!} + \cdots.$$

We find for instance that

$$D \sin x = \cos x, \quad D \cos x = -\sin x, \quad \sin^2 x + \cos^2 x = 1,$$

and that a solution of the equation

$$x = \sin y$$

is

$$y = I_0^x 1/\sqrt{(1 - x^2)}, \quad -1 < x < 1.$$

The functions $\sin x$ and $\cos x$ have the "addition formulae"

$$\sin (x + y) = \sin x \cos y + \cos x \sin y$$

$$\cos (x + y) = \cos x \cos y - \sin x \sin y.$$

The equation

$$\cos x = 0$$

has precisely one solution between $x = 0$ and $x = 3$, and this solution is denoted by $\frac{1}{2}\pi$ (one half π). The functions $\sin x$ and $\cos x$ are both periodic with period 2π, that is to say

$$\sin (x + 2\pi) = \sin x, \quad \cos (x + 2\pi) = \cos x$$

for all values of x.

In the interval $-\frac{1}{2}\pi < x < \frac{1}{2}\pi$ the function

$$\tan x = \sin x/\cos x$$

has derivative
$$1/\cos^2 x = 1 + \tan^2 x$$
and the equation
$$x = \tan y$$
has the unique solution
$$y = I_0^x \frac{1}{1 + t^2} = \arctan x.$$

Since $\cos \frac{1}{2} \pi = 0$ therefore

$$0 = \cos\left(\frac{1}{4}\pi + \frac{1}{4}\pi\right) = \cos^2 \frac{1}{4}\pi - \sin^2 \frac{1}{4}\pi$$

and so

$$\tan^2 \frac{1}{4}\pi = 1.$$

In the interval $0 < x < \frac{1}{2}\pi$, $\tan x$ is positive and therefore

$$\tan \frac{1}{4}\pi = 1.$$

It follows that

$$\frac{1}{4}\pi = I_0^1 \frac{1}{1 + t^2} = 1 - \frac{1}{3} + \frac{1}{5} - \cdots$$

which provides a means for calculating π. In fact the value of π to 20 places of decimals is

$$3 \cdot 14159\ 26535\ 89793\ 23846.$$

Far more powerful methods of calculating π are known. For instance, from the relation

$$\frac{1}{4}\pi = 8 \arctan \frac{1}{10} - 4 \arctan \frac{1}{515} - \arctan \frac{1}{239}$$

we obtain

$$\frac{1}{4}\pi = 8\left\{\frac{1}{10} - \frac{1}{3} \cdot \frac{1}{10^3} + \frac{1}{5} \cdot \frac{1}{10^5} - \cdots\right\}$$
$$- 4\left\{\frac{1}{515} - \frac{1}{3} \cdot \frac{1}{515^3} + \frac{1}{5} \cdot \frac{1}{515^5} - \cdots\right\}$$
$$- \left\{\frac{1}{239} - \frac{1}{3} \cdot \frac{1}{239^3} + \frac{1}{5} \cdot \frac{1}{239^5} - \cdots\right\},$$

and fifteen terms of the first series, with six terms of each of the second and third series, give π to thirty places of decimals. Using an electronic computer the value of π has been evaluated to 10,000 places of decimals.

The geometrical significance of π is that π is the area of the circle

$$x^2 + y^2 = 1$$

(i.e. the area bounded by the semicircles

$$y = \sqrt{(1 - x^2)}, \quad y = -\sqrt{(1 - x^2)}).$$

Pretender numbers

The endless decimals share many of their properties with a field we shall call the field of pretender numbers; the usual name of these numbers is dyadic numbers, and they form one of a series of fields, the triadic, tetradic, pentadic, etc., numbers, but we shall content ourselves with describing the dyadic numbers, calling them, as we have said, pretender numbers.

The infinite decimal is simply a convergent sequence of rationals of a particularly simple kind. We could fittingly call an infinite decimal a *normal form* of a convergent sequence, all sequences having this decimal for limit being said to have the same normal form. (In fact we could dispense with the normal forms and deal directly with the convergent sequences, since their property of convergence is preserved under addition, subtraction, multiplication and division, taking care not to divide by zero.)

We start again with the rational numbers and proceed to define, in place of the *positive value* $|r|$ of a rational r, the *pretender value* of the rational r, which we denote by $||r||$; let $r = A/B$, (not necessarily in its lowest terms) and let a, b be the exponents of the greatest powers of 2 in A, B respectively, so that

$$A = 2^a A_1, \quad B = 2^b B_1$$

where A_1, B_1 are odd numbers; then

$$\frac{1}{2^{a-b}}$$

is called the pretender value of r (notice that the value is not 2^{a-b} as one might expect, but $1/2^{a-b}$). We must show that the pretender value is independent of the particular representation A/B of the fraction r. To this end, let $A'/B' = A/B$ and further let

$$A' = 2^{a'} A_1', \quad B' = 2^{b'} B_1'$$

where A_1', B_1' are odd.

Then since $A/B = A'/B'$ we have

$$2^{a+b'} A_1 B_1' = 2^{a'+b} A_1' B_1$$

and since $A_1 B_1'$ and $A_1' B_1$ are both odd, therefore

$$a + b' = a' + b$$

that is $a - b = a' - b'$, as required.

We prove next that $\|r + r'\|$ *is not greater than the greater of* $\|r\|$ *and* $\|r'\|$ and that

$$\|r \times r'\| = \|r\| \times \|r'\|.$$

For if $r = A/B$, $r' = A'/B'$ where $A = 2^a A_1$, $B = 2^b B_1$, $A' = 2^{a'} A_1'$, $B' = 2^{b'} B_1'$ and all of A_1, B_1, A_1', B_1' are odd, then writing $n = a - b$, $n' = a' - b'$ we have

$$r + r' = \frac{A B' + A' B}{B B'} = \frac{2^{n+b+b'} A_1 B_1' + 2^{n'+b+b'} A_1' B_1}{2^{b+b'} B_1 B_1'}$$

and the greatest power of 2 in the numerator exceeds by $b + b'$ at *least* the smaller of n, n' which we denote by N.

Thus

$$\|r + r'\| \leqslant \frac{1}{2^N}$$

and either

$$\|r\| = \frac{1}{2^N} \quad \text{or} \quad \|r'\| = \frac{1}{2^N}$$

proving that

$$\|r + r'\| \leqslant \text{the greater of} \quad \|r\|, \|r'\|.$$

This result readily extends to a sum of any number of terms, giving

$$\|r_1 + r_2 + \cdots + r_k\| \leqslant \text{the greatest of}$$

$$\{\|r_1\|, \|r_2\|, \|r_3\|, \ldots, \|r_k\|\}.$$

For the product, we have

$$r \times r' = 2^{a+a'} A_1 A_1'/2^{b+b'} B_1 B_1'$$

and so

$$\|r \times r'\| = \frac{1}{2^{n+n'}} = \frac{1}{2^n} \times \frac{1}{2^{n'}} = \|r\| \times \|r'\|.$$

Finally the pretender difference of r, s is defined as the pretender value of their positive difference, denoted by $\|r - s\|$. The pretender difference, like the familiar positive difference, satisfies the *triangle inequality*

$$\|r - s\| \leqslant \|r - t\| + \|t - s\|.$$

In terms of pretender difference we now define *pretender convergence*. A sequence of rationals $s_1, s_2, s_3, \ldots$ is *pretender convergent* if given any integer $k \geqslant 1$ we can find n_k so that, for all $N \geqslant n \geqslant n_k$ we have

$$\|s_N - s_n\| < \frac{1}{k}.$$

For example the sequence 1, $1 + 2$, $1 + 2 + 2^2$, $1 + 2 + 2^2 + 2^3$, $\ldots$ is pretender convergent, for

$$\|2^n + 2^{n+1} + \cdots + 2^N\| \leqslant \|2^n\| = \frac{1}{2^n}$$

and $\dfrac{1}{2^n} \to 0$.

In fact for any series $u_1 + u_2 + u_3 + \cdots$ we have the simple, necessary and sufficient pretender convergence condition

$$\|u_n\| \to 0,$$

for $\|u_n + u_{n+1} + \cdots + u_N\| \leqslant$ the greatest of $\|u_n\|, \|u_{n+1}\|, \ldots,$ $\|u_N\|$, quite *unlike* ordinary convergence. If for some rational l

$$\|l - s_n\| \to 0$$

we say that l is the *pretender limit* of s_n.

Since

$$1 + 2 + 2^2 + \cdots + 2^{n-1} = 2^n - 1$$

and

$$\|(2^n - 1) - (-1)\| = \frac{1}{2^n} \to 0$$

therefore the pretender limit of the series $1 + 2 + 2^2 + \cdots$ is -1.

We shall not stop to prove that the sum, difference, product and quotient of pretender convergent sequences are themselves pretender convergent.

The pretender convergent series

$$2^i(a_0 + 2a_1 + 2^2a_2 + 2^3a_3 + \cdots)$$

where $a_0, a_1, a_2, \ldots$ are all zero or unity and i is an integer (positive, negative or zero) are the pretender decimals (or, better, pretender infinite dual fractions).

As an example of a pretender decimal we shall show that the pretender limit of

$$1 + 2 + 2^2 + 2^5 + 2^6 + 2^9 + 2^{10} + \cdots$$

is $3/5$.

For

$$\left\| 1 + 2 + 2^2 + 2^5 + 2^6 + 2^9 + 2^{10} + \cdots + 2^{4n+1} + 2^{4n+2} - \frac{3}{5} \right\|$$

$$= \left\| \frac{2}{5} + (2 + 2^2)(1 + 2^4 + 2^8 + \cdots + 2^{4n}) \right\|$$

$$= \left\| \frac{2}{5} + \frac{6(16^{n+1} - 1)}{16 - 1} \right\| = \left\| \frac{2^{4n+5}}{5} \right\| = \frac{1}{2^{4n+5}} \to 0.$$

By analogy with ordinary decimals we might write

$$1 + 2 + 2^2 + 2^5 + 2^6 + \cdots$$

in the form

$$11100110011 \ldots$$

The chief difference between the positive value and the pretender value is that, whereas for any numbers a, b we can find a positive integer n such that

$$|a + a + \cdots + a| > |b|$$

with n a's in the sum, for the pretender value we have

$$\|a + a + \cdots + a\| = \|a\|$$

no matter how many a's we add together.

Notes on Chapter 3

An account of the derivation from the infinite series of the addition formulae for sin x and cos x, and of their periodicity, is given in the author's book *The Uniform Calculus* (Clarendon Press).

The formula for $\frac{1}{4}\pi$ was given by G. F. Freeman, *Math. Gaz.* XLII (1959) p. 285.

Pretender numbers (p-adic numbers) were discovered by E. Kummer and K. Hensel.

CHAPTER 4

CLASSES AND TRUTH FUNCTIONS

WE ARE going to consider some properties of collections; collections or *classes* as we shall call them, will be denoted by capital letters $A, B, C, \ldots$. All the classes we consider will have their members chosen from a certain so-called universe (or universal class) which we denote by 1. For instance, the universe might consist of all grains of sand in the world, and the classes under consideration, all heaps of grains of sand. We shall also introduce the idea of an *empty class*, a class without any members, which we denote by 0. The reason for denoting the empty class by 0 and the universal class by 1 will become apparent shortly.

If two classes A, B have some members in common we shall denote the class of common elements by $A \cdot B$ (called the *product* or *intersection* of A and B). If A and B have no common members their intersection is empty and we write $A \cdot B = 0$.

We may symbolize two classes with common members by overlapping squares, thus

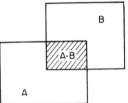

and two classes without common members may be symbolized by non-overlapping squares

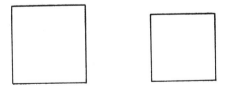

The class consisting of the members of a class A together with the members of a class B is denoted by $A + B$ (called the sum or union of A and B); common members of A and B count only once in $A + B$.

Addition and multiplication of classes is commutative and associative. For the common part of A and B is the same as the common part of B and A; and the class consisting of the members of A and the members of B is the same as the class consisting of the members of B and the members of A. The associative property of addition is obvious since $(A + B) + C$ and $A + (B + C)$ both denote the class consisting of the members of A, B and C. The corresponding property of multiplication is shown in the following diagram:

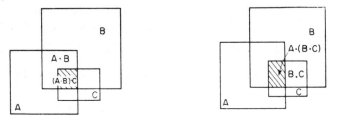

The shaded region is both $(A \cdot B) \cdot C$ and $A \cdot (B \cdot C)$.

The distributive law

$$A \cdot (B + C) = A \cdot B + A \cdot C$$

is likewise exhibited in the diagram

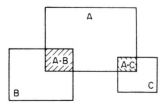   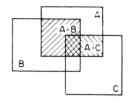

(B, C without members in common)   (B, C with common members)

Unlike the arithmetic of numbers, however, the arithmetic of classes has a second distributive law

$$A + B \cdot C = (A + B) \cdot (A + C)$$

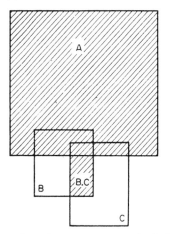

The diagram shows that the common part of $A + B$ and $A + C$ consists of A together with the common part of B and C.

The members of the universal class which do not belong to a class A form a class called the *complement* of A. Complements link sum and product together for we have

$$(A + B)' = A' \cdot B'$$

(the complement of the sum is the product of the complements) and

$$(A \cdot B)' = A' + B'$$

(the complement of the product is the sum of the complements). To represent these important results in a diagram we take A and

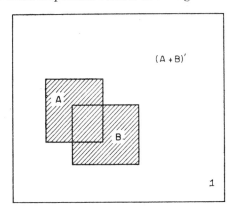

B to be squares in the universal square 1.The shaded region denotes $A + B$, and so $(A + B)'$ is the unshaded region in the universal square 1; the horizontal shading marks the complement of A,

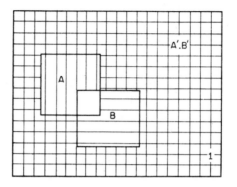

and the vertical shading marks the complement of B. The region with both horizontal and vertical shading is therefore the common part of the complements A', B' and the diagram shows that this common part coincides with the complement of $A + B$.

Since the complement of the complement is the original class, the second property

$$(A \cdot B)' = A' + B'$$

follows from the first, for we have (applying the first result to the classes A', B')

$$(A' + B')' = A'' \cdot B'' = A \cdot B$$

and therefore

$$A' + B' = (A \cdot B)'.$$

The fundamental properties of the universal and empty classes are

$$A + 0 = A, \quad A \cdot 0 = 0, \quad A \cdot 1 = A$$

as our notation anticipated.

The equation $A = 0 + A$ says that if we add no new members to A, A remains unchanged. And since the empty class 0 is without members, A and 0 have no members in common, and so the class of their common members is the empty class. On the other hand the universal class 1 contains necessarily all the members of A, so that A and 1 have the whole of A in common.

If all the members of a class A are also members of a class B we say that the class A is *contained* in the class B and write $A \subset B$. Every class is, of course, contained in the universal class

$$A \subset 1$$

and we shall also say that the empty class is contained in any class, so that

$$0 \subset A \subset 1.$$

If $A \subset B$ and $B \subset C$, then $A \subset C$ for the members of A are contained in B, and *so* contained in C.

If $A \subset B$, then $A \cdot B = A$, and *conversely*, for if $A \subset B$, then all the members of A are in common with B, and if $A \cdot B = A$, then A and B have the whole of A in common, so that $A \subset B$.

If $A \subset B$ and $B \subset A$, then A and B are the same class, that is $A = B$.

The classes A, B, C, ... are *partially ordered* by the relation of inclusion; like the relation 'less than' for integers the relation of inclusion is

(i) *reflexive*, that is $A \subset A$ for any A,

(ii) *antisymmetric*, that is $A \subset B$ and $B \subset A$ leads to $A = B$,

(iii) *transitive*, that is $A \subset B$ and $B \subset C$ leads to $A \subset C$.

Unlike the relation 'less than or equal', however, it is not necessarily the case that for any two classes, A, B one of the relations $A \subset B$, $B \subset A$ must hold, which is why we call inclusion a *partial* order relation.

The arithmetic of classes is an example of a *Boolean* arithmetic (named after G. Boole, the famous Irish mathematician). Before, however, we seek to mark the essential features of a Boolean arithmetic, we shall consider the question of the *independence* of the various relations we have shown to hold between classes. In the presence of the operation of taking a complement, it is immediately obvious that the addition and multiplication of classes may each be defined in terms of the other. For instance, we have seen that

$$A + B = (A' \cdot B')'$$

which defines addition of classes in terms of multiplication (the sum of two classes is the complement of the product of their complements) and correspondingly

$$A \cdot B = (A' + B')'$$

which defines the product in terms of the sum (the product of two classes is the complement of the sum of the complements). The empty class and the universal class may, in turn, be defined in terms of addition and complementation (or multiplication and complementation) since

$$1 = A + A' \quad \text{and} \quad 0 = 1'.$$

Similarly, inclusion may be defined in terms of multiplication (or addition) since $A \subset B$ if, and only if, A is the common part of A and B, that is $A \cdot B = A$. Thus only two operations, for instance, multiplication and taking the complement, suffice, and in terms of these we may define the empty class, the universal class, and the addition of classes.

A Boolean arithmetic may be defined as a set of elements a, b, c, ... which admit two operations, called multiplication and complementation, such that the complement of any element is again an element, and the product of two elements is an element. Multiplication is commutative and associative. An element has only one complement, that is, if $a = b$, then $a' = b'$, and only one product with another element, that is, if $a = b$, then $a \cdot c = b \cdot c$. Finally

$$a \cdot b = a$$

if, and only if,

$$a \cdot b' = c \cdot c'$$

for any c.

It readily follows that $a \cdot a' = b \cdot b'$ for any a and b, for (writing x for any element) from

$$x \cdot x' = x \cdot x'$$

(taking a, b, c all equal to x above) it follows that

$$x \cdot x = x$$

and hence

$$x \cdot x' = c \cdot c'$$

for any x and c. Thus all the products $a \cdot a'$, $b \cdot b'$, $c \cdot c'$, ... are equal to the same element, which we denote by 0.
From the equation

$$x \cdot x = x$$

it follows that
$$x \cdot x \cdot x' = x \cdot x',$$
that is
$$x \cdot 0 = 0.$$

To prove that $x'' = x$ is rather more difficult. First we define a partial order relation $\subset$ (called inclusion) by the condition that $a \subset b$ if, and only if, $a \cdot b = a$ (thus $a \subset b$ if, and only if, $a \cdot b' = c \cdot c' = 0$) and observe that from $a \subset b$ and $b \subset a$ it follows that $a = b$; for if $a \cdot b = a$ and $b \cdot a = b$, then since $a \cdot b = b \cdot a$, we have $a = b$. Moreover if $a \subset b$ and $b \subset c$, then $a \subset c$, for if $a \cdot b = a$ and $b \cdot c = b$, then $a \cdot b \cdot c = a \cdot c$ and $a \cdot b \cdot c = a \cdot b = a$ so that $a \cdot c = a$, that is $a \subset c$.

Since $x' \cdot x = 0$, taking x' for x, we find $x'' \cdot x' = 0 = c \cdot c'$ and therefore $x'' \subset x$; hence $x''' \subset x'$ and $x'''' \subset x''$ (taking x' for x twice) and so $x'''' \subset x$. We deduce in turn that $x'''' \cdot x' = 0$, $x' \subset x'''$ and therefore $x' = x'''$; but $x \cdot x' = 0$ and so $x \cdot x''' = 0$, that is $x \subset x''$, and since we have already proved that $x'' \subset x$ it follows at last that $x = x''$.

We now define 1 as the complement of 0,
$$1 = 0'$$
and proceed to prove that
$$a \cdot 1 = a.$$

The definition of 1 makes $1' = 0'' = 0$, and since $a \cdot 0 = 0$ we have
$$a \cdot 1' = c \cdot c'$$
and therefore
$$a \cdot 1 = a.$$

It readily follows that, defining addition by the equation
$$a + b = (a' \cdot b')',$$
we have
$$a + 0 = a,$$
for
$$a + 0 = (a' \cdot 0')' = (a' \cdot 1)' = a'' = a,$$
confirming that 0 and 1 have the properties implied by the notation.

It may be shown that both the distributive laws

$$a \cdot (b + c) = a \cdot b + a \cdot c$$

and

$$a + b \cdot c = (a + b) \cdot (a + c)$$

hold, but we shall omit the details.

A Boolean arithmetic may be regarded as a ring in two ways (by taking either $+$ and $\cdot$ as ring addition and multiplication, or $\cdot$ and $+$) with complementation taking the part of subtraction (or division as the case may be). Boolean arithmetic is, however, a very special kind of ring, because of the properties

$$a + a = a, \quad a \cdot a = a,$$

which hold in a Boolean arithmetic, but not in a general ring.

Sentence logic

Sentence logic is the study of the conditions under which compound sentences are true simply in virtue of their pattern, without regard to the meaning of their parts. For instance, the sentence "it is raining or it is not raining" is true not just with the particular ingredients in question, but with any statement in place of 'it is raining'. It is like the equation $x \cdot x' = 0$ in Boolean arithmetic, which holds for any element x whatever, and in fact, as we shall see, sentence logic may be formulated as a Boolean arithmetic.

Since we are not interested in the meaning of the constituent parts, but only in the combinations of simple sentences we shall denote simple sentences by letters $p, q, r, \ldots$. The combinations in question are "p and q", "p or q", 'p implies q' (that is, "if p, then q", for instance "if there is lightning there is thunder") and finally the denial of p, 'not-p'. The logical terms "and", "or", "not" and "implies" are usually abbreviated, with "$\&$" (ampersand) for "and", "$\vee$" (the first letter of the Latin word *vel*, meaning or), "$\neg$" for "not" and an arrow "$\rightarrow$" for "implies". Thus the combinations we shall consider are $\neg p$, $p \& q$, $p \vee q$, $p \rightarrow q$ and further compounds constructed from these in the same ways, like $p \rightarrow (p \vee q)$, or $(p \rightarrow q) \rightarrow [(p \vee r) \rightarrow (q \vee r)]$ where brackets are used to mark out the constituent parts of the sentence.

A simple sentence may be true or false, or as we shall say, have two truth *values*, truth and falsity, which we abbreviate by '0' and '1' respectively. The denial of p, $\neg\, p$, is true when p is false and false when p is true, and so the truth table for denial is

p	0	1
$\neg\, p$	1	0

The disjunction $p \vee q$ is truth if either of p or q is true (that is, at least one, and perhaps both) and false otherwise, so that the truth table for disjunction reads

$\vee$	0	1	q
0	0	0	
1	0	1	
p			

The conjunction $p\,\&\,q$, however, is true only if both p and q are true, giving the table

$\&$	0	1	q
0	0	1	
1	1	1	
p			

The sense of implication is not clear from its usage in everyday language; certainly we exclude the possibility of a true sentence implying a false one, but the question as to what follows from a false sentence is left open. The choice made in sentence logic is to say that anything is implied by a false sentence, or to put it another way, that the implication $p \to q$ is true when p is false, whether q is true or false. Thus the table for implication is

$\to$	0	1	q
0	0	1	
1	0	0	
p			

The values of p are in the left-hand vertical column, and the values of q in the top row. In the implication $p \to q$, p is called the *antecedent* and q the *consequent*.

Double implication, or equivalence, $p \leftrightarrow q$ means that p and q have the same truth values, that is to say $p \leftrightarrow q$ is true if, and only if, p, q are both true or both false.

Conjunction, disjunction, implication and double implication are connected in various ways. To bring out these connections we set up the truth tables side by side:

p	q	$\neg p$	$\neg q$	$p \lor q$	$p\,\&\,q$	$p \to q$	$p \leftrightarrow q$	$\neg(p \leftrightarrow q)$	$\neg p\,\&\,q$	$p\,\&\,\neg q$	$q \to p$	$\neg(p \lor q)$	$\neg(p\,\&\,q)$	$p \lor \neg p$	$p\,\&\,\neg p$
0	0	1	1	0	0	0	0	1	1	1	0	1	1	0	1
0	1	1	0	0	1	1	1	0	1	0	0	1	0	0	1
1	0	0	1	0	1	0	1	0	0	1	1	1	0	0	1
1	1	0	0	1	1	0	0	1	1	1	0	0	0	0	1

The values of p and q are now entered in columns; the values of $\neg p$ are obtained from the values of p by changing from 0 to 1 and 1 to 0, according to the truth table for $\neg p$, and the entry for $p \lor q$ is made according to the table for disjunction which shows that $p \lor q$ has the value 1 only in the fourth row when p and q both have the value 1. The tables reveal that the truth values of $p \to q$ are the same as the truth values of $\neg p \lor q$, so that $p \to q$ and $\neg p \lor q$ are truth table equivalents, which we may express by writing $p \to q = \neg p \lor q$. Other truth table equivalents are $p\,\&\,q$ and $\neg(\neg p \lor \neg q)$; $p \lor q$ and $\neg(\neg p\,\&\,\neg q)$; and $p \leftrightarrow q$ and $(p \to q)\,\&\,(q \to p)$.

A sentence is said to be *valid* or a *tautology* if its truth value is 0 irrespective of the truth values of its constituent sentences, that is if it is true in virtue of its structure; such a sentence is $p \lor \neg p$ which takes the value 0 whether p has the value 0 or 1. A sentence like $p\,\&\,\neg p$ which takes only the value 1 is said to be *contradictory*, and a sentence which may take both values 0 and 1 is *contingent*. A sentence is necessarily valid, contradictory or contingent, and by means of the truth tables we may find to which category any compound sentence belongs. As a first example we consider the sentence

$$\{p \mathbin{\&} (p \rightarrow q)\} \rightarrow q.$$

To test this sentence we set up in successive columns the truth values of the sentences $p \rightarrow q$, $p \mathbin{\&} (p \rightarrow q)$ and finally $\{p \mathbin{\&} (p \rightarrow q)\} \rightarrow q$

p	q	$p \rightarrow q$	$p \mathbin{\&} (p \rightarrow q)$	$\{p \mathbin{\&} (p \rightarrow q)\} \rightarrow q$
0	0	0	0	0
0	1	1	1	0
1	0	0	1	0
1	1	0	1	0

The possible combinations of values for p and q is $2 \times 2 = 4$ since with each of 2 values 0, 1 for p, q may have two values; in the third column we enter the values of $p \rightarrow q$ from the table for implication. The fourth column is drawn up from the first and third columns, using the table for conjunction, and finally the last column is drawn up from the second and fourth columns, using the table for implication. The sentence is valid.

To test a compound sentence with more than two constituent sentences the truth table test is very slow. For instance, to test

$$(p \rightarrow q) \rightarrow \{(r \lor p) \rightarrow (r \lor q)\}$$

we need $2 \times 2 \times 2 = 8$ rows, and 8 columns

p	q	r	$p \rightarrow q$	$r \lor p$	$r \lor q$	$(r \lor p) \rightarrow (r \lor q)$	$(p \rightarrow q) \rightarrow \{(r \lor p) \lor (r \lor q)\}$
0	0	0	0	0	0	0	0
0	0	1	0	0	0	0	0
0	1	0	1	0	0	0	0
0	1	1	1	0	1	1	0
1	0	0	0	0	0	0	0
1	0	1	0	1	0	0	0
1	1	0	0	0	0	0	0
1	1	1	0	1	1	0	0

The last column of zeros shows that the sentence is valid.

As the use of the numerals 0, 1 for truth and falsehood indicated we may readily construct a numerical test for validity. Using the arithmetic *modulo* 2 the truth values of $p \vee q$ are given by the product $p \cdot q$ for $p \cdot q$ takes the value 0 if either p or q is 0, just as $p \vee q$ is true if either of p, q is true. The corresponding functions for $\neg p$ and $p \mathbin{\&} q$ are $1 - p$ and $p + q - pq$ as may readily be verified. Since $p \to q$ has the same truth values as $\neg p \vee q$, the truth values of $p \to q$ are given by $(1 - p)\, q$; finally for $p \leftrightarrow q$ we use the function $p + q$.

We list these representing functions in the following table:

logical connective	representing function
$p \vee q$	$p \cdot q$
$p \mathbin{\&} q$	$p + q - pq$
$\neg p$	$1 - p$
$p \to q$	$(1 - p)\, q$
$p \leftrightarrow q$	$p + q$

To test the validity of a sentence we simply work out the value of its representing function. Let us consider again the examples above.

We start by forming the representing function of the sentence

$$\{p \mathbin{\&} (p \to q)\} \to q;$$

the function is built up in stages, exactly as the sentence itself is built up. The representative of $p \to q$ is $(1 - p)\, q$ and so that of $p \mathbin{\&} (p \to q)$ is

$$p + (1 - p)\, q - (1 - p)\, qp = p + q - pq,$$

since $(1 - p)\, p = 0$ whether p has the value 0 or 1 (and this, of course, corresponds to the fact that $p \vee \neg p$ is a valid sentence); hence the representative of the whole sentence is

$$(1 - p - q + pq)\, q = (1 - p)\,(1 - q)\, q = 0$$

since $(1 - q)\, q = 0$, showing that the sentence is valid.

We come now to the second example

$$(p \to q) \to \{(r \vee p) \to (r \vee q)\}.$$

The sentence $(r \lor p) \to (r \lor q)$ has the representative

$$(1 - pr)\, qr$$

and so the representative of the whole sentence is

$$\{1 - (1 - p)\, q\}\, (1 - pr)\, qr.$$

Can this function take the value 1? If it does, then every factor has this value, that is $q = r = 1$ and $pr = 0$ (forcing the value $p = 0$), and $(1 - p)\, q = 0$, which is impossible since $p = 0$ and $q = 1$; this shows that the representing function cannot take the value 1 (and so takes only the value 0) and therefore the sentence is valid. It is not *necessary* to proceed in this indirect way, but often quicker to do so. To work out the representing function's values directly we observe that if either $q = 0$ or $r = 0$ the value is 0, and if $q = r = 1$ the value is

$$\{1 - (1 - p)\}\, (1 - p)$$

which is clearly 0 whether p has the value 0 or 1.

In the truth tables on page 208 the truth values of sentences like $p \lor q$ are entered in a column, and in each row in the column we enter the value corresponding to each particular pair of values of the constituent sentences p and q. The pairs of values of p and q are arranged in a particular order, namely 0 0, 0 1, 1 0, 1 1; the order is of course that of the numbers 0, 1, 2, 3 *written in the scale of 2*. In the same way if we made a truth table for sentences with three constituent parts – or *variables*, as they are called – we should enter the values of the variables p, q, r in the order 000, 001, 010, 011, 100, 101, 110, 111 obtained by writing the numbers 0, 1, 2, 3, 4, 5, 6, 7 in the scale of 2. To return to the case of two variables, each column, as we have seen, has four rows corresponding to the pairs of values 00, 01, 10, 11 of the variables p, q. There are therefore $2 \times 2 \times 2 \times 2 = 16$ possible columns, or *truth functions* as we shall say, since each row may be filled in two ways, with a 0 or 1. Of these sixteen, $p,\ q,\ \neg p,\ \neg q$ comprise four, and $p \lor q$, $p \,\&\, q,\ p \to q,\ p \leftrightarrow q$ another four; then we note the two one-variable functions $p \lor \neg p$, $p \,\&\, \neg p$. The remaining six are $\neg p \,\&\, q$, $p \,\&\, \neg q,\ q \to p,\ \neg (p \,\&\, q),\ \neg (p \lor q)$ and $\neg (p \leftrightarrow q)$, showing that the whole sixteen may be expressed in terms of the connectives

&, $\vee$, $\rightarrow$, $\leftrightarrow$ and negation. In fact these five are not independent of one another. We have already remarked that $p \rightarrow q$ is truth table equivalent to $\neg p \vee q$, and it is immediately verified that $p \,\&\, q$ is equivalent to $\neg (\neg p \vee \neg q)$ and that $p \leftrightarrow q$ is equivalent to $(p \rightarrow q) \,\&\, (q \rightarrow p)$, showing that all truth functions may be constructed from '$\neg$' and '$\vee$'. What is perhaps much more surprising, all truth functions may be generated by a single truth function. Let us denote by p/q the function whose values are those of $\neg p \vee \neg q$ (so that p/q may be read as 'neither p nor q', but to avoid the suggestion of two operations we shall call p/q simply 'p stroke q'). Thus the table for the stroke function is

p	q	p/q	p/p	q/q	$(p/p)/(q/q)$
0	0	1	1	1	0
0	1	0	1	0	0
1	0	0	0	1	0
1	1	0	0	0	1

If we can show that negation "$\neg$", and disjunction "$\vee$" may be generated by the stroke function it will follow that all two variable truth functions may be generated by the stroke function. The values of p/p are simply those of $\neg p$ (for p/q has the value 0 only if one at least of p, q has the value 1), so that $\neg p$ is equivalent to p/p. Next we calculate the values of the function $(p/p)/(q/q)$ which proves to be the same as those of $p \vee q$. Since $\neg p$ and $p \vee q$ are both expressible in terms of the stroke function p/q, it follows that all truth functions of (1 or) 2 arguments are so expressible. What of truth functions of more than two variables? Consider any truth function whatever of three variables p, q, r and let us denote it for short by (p, q, r); give r the value 0, then $(p, q, 0)$ is a truth function of 2 variables, which as we have just seen may be generated by the stroke function; similarly $(p, q, 1)$ may be generated by the stroke function and therefore the function

$$\{r \,\&\, (p, q, 0)\} \vee \{\neg r \,\&\, (p, q, 1)\} \tag{i}$$

may be so generated since it involves only "&", "$\vee$", "$\neg$" in addition to $(p, q, 0)$ and $(p, q, 1)$.

But
$$\{r \,\&\, (p, q, 0)\} \lor \{\neg \, r \,\&\, (p, q, 1)\}$$

has exactly the same truth values as (p, q, r) itself; for writing $\{p, q, r\}$ for expression (i) we observe that if $(p, q, 0)$ has the value 0 (for some pair of values of p, q,), then the value of $0 \,\&\, (p, q, 0)$ is 0, and the value of $\neg \, r \,\&\, (p, q, 1)$ when $r = 0$ is $1 \,\&\, (p, q, 1)$ which has the value 1, so that the value of $\{p, q, 0\}$ is 0, the same as $(p, q, 0)$; and if $(p, q, 0)$ has the value 1, then $0 \,\&\, (p, q, 0)$ has the value 1, and $\neg \, 0 \,\&\, (p, q, 1)$ has the value 1, showing again that $\{p, q, 0\}$ has the same value as $(p, q, 0)$. A similar argument shows that $\{p, q, 1\}$ always has the same truth value as $(p, q, 1)$ which confirms that $\{p, q, r\}$ is truth table equivalent to (p, q, r). Thus every truth function of three arguments may also be expressed purely in terms of the stroke function, and step by step we may pass from functions of 3 arguments to functions of 4 arguments, and so on up to any truth function whatever.

Of course this result is not a special property of truth functions as such. We have been concerned with the class of functions which take only one of two possible values when the variables take only these 2 values (not necessarily just 0 and 1, or true and false) and we have shown that this whole class of functions may be generated by a single function of the class. This result is true also for functions which take only 3 values when their variables take these same three values, and quite generally for functions which take only n values when their variables take these same n values ($n \geqslant 2$), but the proof is rather more difficult.

We have seen that the stroke function alone generates all other truth functions. Has any other truth function this property? It is easily shown that the function $\neg \, p \,\&\, \neg \, q$ has the property, but no other function of 2 variables has. Considering only the second part of this observation we content ourselves with showing that $p \to q$ does *not* generate all truth functions; it suffices to show that we cannot obtain $\neg \, p$. Now $p \to p$ is a tautology and takes only the value 0; $p \to 0$ takes the value 0, and $0 \to p$ takes the same value as p, and so the only one variable functions we can construct from $p \to q$ are p itself and 0. A similar argument shows that none of $p \lor q$, $p \,\&\, q$, $p \leftrightarrow q$ suffices to generate $\neg \, p$.

We have seen that there are just 2 truth functions of two variables which generate all truth functions; quite recently the problem of finding how many complete generators (functions which generate all truth functions) there are of more than 2 variables has been solved, and the number of such generators has proved to be surprisingly high. There are, for instance, 16 complete generators of three variables, and 980 complete generators of four variables. It can be proved that a function $(p_1, p_2, \ldots, p_n)$ of n variables is a complete generator if, and only if,

$$(p, p, p, \ldots, p) = \neg\, p$$

$$(\neg\, p_1, \neg\, p_2, \ldots, \neg\, p_n) \neq \neg\, (p_1, p_2, \ldots, p_n).$$

A simple example of a complete generator of all functions which take 3 values $0, 1, 2$, of variables which take only these values is

$$1 + (p + q + r) + pqr.$$

To prove that this is a complete generator we start by showing that the representative function of any truth function with 3 values is a polynomial. Consider first functions of two variables; there are $3 \times 3 = 9$ pairs of values for the two variables, and so 9 rows in any column in the truth tables. Each row may be filled in 3 ways (with 0, 1 or 2) so that there are 3^9 truth functions (of 2 variables). Next consider polynomials with coefficients in the ring of remainders modulo 3; if p has one of the values $0, 1, 2$, then $p^3 = p$, modulo 3, and so the only polynomials are of degree 2 or less. If $ap^2 + bp + c$ is any polynomial with coefficients 0, 1 or 2, then each of a, b, c may have three values, giving $3 \times 3 \times 3 = 3^3$ polynomials altogether. Hence the number of polynomials in q, with polynomials in p as coefficients, is $3^3 \times 3^3 \times 3^3 = 3^9$, which is precisely the total number of truth functions of 2 variables. Similarly we can show that the polynomials in r with polynomials in p, q as coefficients (that is, polynomials in q with polynomials in p for coefficients) comprise *all* the truth functions in p, q, r; for the number of polynomials in p, q, r is $3^9 \times 3^9 \times 3^9 = 3^{27}$ and the number of truth functions in p, q, r is $3^{3 \times 3 \times 3} = 3^{27}$. Step by step we can show that there are exactly as many truth functions of a given set of variables as there are polynomials in these variables. Thus to show that the polynomial

$$[p, q, r] = 1 + (p + q + r) + pqr$$

generates the complete set of truth functions, we have only to show that it generates *all* polynomials (in any number of variables), and this will be the case if we can generate 0, 1, 2 and the sum and product $p + q$, pq; for from these we can certainly generate any polynomial.

Since

$$p + p + p = 0, \text{ modulo } 3,$$

$$[p, p, p] = 1 + p,$$

and hence

$$[1 + p, 1 + p, 1 + p] = 2 + p;$$

but

$$p(p + 1)(p + 2) = p(p^2 + 2) = p + 2p = 0, \text{ modulo } 3,$$

and therefore

$$[p, 1 + p, 2 + p] = 1 + (p + 1 + p + 2 + p) +$$
$$+ p(p + 1)(p + 2) = 1$$

whence we construct in turn

$$2 = 1 + 1 = [1, 1, 1]$$

$$0 = 1 + 2 = [2, 2, 2]$$

$$p + q = [p, q + 2, 0]$$

and finally

$$pq = 2 + [p + 2, q + 2, 1].$$

The truth tables determine the truth value of any sentence for given truth values of the constituent sentences. Conversely given the truth values we may construct the sentences — in fact, we have already remarked on this possibility, but we shall now describe a simple way of building up a sentence with given truth values. As a first example consider the table

p	0	0	1	1
q	0	1	0	1
	0	1	1	0

To find a sentence which takes these truth values we look at the columns with a zero in the third row, and write down p or $\neg p$ according as p has the value 0 or 1 in this column, and the same for q, joining p and q by a conjunction. Thus in the first column p and q both have zero values and so we start by writing down $p \& q$; in the fourth column (the only other column with a zero in the bottom row) p has the value 1, q the value 1 and so we write down $\neg p \& \neg p$. Finally we join the sentences written down by disjunctions, forming

$$(p \& q) \vee (\neg p \& \neg q)$$

and this is the desired sentence.

To see why the construction succeeds we note that the sentence $p \& q$ we wrote down from the first column takes the value zero only for the values of p, q in this column, and similarly $\neg p \& \neg q$ take the value zero only for the values of p, q in the fourth column. A disjunction is zero only if one of its factors is zero and therefore

$$(p \& q) \vee (\neg p \& \neg q)$$

takes the value zero in the first and fourth columns, and only in these columns, and so takes the value 1 in the second and third columns.

For another example consider the table

p	0	0	0	0	1	1	1	1
q	0	0	1	1	0	0	1	1
r	0	1	0	1	0	1	0	1
	0	1	1	0	1	0	0	1

As before we construct the sentence $p \& q \& r$ on the first column, $p \& \neg q \& \neg r$ on the fourth (the next column with a zero on the bottom row), $\neg p \& q \& \neg r$ on the sixth and $\neg p \& \neg q \& r$ on the seventh. Then the desired sentence is

$$(p \& q \& r) \vee (p \& \neg q \& \neg r) \vee (\neg p \& q \& \neg r)$$
$$\vee (\neg p \& \neg q \& r).$$

Switching circuits

Sentence logic has a perhaps surprising application to the design of electrical circuits. The variables $p, q, r, \ldots$ now denote switches; when the switch p is closed we write $p = 0$, and when it is open we write $p = 1$. A circuit with two switches in parallel is represented by $p \lor q$

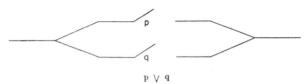

p ∨ q

because the current flows if either of the switches p, q is closed (or both are closed), but current does not flow if neither p nor q is closed. A circuit with two switches in series is represented by $p \,\&\, q$

p & q

since current flows in the circuit only when both the switches are closed. A switch which is closed when p is open, and open when p is closed is represented by $\neg p$.

A tautology $p \lor \neg p$ represents two switches in parallel one of which is necessarily closed

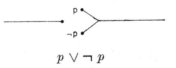

$p \lor \neg p$

so that current always flows.

The circuit

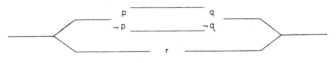

for example, is represented by $(p \leftrightarrow q) \lor r$, for current flows if r is closed, or if p, q are both closed or $\neg p$, $\neg q$ are both closed, (i.e. p and q have the same value).

Anyone who has tried to work out for himself the circuit of the familiar household two-way landing switch, or of the hotel corridor multi-switch, will be surprised to find how easy the use of sentence logic makes it to find these circuits. Let us consider first the circuit with two switches p, q; since two-way switches control the circuit independently, current is switched on and off by p, and independently by q. Let us start by making current flow when both p, q have the value 0; then for each change in value of one of p, q the value of the circuit changes, and so we have the following table:

p	0	0	1	1
q	0	1	1	0
	0	1	0	1

We have already seen that a sentence with these truth values is

$$(p \,\&\, q) \lor (\neg p \,\&\, \neg q)$$

and the circuit represented by this sentence is

showing that the necessary circuit requires two 3-pole switches.

The corresponding problem for three (or more) switches may be solved in the same way. With three switches we draw up the table:

p	0	0	0	0	1	1	1	1
q	0	0	1	1	1	1	0	0
r	0	1	1	0	0	1	1	0
	0	1	0	1	0	1	0	1

As before the requirement is that a change in value of one switch changes the value of the circuit; hence, starting with the switches all at zero, and the circuit at zero, the circuit has the value 1 when one switch has the value 1, the value 0 again when two switches have the value 1, and finally the value 1 when all switches have the value 1. A sentence satisfying this table is (as we have already found)

$$(p \& q \& r) \lor (\neg p \& q \& \neg r) \lor (p \& \neg q \& \neg r) \lor$$
$$\lor (\neg p \& \neg q \& r)$$

and the circuit represented by this sentence is

Using 3-pole and 4-pole switches the circuit takes the form

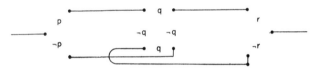

We remarked earlier that sentence logic may be formulated as a Boolean arithmetic. We take disjunction '$\lor$' for multiplication and negation '$\neg$' for complementation. From proved results of Boolean arithmetic we observe that $p = q$ follows from $\neg p \lor q$ and $p \lor \neg q$ (i.e. from $p \to q$ and $q \to p$) so that equality '$=$' in the arithmetic is the relation of equivalence in sentence logic. It may be shown that a sentence p is valid if, and only if, the equation $p = 0$ is provable in Boolean arithmetic. For instance, we have already seen that $p \lor \neg p = 0$ is provable in the arithmetic, and that $p \lor \neg p$ is valid by truth tables. We shall not prove this result for the version of Boolean arithmetic given above, but shall prove the corresponding result (in outline) for a system of sentence logic established (like Boolean arithmetic) on certain basic properties called *axioms*.

As initial sentences, or axioms, we take

A 1 $(p \lor p) \to p$

A 2 $p \to (p \lor q)$

A 3 $(p \lor q) \to (q \lor p)$

A 4 $(p \to q) \to \{(r \lor p) \to (r \lor q)\}$

where we regard disjunction "$\lor$" and negation "$\neg$" as primitive signs having only such properties as these initial sentences give them, and implication "$\to$" is *defined* in terms of "$\lor$" and "$\neg$" by the definition

$$\text{``}p \to q\text{''} \text{ stands for } \text{``}\neg\, p \lor q\text{''}$$

so that "$p \to q$" is simply an *abbreviation* for "$\neg\, p \lor q$" and not itself an element of the system. The reasons for introducing implication are that the axioms look uncomfortably long if written out in full and because the arrow has what one might call natural properties, as we shall see.

Initial sentences alone do not of course suffice to set up a branch of mathematics. We need in addition some rule or rules of procedure which enable us to proceed from the initial sentences to the *theorems*. The only rules we need for sentence logic are first the rule

$$\frac{\begin{array}{c} P \\ P \to Q \end{array}}{Q}$$

which allows us to proceed from proved sentences P and $P \to Q$ to the sentence Q. We shall simply call this rule *inference* (or detachment), and we shall say that Q is derived from P and $P \to Q$ by inference. The second and only other rule we need is a rule of substitution which allows us to substitute any composite sentence (like $p \lor (p \to q)$) for a sentence letter ($p, q, r, \ldots$) at each of its points of occurrence in a sentence.

A sequence of sentences $S_1, S_2, \ldots, S_n$ such that each is either one of the initial sentences, or is obtained from *previous* sentences in the sequence by inference or by substitution, is called a proof, and the last sentence of the proof is said to be proved by the proof.

Before we consider some actual examples of proofs we shall

build up a few general results. We remark first that if we have proved some sentence of the form

$$P \lor Q$$

(where P and Q stand for some composite sentences or are perhaps just sentence letters), then we can certainly prove $Q \lor P$. For consider the sentences

. . . . .

. . . . .

$$P \lor Q$$
$$(p \lor q) \to (q \lor p)$$
$$(P \lor Q) \to (Q \lor P)$$
$$Q \lor P$$

where the dotted lines indicate the proof of the sentence $P \lor Q$; this sequence of sentences constitutes a proof, for by assumption the sentences up to $P \lor Q$ constitute a proof, the next sentence is an axiom, and the following is obtained from it by substituting "P" for "p" and "Q" for "q", and finally $Q \lor P$ is obtained from previous sentences, namely $P \lor Q$ and $(P \lor Q) \to (Q \lor P)$, by inference.

Another important general result is that from proved sentences $P \to Q$ and $Q \to R$ we can obtain a proof of the sentence $P \to R$. The proof is built up from the sentences

(i) $P \to Q$

(ii) $Q \to R$

(iii) $(p \to q) \to ((r \lor p) \to (r \lor q))$

(iv) $(Q \to R) \to ((P \to Q) \to (P \to R))$

(v) $(P \to Q) \to (P \to R)$

(vi) $P \to R$:

sentence (iv) is obtained from axiom (iii) by substituting "Q" for "p", "R" for "q", "$\neg P$" for "r" (and writing "$P \to Q$" for "$\neg P \lor Q$"), (v) and (vi) are inferred in turn from (ii) and (i). The proof of (vi) is obtained by prefacing (i) with the proofs of (i) and (ii). The passage from a proved sentence $P \lor Q$ to $Q \lor P$ and the passage from $P \to Q$, $Q \to R$ to $P \to R$ we shall also call *inference*.

We come now to our first example of a formal proof, and proceed to prove the sentence $p \rightarrow p$. The proof consists of the sentences

(a) $$p \rightarrow (p \vee q),$$

(b) $$p \rightarrow (p \vee p),$$

(c) $$p \vee p \rightarrow p,$$

(d) $$(p \rightarrow q) \rightarrow ((r \vee p) \rightarrow (r \vee q)),$$

(e) $$\{(p \vee p) \rightarrow p\} \rightarrow [\{p \rightarrow (p \vee p)\} \rightarrow (p \rightarrow p)],$$

(f) $$\{p \rightarrow (p \vee p)\} \rightarrow (p \rightarrow p),$$

(g) $$p \rightarrow p,$$

of which the first is an initial sentence (in fact A2), (b) is obtained from (a) by substitution ("p" for "q"), (c) is axiom A1, (d) is axiom A4, (e) is obtained from (d) by substituting "$p \vee p$" for "p", "p" for "q" and "$\neg p$" for "r" (and writing "$p \rightarrow p$" for "$\neg p \vee p$" etc.), (f) follows from (c) and (e) by inference, and similarly (g) follows from (b) and (f). Now the passage from (b), (c) to (g) is simply an instance of the general proof we gave that we can pass from $P \rightarrow Q$, $Q \rightarrow R$ to $P \rightarrow R$, the steps (d), (e), (f) simply repeating the steps we took before, and in future applications we shall simply quote the general rule and not copy the steps as we have just done. Of course, the *official proof* still consists of *all* the steps; we are merely saying that the general rule enables anyone to fill in the steps for himself.

From the rule that $Q \vee P$ is provable when $P \vee Q$ is provable it now follows that

$$p \vee \neg p$$

is provable (for $p \rightarrow p$ is the abbreviation of $\neg p \vee p$), a sentence known as the principle of the excluded middle or *tertium non datum*, and hence substituting "$\neg p$" for "p" we prove

$$\neg p \vee \neg \neg p$$

i.e.

$$p \rightarrow \neg \neg p.$$

Again substituting "$\neg p$" for "p" we reach

$$\neg p \rightarrow \neg \neg \neg p$$

and from axiom A4

$$\{\neg p \to \neg \neg \neg p\} \to \{(p \vee \neg p) \to (p \vee \neg \neg \neg p)\}$$

(by the substitutions "$\neg p$" for "p", "$\neg \neg \neg p$" for "q" and "p" for "r") whence by inference

$$(p \vee \neg p) \to (p \vee \neg \neg \neg p)$$

and from the proved sentence $p \vee \neg p$ we now infer

$$p \vee \neg \neg \neg p$$

and thence

$$\neg \neg \neg p \vee p,$$

which may be written

$$\neg \neg p \to p.$$

Another important general principle we shall prove is that from a provable sentence
$$P \to Q$$
we can prove
$$R \vee P \to R \vee Q$$
and likewise that
$$P \vee R \to Q \vee R.$$
For from axiom A4

$$(p \to q) \to \{(r \vee p) \to (r \vee q)\}$$

we obtain by substitution

$$(P \to Q) \to \{(R \vee P) \to (R \vee Q)\}$$

and so from $P \to Q$ we infer

(i) $\qquad\qquad (R \vee P) \to (R \vee Q).$

But from axiom A3,

$$(p \vee q) \to (q \vee p)$$

we obtain, by substitution, both

(ii) $\qquad\qquad (P \vee R) \to (R \vee P)$

and

(iii) $\qquad\qquad R \vee Q \to (Q \vee R)$

and from (ii) and (i) we infer

(iv) $$(P \lor R) \to (R \lor Q)$$

and from (iv) and (iii)

$$(P \lor R) \to (Q \lor R)$$

is proved.

Next we prove the sentence, called *transposition*,

$$(p \to q) \to (\neg q \to \neg p);$$

starting from the provable sentence

$$q \to \neg \neg q$$

and using the rule we have just established, we see that

$$(\neg p \lor q) \to (\neg p \lor \neg \neg q)$$

is provable; but from axiom A3

$$(\neg p \lor \neg \neg q) \to (\neg \neg q \lor \neg p)$$

and from the last two sentences we infer

$$(\neg p \lor q) \to (\neg \neg q \lor \neg p)$$

that is,

$$(p \to q) \to (\neg q \to \neg p).$$

When both $P \to Q$ and $Q \to P$ are provable we say that P, Q are equivalent and write $P \leftrightarrow Q$. Notice that if $P \leftrightarrow Q$ and $Q \leftrightarrow R$ then $P \leftrightarrow R$, and that if $P \leftrightarrow Q$ and either of P, Q is provable, then so is the other. Thus we have proved

$$p \leftrightarrow \neg \neg p.$$

If $P \leftrightarrow Q$ and if $S(P)$ is any sentence in which P is contained (at one or more places), then

$$S(P) \to S(Q)$$

is provable, and therefore, if $S(P)$ is provable, so is $S(Q)$; in other words if $P \leftrightarrow Q$ we may substitute "Q" for "P" in any provable sentence. This short cut effects a great economy in proofs and we proceed to discuss it.

Let us suppose first that P appears only once in $S(P)$ and that $S(P)$ has one of the forms $\neg P$, $R \vee P$, $P \vee R$. If $S(P)$ has the form $\neg P$, then we have to prove that from

$$P \leftrightarrow Q$$

follows

$$\neg P \to \neg Q;$$

however from

$$Q \to P$$

and transposition we immediately infer

$$\neg P \to \neg Q$$

as required.

Similarly from $P \to Q$ we infer $\neg Q \to \neg P$ so that, to sum up, from $P \leftrightarrow Q$ we infer $\neg P \leftrightarrow \neg Q$. Moreover we already know that from

$$P \to Q$$

we may infer both

$$R \vee P \to R \vee Q \text{ and } P \vee R \to Q \vee R$$

and that from

$$Q \to P$$

both

$$R \vee Q \to R \vee P, \, Q \vee R \to P \vee R$$

may be inferred, showing that from

$$P \leftrightarrow Q$$

follows

$$P \vee R \leftrightarrow Q \vee R, \, R \vee P \leftrightarrow R \vee Q.$$

Suppose now that P appears once in some sentence S; then we can build up S in successive stages, starting with P itself and passing at any stage from some sentence U to a sentence V which has one of the forms $\neg U$, $U \vee W$, $W \vee U$ (where W does not contain P, or at any rate is left unchanged). If replacing P by Q turns U into U' and V into V' and if at this stage — as at the first — we have

$$U \leftrightarrow U',$$

then as we have seen

$$\neg U \leftrightarrow \neg U', \, W \vee U \leftrightarrow W \vee U', \, U \vee W \leftrightarrow U' \vee W$$

that is
$$V \leftrightarrow V'$$

showing that equivalence is preserved at each stage, so that finally
$$S \leftrightarrow S'$$

where S' is obtained from S by replacing P by Q.

Essentially the same argument works if P occurs more than once in S; we number off the occurrences and substitute Q for P at each occurrence in turn. After each substitution equivalence is preserved and so equivalence is preserved after all the substitutions have been effected. To illustrate this proof we consider the substitution of Q for P in the sentence

$$Q \vee P \vee \neg (P \vee R).$$

Starting with
$$P \leftrightarrow Q$$

we pass to
$$Q \vee P \leftrightarrow Q \vee Q$$

and thence to

(i) $\{(Q \vee P) \vee \neg (P \vee R)\} \leftrightarrow \{(Q \vee Q) \vee \neg (P \vee R)\}.$

Next we start again with
$$P \leftrightarrow Q$$

and pass in turn to

$$P \vee R \leftrightarrow Q \vee R$$
$$\neg (P \vee R) \leftrightarrow \neg (Q \vee R)$$

(ii) $\{(Q \vee Q) \vee \neg (P \vee R)\} \leftrightarrow \{(Q \vee Q) \vee \neg (Q \vee R)\}$

and from (i), (ii) we infer

$$\{(Q \vee P) \vee \neg (P \vee R)\} \leftrightarrow \{(Q \vee Q) \vee \neg (P \vee R)\}$$

as required.

As an example of the use of this principle of substitution we observe that in any sentence we may replace $\neg \, \neg \, p$ by p, since $p \leftrightarrow \neg \, \neg \, p$. It follows that every sentence may be reduced to an equivalent one in which negation "$\neg$" occurs at most once in front of any sentence.

We may introduce conjunction, denoted by $\&$, into our system by writing $p \, \& \, q$ as an abbreviation for $\neg \, (\neg \, p \vee \neg \, q)$. Disjunction and conjunction are commutative, associative and distributive (each with respect to the other), but we shall not stop to prove these results. An important consequence is that

$$p \rightarrow (q \rightarrow r)$$

$$q \rightarrow (p \rightarrow r)$$

and

$$(p \mathbin{\&} q) \rightarrow r$$

are all equivalent, for the first two are abbreviations for $\neg\, p \vee \neg\, q \vee r$, and the third stands for

$$\neg\,\neg\,(\neg\, p \vee \neg\, q) \vee r$$

which is equivalent to $\neg\, p \vee \neg\, q \vee r$.

A principle of great value in simplifying proofs in sentence logic is the *deduction principle*. This principle affirms that if by adding to the four axioms some sentence A as a fifth axiom we can prove a sentence B, *without substituting for sentence letters which occur in A*, then we can prove the sentence $A \rightarrow B$ on the basis of the axioms A 1–4 above. To prove this principle let us suppose we have before us a proof of B involving A as an additional axiom:

$$\begin{array}{cc}
\cdots\cdots & \cdots\cdots \\
A & A \rightarrow A \\
\cdots\cdots & \cdots\cdots \\
S & A \rightarrow S \\
\cdots\cdots & \cdots\cdots \\
B & A \rightarrow B
\end{array}$$

The steps in this proof will consist of selections from the axioms A 1–4, the sentence A itself, various applications of inference and substitution, but no substitution upon the letters in A. Let us now parallel this proof by a series of sentences such that to each sentence S in the proof now corresponds the sentence $A \rightarrow S$. The last sentence is now $A \rightarrow B$, and we shall show that this second series of sentences may be *expanded into a proof* of $A \rightarrow B$ in which A itself no longer features as an axiom. First we observe that A itself becomes $A \rightarrow A$ which we know is provable from axioms A 1–4. Next we notice that if S is itself one of the axioms A 1–4, then

$A \rightarrow S$ is provable from these axioms (for $\neg A \vee S$ may be inferred from S).

It remains to consider the validity of inferences under the transformation we have made.

If in the original proof we infer Q from P and $P \rightarrow Q$ at some stage, to this inference there corresponds after transformation the three sentences

$$A \rightarrow P$$
$$A \rightarrow (P \rightarrow Q)$$
$$A \rightarrow Q$$

and the question arises whether we can prove $A \rightarrow Q$, given that $A \rightarrow P$, $A \rightarrow (P \rightarrow Q)$ are proved (from axioms A1–4). We accomplish the proof by observing that $A \rightarrow (P \rightarrow Q)$ is equivalent to $(A \& P) \rightarrow Q$ which in turn is equivalent to $(P \& A) \rightarrow Q$, $P \rightarrow (A \rightarrow Q)$ and from $A \rightarrow P$, $P \rightarrow (A \rightarrow Q)$ we already know that $A \rightarrow Q$ may be inferred.

It remains only to consider an inference by substitution. Suppose that S' results from S by some substitution. Then the same substitution takes us from $A \rightarrow S$ to $A \rightarrow S'$ since we know that the substitution which takes us from S to S' is not made upon any sentence letters in A, so that A is not changed under the substitution. Thus after transformation of each sentence S into $A \rightarrow S$ we obtain a series of sentences provable from A1–4, the last of which is $A \rightarrow B$, we as desired to show.

As an example of the use of the deduction theorem we prove

$$r \rightarrow (s \rightarrow (t \rightarrow r)).$$

We start by adding r to the axioms; from axioms A2, A3

$$p \rightarrow (p \vee q), \ (p \vee q) \rightarrow (q \vee p)$$

substituting "r" for "p" and "$\neg t$" for "q" we infer

$$r \rightarrow (t \rightarrow r)$$

and thence from r we infer

$$t \rightarrow r;$$

and from this in turn in the same way we infer $s \rightarrow (t \rightarrow r)$.

Hence by the deduction principle

$$r \rightarrow (s \rightarrow (t \rightarrow r))$$

is provable from axioms A 1–4 above.

If we sought to prove the sentence

$$p \rightarrow (q \rightarrow (r \rightarrow p))$$

by the same method we should run into difficulties when we sought to substitute for "p" in axioms A 2, A 3 since p is now a letter in the new axiom p, and the proof breaks down. But it is obvious that $p \rightarrow (q \rightarrow (r \rightarrow p))$ is just a *variant* of $r \rightarrow (s \rightarrow (t \rightarrow r))$, that is, each of these sentence may be obtained from the other by substitution alone. Hence to prove $p \rightarrow (q \rightarrow (r \rightarrow p))$ by the deduction principle, we prove first the variant $r \rightarrow (s \rightarrow (t \rightarrow r))$ from which the desired sentence may be inferred by substitution.

The deduction principle may be extended to any number of additional axioms. For instance, if we can prove C by adding A, B to the axioms, then

$$A \rightarrow (B \rightarrow C)$$

is provable from A 1–4 alone. For by the principle already proved, since by adding B to the axioms A 1–4 and A we may prove C therefore $B \rightarrow C$ is provable from axioms A 1–4 and A, and *therefore* $A \rightarrow (B \rightarrow C)$ is provable from A 1–4 alone.

For example, to prove

$$p \rightarrow (q \rightarrow p)$$

we may add p and q to axioms A 1–4. Then from p and $p \rightarrow p$ we infer p so that p is derivable from axioms A 1–4 and p, q and therefore

$$p \rightarrow (q \rightarrow p)$$

is provable from A 1–4 alone.

The need for the restriction on substituting for a letter in the additional axioms, in an application of the deduction principle is easily explained. Without this restriction we could infer from

$$\neg\, p$$

by substituting "$\neg\, p$" for "p",

$$\neg\, \neg\, p$$

and thence

$$p$$

and if the deduction principle were still valid we should have

$$\neg\, p \to p$$

that is

$$\neg\,\neg\, p \vee p$$

whence we infer

$$p \vee p$$

and finally from axiom A1, we infer p. But p was completely arbitrary, showing that any sentence whatever is provable.

A set of axioms from which every sentence is provable is said to be *inconsistent*; amongst the provable sentences in an inconsistent system is, of cuorse,

$$p \,\&\, \neg\, p.$$

Conversely we may show that if for some sentence P, $P \,\&\, \neg\, P$ is provable from a set of axioms (which includes A1–4), then every sentence is provable and the set is inconsistent. For $(p \,\&\, \neg\, p) \to q$ is provable from A1–4, and so

$$(P \,\&\, \neg\, P) \to q$$

is provable, whence any q is provable. In fact we may say that a set of axioms is inconsistent if for some sentence P, both P and $\neg\, P$ are provable. For the provable sentence $(P \,\&\, \neg\, P) \to q$ is equivalent to

$$P \to (\neg\, P \to q)$$

so that when P and $\neg\, P$ are both provable, so is q.

A set of axioms which is not inconsistent is said to be *consistent*, or free from contradiction. We shall show that axioms A1–4 are consistent. To this end we set up a numerical model (interpretation) of sentence logic. We regard the sentence letters p, q, r, ... as numerical variables which take the values 0 or 1. The values of $\neg\, 0$, $\neg\, 1$ are taken to be 1, 0 respectively and the value of the disjunction $p \vee q$ is the value of the *product* of the values of p, q. Thus $p \vee q$ has the value 0 unless *both* p, q have the value 1.

We observe first that under this interpretation the axioms all have the value 0, whatever values we assign the sentence letters $p, q, r, \ldots$. Thus considering all possibilities

p	q	$p \vee p$	$p \vee q$	$p \to q$	$(p \vee p) \to p$	$p \to (p \vee q)$	$(p \vee q) \to (q \vee p)$
0	0	0	0	0	0	0	0
0	1	0	0	1	0	0	0
1	0	1	0	0	0	0	0
1	1	1	1	0	0	0	0

showing that Axioms A1–3 take only the value 0. Since axiom A4 contains three sentence letters we require a large table to take account of the eight possibilities.

p	q	r	$p \to q$	$r \vee p$	$r \vee q$	$(r \vee p) \to (r \vee q)$	$(p \to q) \to \{(r \vee p) \to (r \vee q)\}$
0	0	0	0	0	0	0	0
0	0	1	0	0	0	0	0
0	1	0	1	0	0	0	0
0	1	1	1	0	1	1	0
1	0	0	0	0	0	0	0
1	0	1	0	1	0	0	0
1	1	0	0	0	0	0	0
1	1	1	0	1	1	0	0

Thus all the Axioms A1–4 take only the value zero. Next we observe that if P, and $P \to Q$ take the value zero, then Q too must take the value zero, for $0 \to 1$ has the value 1, so that a sentence inferred from sentences which take only the value 0 itself takes only the value 0. Finally we observe that if a sentence S takes only the value zero, for all values of its sentence letters, then necessarily a sentence S' obtained from S by substituting sentences for the sentence letters of S takes only the value zero (for the substituted sentences themselves take only the values 0, 1 at most). Thus starting from axioms A1–4 any sentence proved by inference or substitution is a sentence which takes only the value 0. But the sentence $p \& \neg p$, that is the sentence $\neg(\neg p \vee \neg\neg p)$ takes the value 1 for all values of p, and therefore $p \& \neg p$ is *not* provable from axioms A1–4, and these axioms are *consistent*.

The next question we shall consider is whether all four of the axioms are *independent*; it may have happened that one of the axioms is provable from the remaining three (and in fact an early formulation of sentence logic was based upon five axioms, one of which was found to be provable from the remainder), but we shall show that none of the axioms A1–4 is provable from the other three. The demonstration again makes use of arithmetical models. To show that the first axiom A1 cannot be proved from A2–4 we treat the sentence letters as numerical variables which take the values 0, 1, 2; the values of $\neg p$ are

p	0	1	2
$\neg p$	1	0	2

and the value of $p \vee q$ is given by multiplication *modulo* 4. Under this valuation it will be found that axioms A2–4 all take the value 0; for instance, for the axiom $p \rightarrow (p \vee q)$ the calculation runs as follows:

p	0	0	0	1	1	1	2	2	2
q	0	1	2	0	1	2	0	1	2
$\neg p$	1	1	1	0	0	0	2	2	2
$p \vee q$	0	0	0	0	1	2	0	2	0
$p \rightarrow (p \vee q)$	0	0	0	0	0	0	0	0	0

Furthermore, if P and $P \rightarrow Q$ both have the value 0, then Q has the value 0, for the value of $0 \rightarrow 1$ is 1 and the value of $0 \rightarrow 2$ is 2. And, of course, any sentence which takes only the value 0, retains this property after substitution. Thus any sentence which may be proved from axioms A2–4 takes only the value 0. But axiom A1, $(p \vee p) \rightarrow p$, takes the value 2, when p has the value 2, for $2 \vee 2 = 0$, $0 \rightarrow 2 = 2$. This shows that A1 is not amongst the sentences provable from A2–4.

To prove the independence of axiom A2 from the remaining axioms we may use the following arithmetical model:

p	0	1	2	3
$\neg p$	1	0	3	2

$\vee$	0	1	2	3	p
0	0	0	0	0	
1	0	1	1	1	
2	0	1	2	2	
3	0	1	2	3	
q					

Under this valuation it will be found that Axioms A1, 3, 4 take only the values 0, 2 and further that any sentence inferred from sentences taking only these values, itself takes only these values. But Axiom A2 takes the value 1 when $p = 2$ and $q = 1$.

The independence of the third axiom may be established by means of the valuation

p	0	1	2	3
q	1	0	0	2

$\vee$	0	1	2	3	p
0	0	0	0	0	
1	0	1	2	3	
2	0	2	2	3	
3	0	3	0	3	
q					

under which A1, 2 and A4 all take the value 0, but A3 takes the value 3 when $p = 2$, $q = 3$.

The model for exhibiting the independence of the fourth axiom is

p	0	1	2	3
$\neg p$	1	0	3	0

$\vee$	0	1	2	3	p
0	0	0	0	0	
1	0	1	2	3	
2	0	2	2	0	
3	0	3	0	3	
q					

With this valuation axioms A 1–3 take only the value 0 (and so too any sentence proved from A 1–3) but A 4 takes the value 2 when $p = 3, q = 1, r = 2$.

Thus the axioms A 1–4 are both consistent and independent. A further property which these axioms have is *completeness*; if we seek to add to the axioms any sentence *not* provable from A 1–4, the resulting set of axioms is inconsistent. The axioms A 1–4 thus form a maximal set. To prove completeness we must first discuss the transformation of a sentence to a standard form. We shall show that any sentence has an equivalent of the form

$$D_1 \ \& \ D_2 \ \& \ \ldots \ \& \ D_k$$

where each D_i is a disjunction of sentence letters or negated sentence letters (like $p \vee q \vee \neg r \vee s \vee \neg t$). We shall illustrate the method of reduction to standard form by means of an example. Consider the sentence S:

$$\{p \to \neg (p \ \& \ \neg q)\} \vee \neg (\neg p \vee q):$$

first we pass each negation sign outside a bracket into the bracket, using the equivalences

$$\neg (p \ \& \ q) \leftrightarrow \neg p \vee \neg q, \quad \neg (p \vee q) \leftrightarrow \neg p \ \& \ \neg q,$$

$$\neg \neg p \leftrightarrow p.$$

Then S is equivalent to

$$\{\neg p \vee \neg p \vee q\} \vee (p \& \neg q);$$

next we use the distributive property

$$\{A \vee (B \& C)\} \rightarrow \{(A \vee B) \& (A \vee C)\}$$

and obtain the following equivalent of S:

$$\{\neg p \vee \neg p \vee q \vee p\} \& \{\neg p \vee \neg p \vee q \vee \neg q\}$$

which is of the desired form

$$D_1 \& D_2$$

where D_1 is

$$\neg p \vee \neg p \vee q \vee p$$

and D_2 is

$$\neg p \vee \neg p \vee q \vee \neg q.$$

Next we observe that since $(p \& q) \rightarrow p$, if

$$D_1 \& D_2 \& \ldots \& D_k$$

is provable so is each of $D_1, D_2, \ldots, D_k$, and conversely since $p \rightarrow (q \rightarrow (p \& q))$, if $D_1, D_2, \ldots, D_k$ are each provable so is $D_1 \& D_2 \& \ldots \& D_k$. Moreover a disjunction $A_1 \vee A_2 \vee \cdots \vee A_m$ is certainly provable if one of $A_1, \ldots, A_m$ is the negation of another; for $p \vee \neg p$ is provable and therefore $p \vee \neg p \vee A$, for any A, is provable.

Now let U be any sentence not provable from the axioms A 1–4 and let

$$D_1 \& D_2 \& \cdots \& D_k$$

be an equivalent of U in standard form; since U is not provable, at least one of $D_1, D_2, \ldots, D_k$ is not provable. Suppose that D_i is not provable. Then D_i does not contain both p and $\neg p$ for any letter p (for $p \vee \neg p \vee Q$ is provable). For each unnegated letter in D_i substitute p and for each negated letter substitute $\neg p$, then D_i becomes D_i':

$$p \vee p \vee \cdots \vee p$$

which is equivalent to p. Next for each unnegated letter in D_i substitute $\neg p$, and for each negated letter, p so that D_i becomes D_i'':

$$\neg p \vee \neg p \vee \cdots \vee \neg p$$

which is equivalent to $\neg p$.

If we now make U an additional axiom, in the extended system D_i is provable, and therefore D_i', D_i'' are both provable, that is p and $\neg p$ are both provable, showing that the extended system is inconsistent.

There is also another sense in which the set of axioms A 1–4 is complete; we may show that *every sentence which is truth-table valid* (takes the value 0 for all values 0, 1 of the constituent sentence letters) *is provable from the axioms A 1–4*.

To show this we observe first that the axioms are valid and that a sentence inferred from valid sentences is itself valid—this is precisely what we established when we discussed consistency; in particular then, equivalent sentences are also truth-table equivalent, and so the normal form of a valid sentence is also valid. Furthermore $A \& B$ is valid if, and only if, both A, B are valid. Consider now a valid disjunction D:

$$C_1 \vee C_2 \vee \cdots \vee C_m$$

where each C_i is a sentence letter, or a negated sentence letter; suppose that C_i is not $\neg C_j$ for any pair i, j. Then we may give all unnegated letters the value 1, all negated letters the value 0 (without giving the same letter two different values) and D takes the value 1, contradicting the assumption that D is valid. Thus a valid disjunction contains the pair $p \vee \neg p$ for some letter p. But $p \vee \neg p$ is provable, and therefore $p \vee \neg p \vee Q$ is provable for any Q, so that any valid disjunction is provable. It follows that the normal form of a valid sentence is provable from axioms A 1–4 and so finally the valid sentence itself is provable.

We have shown that every valid sentence is provable from the axioms, and conversely that every sentence provable from the axioms is valid. The truth tables provide a purely mechanical test for validity (we can say in advance how large a table must be prepared to test any given sentence, and allowing, perhaps, one second for filling in each entry in the table we can calculate in advance the time it would take to carry out the test), and *therefore provide a purely mechanical test also for provability*. We describe this situation by saying that the truth tables provide a *decision procedure* for provability (from the axioms), a procedure for deciding whether or not any sentence is provable; since there is a decision procedure for sentence logic we say that sentence logic is a *decidable system*. The truth tables are not the only decision procedure for sentence logic. For instance, the standard form provides another decision procedure. The reduction to standard form is effected in a purely mechanical way, and the inspection of each D_i in the standard form $D_1 \& D_2 \& \ldots \& D_k$ to see whether or not it contains a pair of the form $p \lor \neg p$ is again a purely mechanical operation (we could imagine a machine set up to make the test).

It may be thought that we could easily dispense with a decision procedure and simply test directly whether a sentence is provable by looking at all the proofs. However, the chain of proofs is endless and so we may search through the 'list' of proofs for all time without finding the sentence in question — and without being able to say that it is not there. A system with a decision procedure contains no unsolved problems — or at any rate no problem which will remain unsolved after a long enough attack upon it.

Arithmetic (provided that it contains at least addition and multiplication) is *undecidable*. To show this we shall assume that in arithmetic with addition and multiplication we may define and evaluate (in a certain precise sense we shall not discuss) every function whose values may be calculated in a purely mechanical manner, that is every *computable* function may be defined.

We shall think of arithmetic as having some precise formulation in terms of appropriate axioms and rules of inference, the details of which we shall take for granted, and we shall suppose that all the symbols (variables, functions, etc.) have been numbered off in some way. Then all the statements of arithmetic are finite sets of these symbols and therefore, as we know, all the statements may be numbered, and numbered in such a way that the sentence may be recovered from the number. Moreover, every proof is a set of statements, and so the proofs too may all be numbered.

We may now express the notion of a decision method for arithmetic in a particularly simple way. Arithmetic is decidable if there is a computable function Dn, say, such that $Dn = 0$ if, and only if, sentence number n is provable. If such a decision function exists, all we have to do to find out if some sentence is provable, is to work out the number n of the sentence and then to calculate the value of Dn; if this value comes out 0, then the sentence is provable, otherwise it is not.

We are going to show that a decision function for arithmetic does not exist.

For suppose that, on the contrary, a decision function Dn does exist. Let sub n be the number of the sentence obtained by substituting n for the variable x in sentence number n (leaving the sentence unchanged if it does not contain the variable x); clearly sub n is computable (reconstruct sentence number n, make the substitution and work out the number of the resulting sentence). Consider the sentence

$$(y = \mathrm{sub}\,x) \to \neg\,(Dy = 0);$$

let $\mathbf{p}$ be its number; then sub $\mathbf{p}$ is the number of the sentence

$$(y = \mathrm{sub}\,\mathbf{p}) \to \neg\,(Dy = 0)$$

which we call P.

If P is provable (in the formulation of arithmetic under consideration), then so is the sentence obtained from P by substituting sub $\mathbf{p}$ for the variable y, that is the sentence

$$(\mathrm{sub}\,\mathbf{p} = \mathrm{sub}\,\mathbf{p}) \to \neg\,(D\,\mathrm{sub}\,\mathbf{p} = 0)$$

is provable, and hence $\quad \neg\,(D\,\mathrm{sub}\,\mathbf{p} = 0)$

is provable (since $\mathrm{sub}\,\mathbf{p} = \mathrm{sub}\,\mathbf{p}$ is certainly provable). But if P is in fact provable, then (since D is the decision function)

$$D\,\mathrm{sub}\,\mathbf{p} = 0$$

and arithmetic is inconsistent. Thus, if arithmetic is consistent, P is not provable and consequently sub $\mathbf{p}$ is the number of an unprovable sentence, so that

$$\neg\,(D\,\mathrm{sub}\,\mathbf{p} = 0)$$

is provable. It is a property of equality that for any function $F(n)$, from $a = b$ we may infer $F(a) = F(b)$, and

$$\{F(b) = 0\} \to \{F(a) = 0)\}$$

and so $\qquad \neg\,\{F(a) = 0\} \to \neg\,\{F(b) = 0\}.$

In particular from $y = \mathrm{sub}\,\mathbf{p}$ and the proved sentence $\neg\,(D\,\mathrm{sub}\,\mathbf{p} = 0)$ we may infer $\neg\,(D\,y = 0)$. Thus (by the deduction theorem)

the sentence
$$(y = \text{sub}\,\mathbf{p}) \to \neg\,(Dy = 0)$$

is provable, for any y; that is, sentence number sub $\mathbf{p}$ is provable, and therefore
$$D\,\text{sub}\,\mathbf{p} = 0$$

is provable, and arithmetic is inconsistent. It follows that *there cannot exist a decision function for a consistent formulation of arithmetic*.

If we consider an arithmetic with only one of the two operations of addition and multiplication it is no longer true that every computable function is definable and the above proof breaks down. In fact it is known that arithmetic with only one operation is decidable. Another example of a decidable system is the theory of polynomials of a specified degree in any assigned number of real variables with integral coefficients (the decision procedure being a generalization of Sturm's method for locating the real roots of polynomials). On the other hand the elementary theory of groups and the elementary theory of rings are undecidable.

To return to arithmetic, we shall prove that formalised arithmetic is *incomplete* in the sense that there is a sentence $S(n)$ with variable n, each instance $S(0)$, $S(1)$, $S(2)$, ... of which is provable, whereas $S(n)$ itself is *unprovable*.

We have already remarked that we may number off all proofs in arithmetic, since proofs are just (ordered) sets of sentences. Let Pm be the number of the sentence proved by proof number m, that is the number of the last sentence of the set of sentences in the proof, so that Pm is a computable function (if m is not the number of a proof we set $Pm = 0$).

Let the number of the sentence
$$\neg\,(\text{sub}\,x = Pm)$$
be $\mathbf{a}$.

Then the number of the sentence,
$$\neg\,(\text{sub}\,\mathbf{a} = Pm)$$

is Sub $\mathbf{a}$; call this sentence Q.

If Q is provable, let $\mathbf{q}$ be the number of its proof, so that
$$\text{sub}\,\mathbf{a} = P\mathbf{q}$$

is provable; but if Q is provable, so is

$$\neg\,(\text{sub}\,\mathbf{a} = P\mathbf{q})$$

obtained from Q by substituting $\mathbf{q}$ for m, and arithmetic is inconsistent. Hence if arithmetic is consistent, then Q is *not* provable. But if Q is not provable, then none of the numbers $0, 1, 2, 3, \ldots$ is the number of a proof of Q, that is each of

$$\neg\,(\text{sub}\,\mathbf{a} = P0), \quad \neg\,(\text{sub}\,\mathbf{a} = P1), \quad \neg\,(\text{sub}\,\mathbf{a} = P2), \ldots$$

is provable, but the general case

$$\neg\,(\text{sub}\,\mathbf{a} = Pm)$$

is *not* provable. Thus *if arithmetic is consistent it is incomplete since there is a general statement we cannot prove even though every one of its instances is provable.*

If we seek to block this incompleteness by adding the unprovable statement to the axioms, the enlarged system will still be incomplete since we can carry out the same construction in the larger system.

Notes on Chapter 4

The necessary and sufficient conditions for complete generators were given by E. L. Post *"The Two-Valued Iterative Systems of Mathematical Logic"*, (Princeton Annals of Mathematics Studies No: 5, 1941).

The numbers of complete generators of 3 and 4 variables were found by R. A. Cunninghame-Green, who also found the given example of a complete generator for functions which take 3 values.

Sentence logic: these axioms were first given by B. A. W. Russell and A. N. Whitehead in their encyclopaedic work *Principia Mathematica*, together with a fifth axiom which was later shown by P. Bernays to be redundant. The proof of independence of the remaining axioms is also due to Bernays.

The deduction theorem was discovered by J. Herbrand in 1930.

The first proof that arithmetic is undecidable was found by Alonzo Church; the present account follows a work by A. Tarski, A. Mostowski and R. M. Robinson.

The incompleteness of arithmetic was first proved by Kurt Gödel in 1931. For a more detailed account the reader may consult the author's books *Mathematical Logic*, (University of Leicester Press) or *Recursive Number Theory*, (North-Holland Publishing Co.), where he will find references to the original papers.

CHAPTER 5

NETWORKS AND MAPS

THE elements of school geometry are points, lines, circles, angles, length and area, and the theorems of school geometry concern properties of figures which would be destroyed by any movement of the figures except the movements of which a rigid body is capable. If we draw our figures on rubber, none of the properties that we are taught to regard as the essence of geometry survive a twist in the rubber; thus straight lines cease to be straight, circles are no longer circles, area and length are changed. It may well be thought that in fact *no* property of a figure is preserved if it is drawn on rubber and subjected to bending and stretching. However, this is far from being the case and many interesting properties of figures are preserved and many interesting questions arise. The familiar London Underground Railway map provides a good example. The function of the map is to show which stations are connected by railway lines; the map does not show the distances between stations, nor the paths of the trains, nor the orientation of the various stations, but simply the linkages. And this is clearly a property which is preserved if the map is twisted and stretched, provided only that it is not torn.

The study of properties of figures which survive twisting and stretching is called topology.

Connectivity

Consider a circular disc cut out of a sheet of rubber. What properties of its boundary are preserved when we twist or stretch the disc? Well, the boundary remains a closed curve; another property that is perserved is this; if we cut the disc from one point of the boundary to another the disc falls into *two* parts. However we distort the disc one cut will produce exactly two pieces.

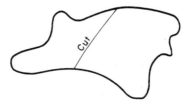

But if we start with a disc with a hole in it, then one cut may not suffice to break the disc into two pieces — two cuts may be needed.

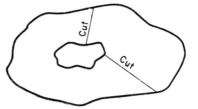

And a disc with two holes in it may need as many as three cuts to break it in two.

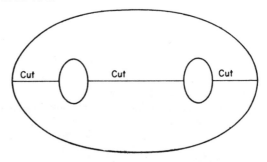

The number of cuts needed to break a disc into two parts is called the *connectivity* of the disc. The disc with no hole is singly-connected; that with one hole is doubly-connected, and the disc with two holes is trebly-connected. The connectivity of a disc is a topological property; it is unchanged by twisting or stretching the disc.

Networks

The oldest topological problem is the Königsberg bridges problem. The river in Köningsberg divides into two branches and is crossed by seven bridges.

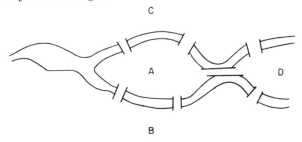

The townspeople, out for a stroll, often asked themselves whether it was possible to cross each bridge once and once only during a walk. The problem came to the ears of the great eighteenth century mathematician L. Euler (favourite of Catherine the Great of Russia, who when asked by her to confound the visiting French atheist Diderot, abused mathematics to deceive a philosopher by advancing a nonsensical pretended mathematical proof of the existence of God). Euler saw that the problem was the same as trying to describe the following figure in a single circuit:

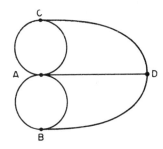

The regions A, B, C, D have become points, and the bridges have become curves connecting these points. The problem is now seen to be a problem in topology, and Euler found the complete solution. A singly-connected network may be completely traversed in a single journey *if, and only if, there are either zero or two crossings*

where an odd number of paths meet. (A network is connected if there is a route from any one crossing to any other.) This test shows that the above figure cannot be traversed in a single journey since at A, B, C and D *three* paths meet; we consider now a proof of Euler's result, observing first that if there is only one crossing, then each time we leave the crossing we must return to it, so that the number of paths meeting there is certainly even.

We start by proving that if each crossing is even, that is to say, if an even number of roads meet at the crossing, then the figure can be traversed in a single journey. Suppose Euler's theorem has been proved for figures with $1, 2, \ldots, N-1$ crossings so that N is the smallest number of crossings for which there is a figure which we have not yet proved to be traversable in a single journey (each crossing being even), and let F be such a figure. Starting at any crossing of F we proceed from crossing to crossing until we return to our starting point (we cannot be blocked *en route* for every crossing we reach is even, so that if there is a road in, then there is another road out). By our assumption we have not covered the whole network of roads, but some part of it, P say. Removing the path we have traversed, the remaining network still contains only even crossings, but may consist of several disconnected pieces, $Q, R, S, \ldots$ say. Now Q and P have a crossing in common, for there is a route from any crossing in Q to any crossing in P and this route must take us from Q to P before it enters $R, S, \ldots$ for otherwise Q would be connected to one of $R, S, \ldots$ after P has been removed; let f be the first crossing on this route from Q to P which does not belong to Q, and let q be the crossing before f. Then q certainly belongs to Q and the road qf does not belong to Q; if the road qf does not belong to P, then it will belong to one of $R, S, \ldots$ and would therefore join Q to one of $R, S, \ldots$ even when P is removed. Since Q is not so connected, therefore qf belongs to P, and so q itself belongs to P, and P and Q have a crossing in common. Similarly we may show that P has a crossing in common with each of $Q, R, S, \ldots$. Since Q has fewer than N crossings, Q may be traversed in a single journey; on the way round P, we reach q, and now instead of completing P, we first traverse Q and when we return to q, we continue our journey round P. In the same way we add in journeys round $R, S, \ldots$ and in this way the whole of F is completed in a single journey. This proves that any figure with N crossings is traversable in a single journey, and so by induction it follows that a figure with any number of crossings is traversable.

Consider next a figure with just two odd crossings a and b, say. Starting at a we take any route P to b. Cutting out P the remaining figure consists of pieces containing only even crossings, each of which has a vertex in common with P and may be added in on our journey from a to b. If a figure has just one odd crossing it cannot be described in a single journey, for if this crossing is c, and if we start at c we cannot finish there (for this would leave a road from c untraversed) and if we start at some other (even) crossing d, we must finish at d (to use an even number of roads) and one road from c will be left untraversed (since we must leave c as often as we enter it). If there are more than two odd crossings we must start at one of them and finish at another, and this will leave at least one crossing through which we may pass only an even number of times. This completes the proof of Euler's criterion. The familiar "envelope"

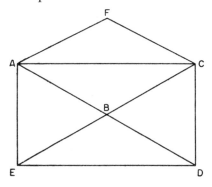

satisfies Euler's conditions, having just two odd crossings D and E. The whole figure may be traversed by the route

ED B E A B C A F C D.

Euler's formula

Another topological discovery of Euler's (which was in fact known to the great French mathematician of the sixteenth century, Réné Descartes) concerns the relationship between the numbers of vertices, edges and faces in solid bodies. Euler's formula is

$$v + f - e = 2$$

where v, f, e are the number of vertices, faces, edges respectively. For instance, a cube has 6 faces, 8 vertices

and 12 edges, and $8 + 6 - 12 = 2$; a tetrahedron (4-face solid) has 4 faces, 4 vertices and 6 edges and $4 + 4 - 6 = 2$; an octahedron (8-face solid) has 8 faces, 6 vertices and 12 edges, and $8 + 6 - 12 = 2$.

The relationship between vertices, faces and edges is a topological property, and we use a topological method to prove it. Suppose the faces were made of rubber sheeting; remove one face and stretch the body out flat. We obtain an island in an ocean which takes the place of the missing face. For instance, a cube becomes

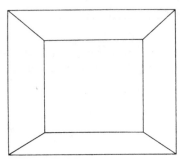

and a tetrahedron

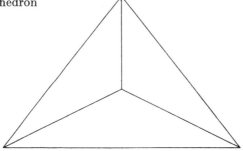

This transformation does not change the number of vertices and the number of edges, and, provided we count the 'sea' outside the island as a face, it does not change the number of faces.

Let us now think of the edges of the plane figure as dykes keeping the sea out of the fields (faces)—of course we are using these physical notions only to facilitate the description, and we shall make no appeal to physical properties in the proof. We suppose next that we flood the fields by removing the dykes one at a time, never removing a dyke when a field is already flooded, so that *a dyke is removed only when there is water on one side of it, and not on the other*. There are $f - 1$ fields to flood (for we started by removing one face) and each field is flooded by removing one dyke, so we must remove $f - 1$ dykes. When all the fields are flooded, the vertices are still connected; for if the removal of a certain dyke leaves two disconnected islands,

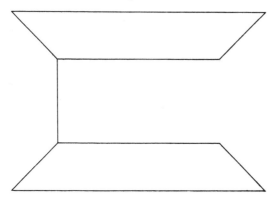

then before this dyke is removed there would have been water on both sides of the dyke, and we would not have been allowed to remove it. Next we observe that there is only *one* path from one vertex to another, for two paths enclose a field which would not have been flooded. Choose some vertex 0 as a starting point; as we pass from 0 to each vertex in turn we associate with this vertex the last dyke we traverse to reach it, so that with each vertex (apart from 0) we associate in this way a unique dyke. Furthermore each dyke must be associated with one or other of its end points, for if there was a dyke AB such that we could pass from 0 to A and from 0 to B without passing along AB, then these paths would again enclose a field (or fields). It follows that the number of dykes left after flooding is equal to the number of vertices (other than 0). Since $f - 1$ dykes are removed we see that

$$e - (f - 1) = v - 1$$

that is

$$f + v - e = 2$$

which is Euler's formula.

Another interesting proof runs as follows. As before we start by opening the body out flat. Next we divide each field into triangles by inserting diagonals. To achieve this we take each face in turn, spread it out into a regular polygon with vertices $1, 2, 3, 4, \ldots, n + 1$ say, and join the vertices $13, 14, 15, 16, \ldots, 1n$; when the face is restored to its shape the diagonals may be distorted but the face is still divided into triangular regions; (that is regions with three edges, not necessarily straight lines). Now adding a diagonal adds one edge and one face, but does not change the number of vertices and so does not change the value of

$$v - e + f.$$

Next remove any triangle with two edges on the coast;

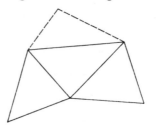

removing 2 edges, 1 vertex and 1 face does not change the value of

$$v - e + f.$$

Then remove any triangle with one edge on the coast;

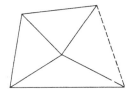

this removes 1 edge and 1 face and leaves $v - e + f$ still unchanged. Remove also any triangle which is wholly surrounded by water;

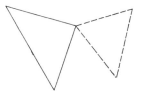

this removes 2 vertices, 3 edges and 1 face, still leaving $v - e + f$ unchanged. Proceeding in this way we reduce the figure to a single triangle surrounded by sea in which

$$v - e + f = 2$$

(counting the sea as one face). We have taken it for granted that all faces are singly-connected.

Characteristic of a surface

We have so far tacitly assumed that we are talking about bodies without holes in them. If we consider for example a cube with a hole through it, we find that the value of $v - e + f$ is no longer 2, but 0. The value of $v - e + f$ is called the characteristic of the surface. A cube with 2 holes in it has characteristic -2 (as may be seen by taking two equal cubes with one hole in each, and joining them together at a face; this removes two faces, four edges and four vertices, reducing $v - e + f$ by 2).

To prove that the characteristic of any surface with a hole through it is zero, we start by covering the ends of the hole, producing *two* surfaces without holes (the original surface and the hole with its ends closed); let v_1, e_1, f_1 relate to the original surface, and

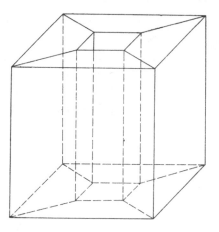

v_2, e_2, f_2 to the closed hole, and let the faces we close have V edges and V vertices. Then we have

$$v_1 - e_1 + f_1 = v_2 - e_2 + f_2 = 2.$$

Hence

$$v - e + f = (v_1 + v_2 - 2V) - (e_1 + e_2 - 2V) + (f_1 + f_2 - 4)$$
$$= (v_1 - e_1 + f_1) + (v_2 - e_2 + f_2) - 4 = 0.$$

The regular solids

Euler's formula provides a simple proof of the well-known result that there are only 5 regular solids. Let each face of the solid have n vertices and edges; then the f faces of the solid produce fn edges, counting each edge twice (once for each face which it bounds), so that

$$nf = 2e.$$

Moreover, if m faces meet at each vertex, we have m edges meeting at a vertex, making a total of mv edges; but each edge has a vertex at each end, so that counting edges by vertices, doubles the number of edges, showing that

$$mv = 2e.$$

Using Euler's formula

$$v - e + f = 2$$

it follows that

$$\frac{1}{m} + \frac{1}{n} = \frac{1}{e} + \frac{1}{2}.$$

But m and n must be at least 3 (for at least three faces are needed to make a vertex, and at least three edges to bound a face). If $m > 3$ and $n > 3$, then

$$\frac{1}{e} \leqslant \frac{1}{4} + \frac{1}{4} - \frac{1}{2} = 0$$

which is impossible (since $e \geqslant 3$); if $m = 3$, then

$$\frac{1}{e} = \frac{1}{n} - \frac{1}{6};$$

since e is positive, $n \leqslant 6$, and to the values

$$n = 3, 4, 5$$

correspond

$$e = 6, 12, 30.$$

Of course $n = 3$ gives the same sets of values for m and e. The complete set of values is exhibited in the following table, which lists also the names of the corresponding solids.

m	n	e	f	v	
3	3	6	4	4	Tetrahedron
3	4	12	8	6	Octahedron
4	3	12	6	8	Cube
3	5	30	20	12	Icosahedron
5	3	30	12	20	Dodecahedron

We have not in fact shown that these five regular solids actually exist, only that there cannot be more than five. However, all five can be constructed.

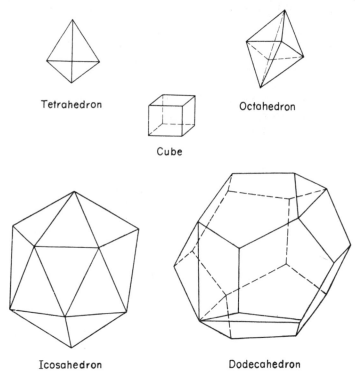

Tetrahedron

Cube

Octahedron

Icosahedron

Dodecahedron

MAP COLOURING

Colouring maps brought to light an exceedingly difficult, and in part still unsolved, topological problem. It was noticed that four colours sufficed to colour any map of any country in the world, but all attempts to prove that four colours will suffice for any map whatever have so far failed. It can be shown, and we shall later give the proof, that five colours are always sufficient, but on the other hand no map has yet been discovered which actually needs more than four colours.

Two-colour maps

Before we consider the proof that five colours always suffice, we shall examine maps which require fewer than four colours. The first question we ask ourselves is what maps need no more than two colours. Certainly straight line maps come into this category — and therefore maps which are distortions of straight line maps also require only two colours. To prove that two colours suffice for any straight line map, we proceed by induction. Certainly a one-line map needs only two colours (one for each side of the line). Suppose that a map of n lines needs only two colours and consider a map of $n + 1$ lines:

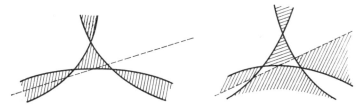

remove one of these lines, leaving a map of n lines which we colour in two colours. Restore the $(n + 1)$th line; on one side of this line leave the map *unchanged*, and on the other side *interchange* the two colours. There results an $(n + 1)$ line map coloured in two colours; for on either side of the restored line we have a correct 2 colouring, and territories separated by the restored line have opposite colours.

If we replace the open lines by simple closed curves the result remains true. That is to say, a map consisting entirely of simple closed curves requires only two colours. For let us number each state in the map according to the number of closed curves within which it lies. Thus a country which lies inside 4 closed curves receives the number 4. Two neighbouring states, states with a common frontier, lie respectively one *inside*, and one *outside* the simple closed curve of which this frontier forms a part. Various parts of the same closed curve may lie on the common frontier, but parts of two *different* closed curves cannot make up the frontier; for if states S_1, S_2 lie on opposite sides of a simple closed curve C and if part of another simple closed curve C_1 forms another boundary of S_1, then this boundary lies on the opposite side of C from S_2 and cannot therefore form a boundary of S_2. Thus two neigh-

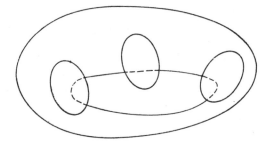

bouring states differ in respect of the curves they are inside and the curves they are outside only in the case of the single curve which forms part of their common boundary, and the two states have numbers which differ only by unity. We may, therefore, colour the map by assigning one colour to states with an even number, and the other colour to states with an odd number.

In the course of this discussion we have taken for granted some of the fundamental topological properties of simple (that is, not crossing) closed curves. A simple closed curve divides the plane into three mutually exclusive sets of points, the points *outside* the curve (called the exterior), the points *on* the curve (called the boundary points), and the points inside the curve (called the interior); any two interior points may be joined by a line (not necessarily straight) which consists entirely of interior points, and any two exterior points may be connected by a line consisting entirely of exterior points but any line joining an *interior* to an *exterior* point necessarily contains a boundary point. These properties are intuitively obvious but nonetheless very difficult to prove.

A necessary and sufficient condition for a map to be coloured in two colours is that an even numbers of states meet at each vertex. It is obvious that the condition is necessary because a vertex where an odd number of states meet already requires three colours. That the condition is sufficient may be seen as follows: start at any vertex and move along the boundary from vertex to vertex until we meet some vertex for the second time; the route from this vertex and back again forms a simple closed curve, which we remove from the map. The map which remains still has only even vertices; we repeat the process obtaining a second closed curve, and

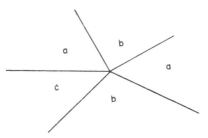

so on. After a sufficient number of repetitions, no vertex will remain, for so long as there remains one vertex (with an even number of boundaries meeting at it) there will necessarily remain a second even vertex (for a boundary has a vertex at each end) and starting at one of these two vertices V, say, we travel to the second, W, and round a closed cycle, and then repeatedly journey from V to W until a closed cycle takes these two vertices out of the map. The map therefore is formed by simple closed curves and may be coloured in two colours.

Triangular maps

There are many interesting relations between colouring maps and numbering their vertices. Confining our attention for the moment to "triangular maps", that is, maps of states each with three boundaries exactly, and such that two states have either no point in common, or just a vertex in common, or a whole boundary in common. By a whole boundary we mean the line joining two vertices. We suppose that the map is drawn on a sphere and the seas, if any, are triangular. Or the map may be a plane, an island in the shape of a triangle, the *sea* also forming a triangle.

If each vertex can be given one of the numbers 0, 1, 2 in such a way that each boundary has different numbers at its ends, then we say that the map can be *properly numbered*.

We shall show that a triangular map can be properly numbered if, and only if, it can be painted in two colours. Consider first a map that is properly numbered. Its triangles fall into two classes, those for which the path 0 1 2 is clockwise, and for which it is anti-clockwise:

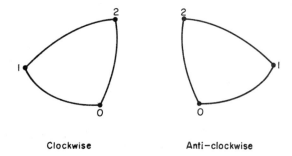

Clockwise   Anti-clockwise

Two triangles with a side in common will have opposite orientations

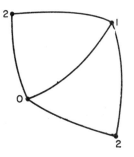

and so we may paint all clockwise triangles in one colour and all anti-clockwise triangles in a second colour. For the converse we have to show that a triangular map painted in two colours can be properly numbered. This is rather more difficult. Let the colours in question be black and white. We start by assigning a *direction* along each side; it suffices to choose the direction so that a journey in this direction round a black triangle is in a clockwise sense, and a journey round a white triangle is in an anti-clockwise sense.

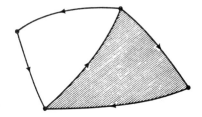

To carry out the assignment, we start with any white triangle, mark the route round its sides by arrows, then proceed to the triangle with a side in common with the initial triangle and so on.

Let *a path from a vertex A to a vertex B* mean a route along sides of the triangles which is always in the assigned direction along the sides. We shall show that we can always find a path from any vertex to any other. Start by picking out a route which *ignores* the assigned directions; let P, Q be consecutive vertices on the route. If the route from P to Q is in the assigned direction we leave the side PQ in the path; but if PQ is in the wrong direction we pass round a triangle PQR which has PQ for one of its sides, taking the two sides PR, RQ in place of PQ.

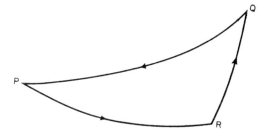

One of the two triangles with side PQ will have the desired orientation. Thus in either case we can pass from P to Q following the assigned directions, and so we can pass from any one vertex to any other.

Next we show that the number of sides in a *closed* path is a multiple of 3. We may suppose that the path does not cross itself, for crossing paths break up into a number of non-crossing closed paths with vertices in common.

Consider a closed path, delimiting a polygon P and suppose that the path proceeds round P in a clockwise sense, so that each boundary triangle is black, and therefore if we black in the whole interior of the polygon P we still have a map painted in two colours.

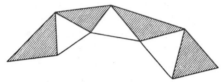

The white regions in this map all have 3 sides, and all the black regions have 3 sides except the polygon P, which has, say, p sides. Then the total number of sides is equally the sum of the number of sides of white regions, and the sum of the number of sides of black regions (for each side is *both* a side of a white region *and* a side of a black region). But the sum of the number of sides of white regions is a multiple of 3, and the sum of the number of sides of black regions is p plus a multiple of 3 which proves that p itself is a multiple of 3.

It follows that if we have two paths from a vertex A to a vertex B, then the numbers of sides in these paths are equal modulo 3. For, suppose that we have paths from A to B of p and q sides respectively; then if we take a path from B to A, consisting say of r sides, we shall have two closed paths of $p + r$ and $q + r$ sides. Thus both $p + r$ and $q + r$ are divisible by 3, and therefore their difference $p - q$ is a multiple of 3.

To number the vertices, we take any vertex I as a starting point and assign to it the number 0. Let A be any other vertex, let p be the number of sides in a path from I to A, and let a be the remainder when p is divided by 3. Then a is independent of the path from I to A and is the number assigned to A. If B and C are neighbouring vertices, they receive different numbers; for if the assigned direction is from B to C and if a path from I to B has p sides, then there is a path from I to C with $p + 1$ sides (the path from I to B and then to C), and p, $p + 1$ are not equal *modulo* 3.

This completes the proof.

Three-colour maps

The general theorem for *three* colours is that a *regular map*, that is a map in which each vertex is the meet of exactly three boundaries, can be painted in three colours if, and only if, each state has an even number of boundaries. We shall not prove this result but shall pass on to consider properties of four- and five-colour maps.

Four-colour maps

Certainly there are maps which need four colours, for instance, the following map, but as we have already remarked no proof has yet been found that four colours suffice for *any* map.

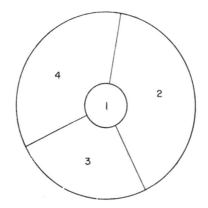

There is, however, a connection between maps which can be painted in four colours and maps which admit a proper numbering of the boundaries, which was rediscovered by a Russian student, Wolynski, who was only 21 years old when he died at the front in the second world war. A proper numbering of the boundaries is one in which two boundaries with a common vertex have different numbers. Wolynski showed that *a map may be painted in four colours if, and only if, its boundaries may be properly numbered with 3 numbers.*

Call the four colours $a + bx$, where a, b have the values 0, 1, and let the *sum* of two colours $a + bx$, $a' + b'x$ be $c + dx$ where $c = a + a'$, $d = b + b'$ *modulo 2*.

We start by proving that a map painted in four colours may have its boundaries properly numbered with 3 numbers. To each boundary we assign the sum of the colours of the regions on either side of it. We obtain only the sums

$$1, x, 1 + x$$

since $a + a' = 0$, and $b + b' = 0$ *modulo 2*, only if $a = a'$, $b = b'$, and the colours on opposite sides of a boundary are different. Moreover this is a proper numbering for if $a + bx$, $a' + b'x$, $a'' + b''x$ are the colours of regions which meet at a vertex, then the boundaries which meet at this vertex have numbers which are respectively equal *modulo 2*, to $(a + a') + (b + b')x$, $(a + a'') + (b + b'')x$, $(a' + a'') + (b' + b'')x$, and if any two of these are equal modulo 2, then two of the colours are equal, which is impossible.

For the converse, we suppose that the boundaries are properly numbered with the numbers

$$1, x, 1 + x.$$

Consider a traveller setting out from his home state, passing from state to neighbouring state (*without passing through a vertex*), and finally returning home; we shall show that the sum of the numbers of the boundaries he crosses is 0, *modulo 2*.

It suffices to consider the case when he visits each country once only, since the addition of a closed path to his journey will not affect the result.

We remark first that the sum of the numbers of the three boundaries which meet at any vertex is $1 + x + (1 + x) = 0$, *modulo 2*. The closed path the traveller describes separates the vertices into two classes, those inside the route and those outside. Let a be the sum of the numbers of those boundaries which have both end

points inside the route, and b the sum of the numbers of the boundaries which have only one end point inside the route; then counting boundaries by the number of vertices inside the route, so that
boundaries with both vertices inside are counted twice, we have
$2a + b = 0$, *modulo* 2, since the sum of the numbers of the boundaries at *each* vertex is zero, and therefore $b = 0$, *modulo* 2. That
is, the sum of the numbers of the boundaries which the traveller
crosses is 0, for such boundaries have one end-point inside the
route, and one outside.

By means of this result we may readily complete the proof of
Wolynski's Theorem. Choose any state O as a starting point, and
assign it the colour 0. To find the colour to be assigned to some
other state P, we journey from O to P, and add the numbers of the
boundaries we cross, obtaining a sum p, *modulo* 2, and assign this
colour to state P. Then we make another journey from O to P
adding the numbers of the boundaries crossed, and obtaining a sum
p', say. These two paths form a closed route which crosses boundaries the numbers of which add up to $p + p'$, so that $p + p' = 0$,
modulo 2, and therefore $p = p'$, *modulo* 2, which shows that the
colour of P is independent of the path to P. It remains to show
that no two neighbouring states have been assigned the same colour. Let states P, Q have a common frontier, with number c, and
let a path from O to P cross boundaries whose numbers add to p;
then continuing across the common frontier into Q we have a
path from O to Q which crosses boundaries whose numbers add to
$p + c$. Since $c \neq 0$, therefore $p + c \neq p$, *modulo* 2, and therefore
P and Q are assigned different colours. Wolynski's Theorem was first
found by P. G. Tait in 1884.

General plane or spherical maps

In every map (on a plane or sphere) there is a state which has
fewer than 6 neighbours. For if every country has at least 6 neighbours, then counting boundaries by states we have

$$6f \leqslant 2e$$

since each boundary is a boundary of two states.

But at least 3 boundaries meet at a vertex and so

$$3v \leqslant 2e$$

since each boundary has two vertices (end points).

It follows that

$$v + f - e \leqslant 0$$

which contradicts Euler's formula $v + f - e = 2$.

Another property of a general map (on a plane or sphere) is that there cannot be five states any pair of which have a common boundary; for otherwise each state touches four others and so counting boundaries by states we have (ignoring the rest of the map)

$$2e = 5 \times 4$$

so that $e = 10$, and counting boundaries by vertices

$$3v \leqslant 2e$$

so that $v \leqslant 6$, and therefore

$$v + f - e \leqslant 6 + 5 - 10 = 1$$

which again contradicts Euler's formula.

Four-colour maps with eleven states at most

We shall now show that four colours suffice to paint any map of not more than 11 states. The special feature of such a map is that it contains a state with fewer than 5 neighbours. For if every state has at least 5 boundaries, then counting boundaries by states we have

$$5f \leqslant 2e,$$

and counting boundaries by vertices

$$3v \leqslant 2e,$$

whence it follows that

$$15(f + v) \leqslant 16e;$$

but $f + v = e + 2$ and so $e \geqslant 30$.

But $f \leqslant 11$ and so from $3v \leqslant 2e$ and $v = e + 2 - f$ follows

$$e \leqslant 3f - 6 \leqslant 33 - 6 = 27$$

and this contradiction establishes the existence of a state with fewer than 5 neighbours.

We now proceed by induction. Obviously 4 colours suffice if there are only 4 states; suppose that 4 colours suffice for any map of not more than N states, and consider the case of $N + 1$ states ($N < 11$). The map with $N + 1$ states contains a state with less than 5 neighbours. If there is a state S with 3 or less neighbours we blot out the boundary between S and one of its neighbours S_1;

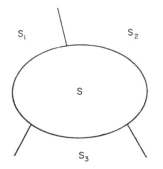

the resulting map has N states and we paint it in 4 colours. We then restore the boundary between S and S_1; the states S_1, S_2, S_3 use only 3 colours and there remains a fourth colour for S (S has no neighbours but S_1, S_2, S_3). If no state has 3 or less neighbours, then there is necessarily a state S with 4 neighbours S_1, S_2, S_3, S_4.

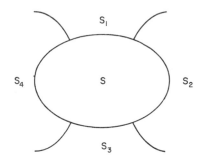

At least one pair of the five states S, S_1, S_2, S_3, S_4 do not touch; let S_1, S_3 be such a pair. Break down the boundaries between S and S_1, and between S and S_2, forming a map with $N - 1$ states, which we paint in 4 colours. Restore the boundaries, leave S_1, S_3 painted in the same colour, and there still remains a fourth colour for S. Eleven states is not the greatest number for which it is known that four colours suffice; by more delicate methods it can be shown that any map with not more than 38 states can be painted in 4 colours.

Five colours suffice for all plane or spherical maps

By an induction similar to the one we have just used, we shall now show that 5 colours certainly suffice to paint any map (on a plane or sphere). Certainly 5 colours suffice for a map of 5 states; suppose that we have established the sufficiency of 5 colours for painting any map of not more than N states, and consider a map of $N + 1$ states. If this map contains a state S with fewer than 5 neighbours,

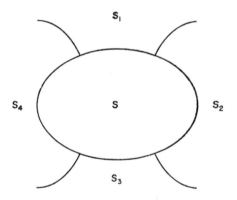

we shrink S to a point, colour the resulting map of N states with 5 colours, restore the state S which, having only four neighbours S_1, S_2, S_3, S_4 may be painted in the fifth colour, not used for these four neighbours. At worst there is a state S with exactly 5 neighbours, two of which at least will have no boundary in common. Let S_1, S_2 be the neighbours of S with no common boundary.

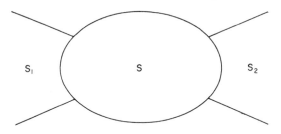

S_1 S S_2

Delete the boundaries between S and S_1, and then between S and S_2, forming a map of $N - 1$ states which we proceed to paint in 5 colours. Leaving the colours of all the other states unchanged (so that S_1, S_2 have the same colour) we now restore the boundaries between S and S_1 and between S and S_2; the 5 countries which surround S are painted in *at most* 4 colours, and so there remains a fifth colour for S, which completes the proof.

Maps on anchor rings

It is a rather remarkable fact that although the map-colouring problem for maps on a plane or a sphere is not completely solved, the corresponding problem for maps on an anchor ring (or a cube with a hole through it) has long been settled.

We shall show that 7 colours suffice to paint any map on an anchor ring, and that there is a map on an anchor ring which actually needs 7 colours.

We have already observed that the characteristic of a cube with a hole in it is 0, and since a rubber cube with a hole in it may be stretched into an anchor ring it follows that Euler's formula for a map on an anchor ring is

$$v - e + f = 0.$$

An anchor ring may be formed

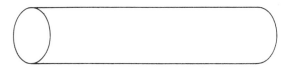

by bringing the flat ends of a cylinder together, and a cylinder may
be formed from a rectangle by bringing an opposite pair of edges
together. Thus we may form an anchor ring by identifying the opposite edges of a rectangle

and reversing the process, we may open a map on an anchor ring
out flat.

The following diagram represents a map on an anchor ring which
has been opened out flat in this way.

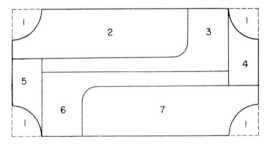

The map consists of seven states (the state 1 has been cut into
4 pieces in opening the map out flat). Since opposite edges of the
rectangle are brought together on an anchor ring it will be seen
that any pair of these seven states has a common boundary, and
therefore 7 colours are needed to paint the map. The map has
7 faces, 21 boundaries and 14 vertices, verifying the formula $v -$
$- e + f = 0$.

To prove that 7 colours suffice for any map on an anchor ring,
we start by showing that in any map on an anchor ring there is a
state with at most 6 neighbours. For if a is the *average* number of
boundaries of each state, since each boundary separates two states
and is terminated by two vertices, counting boundaries by vertices, and by states, we have

$$3v \leqslant 2e = af,$$

and therefore, using Euler's formula for an anchor ring,

$$v - e + f = 0$$

we have

$$e \leqslant 3(e - v) = 3f$$

and so

$$a = \frac{2e}{f} \leqslant 6.$$

Since the average does not exceed 6, at least one state must have not more than 6 neighbours. Let state S have for its neighbours $S_1, S_2, S_3, S_4, S_5, S_6$.

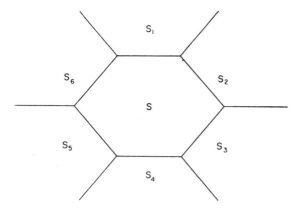

Then we may carry through an inductive proof (exactly as in the case of 5 colours in the plane) letting S shrink to a point, painting the reduced map in 7 colours, and then restoring S and painting it with the seventh colour, not used for S_1, S_2, S_3, S_4, S_5 and S_6. Of course if there is a state with fewer than 6 neighbours we shrink this state to a point and proceed as before.

Maps on a Möbius band

Another case for which the colour problem is completely solved is the case of maps on a Möbius band. A Möbius band is formed by bringing together one pair of opposite edges of a rectangle after twisting the rectangle through a half turn.

Maps on a Möbius band have characteristic 1, so that at least one state in a map on a Möbius band has fewer than 6 neighbours, from which it follows that 6 colours suffice to paint any map on a Möbius band. That 6 is the fewest possible number of colours is shown by the following map in which there are 6 countries any two of which have a boundary in common.

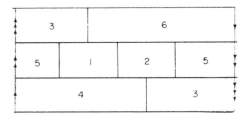

METRIC SPACES

WE come now to a generalization of the notions of limit and continuity which we considered in Chapter 3.

A set of elements a, b, c, ... (which we shall call *points*) forms a *metric space* if with each pair of points a, b is associated a decimal $d(a, b)$ called the *distance* between a and b such that (i) $d(a, b) \geqslant 0$, (ii) $d(a, b) = 0$ if, and only if, a, b are the same point,

(iii) for any a, b, c

$$d(a, b) + d(b, c) \geqslant d(a, c).$$

We observe that the points of school geometry form a metric space, the distance between two points in the ordinary sense forming the distance of the metric space; property (iii) is then the familiar property of a triangle, that the sum of two sides exceeds the third. Another, quite different example of a metric space is the set of all functions continuous in some interval (a, b) with

$$I_a^b |f(x) - g(x)|$$

for $d(f, g)$; we observe that, since f, g are continuous,

$$I_a^b |f(x) - g(x)| = 0$$

if, and only if, $f(x) = g(x)$ throughout (a, b), and since

$$|f(x) - h(x)| \leqslant |f(x) - g(x)| + |g(x) - h(x)|$$

therefore

$$I_a^b |f(x) - h(x)| \leqslant I_a^b |f(x) - g(x)| + I_a^b |g(x) - h(x)|.$$

If p is any point of a metric space M and if δ is any positive number, then the set of points x of M which satisfy the inequality

$$d(x, p) < \delta$$

is called a *neighbourhood* of p.

A subset E of a metric space M is said to be an *open* set if for every point e of E there is a neighbourhood of e which lies entirely in the subset E. *Thus in particular a neighbourhood is an open set.* A point l of M is a *limit* point of a subset E of M if every neighbourhood of l contains a point (not just l) of E. The set of points which belong to E, or are limit points of E, form the *closure* $\bar{E}$ of E; in other words, c belongs to the closure of E if every neighbourhood of c contains a point of E (perhaps c itself). A set which coincides with its closure is said to be *closed*; thus a closed set is one which contains its limit points.

The complement (in M) of a closed set is an open set, and conversely. For if E is closed, and if E' is the complement of E, then no point e' of E' is a limit point of E, and so for every e' belonging to E' there is some neighbourhood $N_{e'}$, of e' which contains no point of E, and therefore, $N_{e'}$ consists entirely of points of E', proving that E' is open.

Conversely, if E is open, and E' its complement, then E' is closed, for if l belongs to E, then there is a neighbourhood of l consisting entirely of points of E, and so containing no point of E', which proves that no point of E is a limit point of E'; hence the limit points of E' all belong to E' and E' is closed.

The closure $\bar{E}$ of any set E is closed; for if l is a limit of $\bar{E}$, then any neighbourhood N_l of l contains points of $\bar{E}$; if any of these points belong to $\bar{E}$, but not to E, then N_l is a neighbourhood of a limit point of E, and so N_l contains points of E. Thus in any case any neighbourhood N_l of l contains points of E, proving that l is a limit also of E, and therefore l belongs to $\bar{E}$ and $\bar{E}$ is closed.

If the arguments of a function $f(x)$ lie in a metric space M and its values in a metric space $\mathcal{M}$ we say that f maps M into $\mathcal{M}$. A function f which maps M into $\mathcal{M}$ is continuous at a (in M) if given any neighbourhood $\mathcal{N}$ of $f(a)$, there is a neighbourhood N of a such that $f(x)$ lies in $\mathcal{N}$ whenever x lies in N.

If a function $f(x)$ maps the points of a set X onto the points $\mathcal{X}$ (that is to say $\mathcal{X}$ is the set of all $f(x)$ for all x belonging to X), then we write
$$\mathcal{X} = f(X), \quad \text{and} \quad X = f^{-1}(\mathcal{X}).$$

A function f which maps a space M into a space $\mathcal{M}$ is continuous if, and only if, for any open set $\mathcal{X}$ in $\mathcal{M}$ the set $f^{-1}(\mathcal{X})$ is open in M.

For let $\mathcal{X}$ be an open set in $\mathcal{M}$, the map of a set X in M. If x lies in X, then $f(x)$ lies in $\mathcal{X}$; there is a neighbourhood of $f(x)$ lying entirely in $\mathcal{X}$ and so, if f is continuous, there is a neighbourhood N of x such that for any x of N, $f(x)$ lies in $\mathcal{X}$, which shows that N is contained in $f^{-1}(\mathcal{X})$, that is in X, and so X is open. Conversely, if to any open $\mathcal{X}$ there corresponds an open $f^{-1}(\mathcal{X})$, then $f(x)$ is continuous. For let x by any point of M and $\mathcal{N}$ a neighbourhood of $f(x)$; then since $\mathcal{N}$ is open, $f^{-1}(\mathcal{N})$ is open in M and so $f^{-1}(\mathcal{N})$ contains a neighbourhood N of x. Then the neighbourhood $\mathcal{N}$ of $f(x)$ contains all $f(n)$ for n in N, proving continuity. Similarly, f is continuous if, an only if $f^{-1}(\mathcal{X})$ is *closed* in M, whenever $\mathcal{X}$ is closed in $\mathcal{M}$.

The product of two closed sets is closed. For if C_1, C_2 are closed sets and if C is their product, and l a limit of C, then any neighbourhood of l contains points of C, and therefore points of C_1 and C_2, showing that l is a limit of C_1 and a limit of C_2; but C_1, C_2 are closed and therefore l belongs both to C_1 and to C_2 and therefore to C, proving that C is closed. The result obviously extends to the product of any finite or infinite number of closed sets.

The corresponding result for open sets is that the *sum* of any collection (including an infinite collection) of open sets is open. Let $A_1, A_2, A_3, \ldots$ be open sets, and a any point of their sum. Then a belongs to A_k for some k, and since A_k is open, therefore there is a neighbourhood of a which lies entirely in A_k, and hence in A, proving that A is open.

Topological space

Even more general than the concept of a metric space is the concept of a topological space. A set T forms a topological space if there is a family U of subsets of T, called the *open sets* of the space, such that

    (i) the empty set and T itself are open sets,
    (ii) the product of two open sets is open,
    (iii) the sum of any family of open sets is open.

We remark that these are precisely the properties which open sets in a metric space satisfy, so that a metric space is a topological space.

The complement of an open set is defined to be a closed set.

An alternative definition of a topological space may be given in terms of the notion of a *neighbourhood*.

A space T is a topological space if there is a family of subsets, called neighbourhoods, such that

(a) every point p of T lies in some neighbourhood, called a neighbourhood of p,
(b) every set which contains a neighbourhood of p is itself a neighbourhood of p,
(c) the product of two neighbourhoods of p is a neighbourhood of p,
(d) if P is a neighbourhood of p, then there is a neighbourhood Q of p which is completely contained in P and such that P is a neighbourhood of every point of Q.

To show that these definitions are equivalent we call a space satisfying (i), (ii), (iii) and O-space, and one satisfying (a), (b), (c), (d) an N-space.

We start by *defining* neighbourhood in an O-space, in terms of open sets. A neighbourhood of a point p is any subset of the space which contains an open set which contains p; thus any open set is a neighbourhood of each of its points. Since each point of an O-space T lies in the open set T itself, therefore (a) is satisfied. Furthermore (b) is satisfied by the very definition of a neighbourhood. As to (c) two neighbourhoods N_1, N_2 of p contain open sets O_1, O_2 which contain p, and the product $O_1 O_2$ is an open set by (ii) which contains p and lies in $N_1 N_2$ so that $N_1 N_2$ is a neighbourhood.

To prove (d) we remark that since P is a neighbourhood of p, therefore P contains an open set O which itself contains p, and by definition P is a neighbourhood of any point in O.

Conversely, we show that we may define open sets in an N-space which satisfy (i), (ii) and (iii). Let the open sets of an N-space consist of all subsets of the space which are neighbourhoods of each of their points. Then the empty set is open since it contains no points and therefore satisfies the condition of being a neighbourhood of each of its points; similarly the whole space is open since it contains all the neighbourhoods, and so condition (i) is satisfied. If N_1, N_2 are neighbourhoods of each of their points and if p is any common point of N_1, N_2 then $N_1 N_2$ is a neighbourhood of p (by (c)) so that (ii) is satisfied. Finally if p is any point of a sum of open sets, then p belongs to a set O_k of the sum, and O_k is a neighbourhood of p; but the sum set contains O_k and is therefore also a neighbourhood of p, proving that condition (iii) is fulfilled.

Yet another characterization of a topological space is in terms of the notion of closure.

Let us call a set T a K-space (after its discoverer, the Polish mathematician Kuratowski) if its points have the following properties:

With each subset X of T is associated another subset $\bar{X}$, called its *closure*, such that

$$(k_1) \ \ X \subset \bar{X}, \ \ (k_2) \ \ 0 = \bar{0}, \ \ (k_3) \ \ \overline{X + Y} = \bar{X} + \bar{Y},$$
$$(k_4) \ \ \bar{\bar{X}} = \bar{X}.$$

The proofs that a topological space satisfies the conditions (k_1) to (k_4) are similar to the proofs we have already given of some of these properties in a metric space and we shall not repeat them. We shall content ourselves with showing that a K-space is a topological space.

We start with two definitions. In a K-space a set S is closed if, and only if, $S = \overline{S}$, and a set S is open if the complement S' is closed. Now the empty set is open because its complement is the whole space T, and since $\overline{T} \subset T$, and $T \subset \overline{T}$, therefore $T = \overline{T}$, proving that T is closed, and so 0 is open. But 0 is also closed since $0 = \overline{0}$, and therefore T is also open. Furthermore if S_1, S_2 are open, then the complements S_1', S_2' are closed and since $\overline{S_1' + S_2'} = \overline{S_1'} + \overline{S_2'} = S_1' + S_2'$, therefore $S_1' + S_2'$ is closed; but the complement of the product $S_1 S_2$ is the sum of the complements $S_1' + S_2'$ and so $S_1 S_2$ is open. Finally we have to show that the sum of any collection of open sets is open. Since the complement of a sum is the product of complements we shall in fact show that a product of closed sets is closed. Let P be the product of a family of closed sets, and C any set of the family. Then $P \subset C$ so that $C = C + P$ whence, by (k_3), $\overline{C} = \overline{C} + \overline{P}$ and so $\overline{P} \subset \overline{C}$; but C is closed, so that $\overline{C} = C$, and therefore $\overline{P} \subset C$. Since $\overline{P}$ is contained in every set of the family, it is contained in the product, that is $\overline{P} \subset P$; but by (k_1), $P \subset \overline{P}$ and so $P = \overline{P}$, proving that the product is closed.

The closure of a set X (as defined in a K-space) is the smallest closed set which contains X and all its limit points. More precisely, (i) X and all its limit points belong to $\overline{X}$, and (ii) every point of $\overline{X}$ is a point of X or a limit point of $\overline{X}$. We observe first that $\overline{X}$ is the smallest closed set which contains X. For let C be *closed* and contain X, so that
$$C = C + X;$$
then, by (k_3), $$C = \overline{C} = \overline{C} + \overline{X} = C + \overline{X}$$

showing that C contains $\overline{X}$. A consequence of this is that **every open set which contains a point of $\overline{X}$ also contains a point of X.** For if an open set S contains no point of X, then its closed complement S' contains the whole of X, and therefore the whole of $\overline{X}$, so that S itself contains no point of $\overline{X}$.

Next we show that p belongs to $\overline{X}$ if, and only if, every open set which contains p, contains a point of X. For if p does not belong to $\overline{X}$, then there is a closed set (in fact $\overline{X}$ itself) which contains X and not p, and so (by complements) an open set which contains p and no point of X. And if p belongs to $\overline{X}$, then every open set which contains p, contains a point of $\overline{X}$ (namely p) and so contains a point of X.

It follows at once that if p belongs to $\overline{X}$, then p either belongs to X or is a limit point of X, for every open set which contains p contains a point of X, and so if p is not itself a member of X, then p is a limit point of X. Furthermore $\overline{X}$ contains all the limit points of X, for if l is a limit of X, and if l does not already belong to X (and so to $\overline{X}$), then the fact that every open set which contains l necessarily contains a point of X, makes l a member of $\overline{X}$.

Topological mappings

A function f which maps the points of a topological space S into a space T is (by analogy with the metric case) said to be continuous if every open set in T is the map of an open set in S. If the mapping of S into T is also a mapping of T into S such that each point in S has its *unique* mate in T, and if the mappings of S into T, and T into S are both continuous, then the mapping is said to be a *topological mapping*. Thus a topological mapping is a pair of continuous functions f, g such that for any s in the space S, $f(s)$ lies in T and

$$g(f(s)) = s$$

and further for any t in T, $g(t)$ lies in S and

$$f(g(t)) = t.$$

Such mappings f and g are said to be *inverse*.

We shall prove that closure is preserved under a topological mapping. First, however, we shall establish the following necessary and sufficient condition for a mapping to be continuous.

A mapping f of a topological space S into a topological space T is continuous if, and only if, for every subset X of S,

$$f(\overline{X}) \subset \overline{f(X)},$$

that is to say, the map of the closure of a set is contained in the closure of the map of the set.

For let f be a continuous mapping of S into T, X any subset of S, and $\bar{x}$ any point of $\bar{X}$. Further let V be an open set, in T, containing $f(\bar{x})$ and let U be the set of all points in S which map into V; then since f is continuous, U is also open. Since U contains all the points which map into V, and V includes $f(\bar{x})$ then U contains $\bar{x}$; but every open set which contains a point of $\bar{X}$ contains a point of X, and therefore U contains a point of X. Hence V contains a point of $f(X)$ and so $f(\bar{x})$ belongs to the closure of $f(X)$, and since this is true for every $\bar{x}$ in $\bar{X}$, therefore

$$f(\bar{X}) \subset \overline{f(X)}.$$

Consider now the converse. We are given that

$$f(\bar{X}) \subset \overline{f(X)}$$

for every subset X, and have to show that f is continuous. Let V be any open set in T, and U the set of all points in S which map into V, that is $f(U) = V$. Then we must show that U is open.

Consider the complements U', V' (U' being the complement of U in S, and V' the complement of V in T). Since V is open, V' is closed, and since every x, such that $f(x)$ belongs to V, belongs to U, therefore
$$f(U') \subset V'.$$
Hence
$$f(\overline{U'}) \subset \overline{f(U')} \subset \overline{V'} = V',$$
that is
$$f(\overline{U'}) \subset V'.$$

If p belongs to $\overline{U'}$ and does not belong to U', then p belongs to U and therefore $f(p)$ belongs to V; but since p belongs to $\overline{U'}$, $f(p)$ belongs to V', which is impossible, and therefore if p belongs to $\overline{U'}$, then p belongs to U', which proves that $U' = \overline{U'}$. Thus U' is closed and therefore U is open. This complete the proof that f is continuous.

Next we prove that a mapping f, of S into T, is *topological* if, and only if,
$$f(\bar{X}) = \overline{f(X)}$$
for all subsets X of S.

For if f is continuous, we have

$$f(\overline{X}) \subset \overline{f(X)}$$

for all subsets X of S, and if the inverse g of f is continuous, then

$$g(\overline{Y}) \subset \overline{g(Y)}$$

for all subsets Y of T.

Then, since $f(X)$ is a subset of T,

$$g(\overline{f(X)}) \subset \overline{g(f(X))} = \overline{X}$$

and so

$$f(g(\overline{f(X)})) \subset f(\overline{X}),$$

that is

$$\overline{f(X)} \subset f(\overline{X})$$

and since also

$$f(\overline{X}) \subset \overline{f(X)}$$

therefore

$$f(\overline{X}) = \overline{f(X)}$$

showing that closure is preserved under a topological mapping.

Conversely, we may show that if

$$f(\overline{X}) = \overline{f(X)}$$

for all subsets X of S, then the mapping f of S into T is topological.
Let Y be any subset of T, and let $X = g(Y)$, so that $f(X) = Y$.
Then

$$f(\overline{X}) = \overline{f(X)} = \overline{Y}$$

and so

$$\overline{X} = g(\overline{Y}),$$

that is

$$\overline{g(Y)} = g(\overline{Y})$$

(and so, of course $g(\overline{Y}) \subset \overline{g(Y)}$) which proves that g is continuous;
f is of course continuous since $f(\overline{X}) \subset \overline{f(X)}$ follows from the hypothesis $f(\overline{X}) = \overline{f(X)}$.

Notes in Chapter 5

Map colouring: Several of the proofs in this section are taken from E. B. Dyn-
kin and W. A. Uspenski "*Mehrfarbenprobleme*" (Deutscher Verlag der Wissenschaften, Berlin, 1955), a delightful book which contains several more almost
equally simple theorems on map colouring.

INDEX

OTHER TITLES IN THE SERIES ON
PURE AND APPLIED MATHEMATICS